ME
E
KS

RLD WAR II

ME REPAIR AND IMPROVEMENT

TIME-LIFE LIBRARY OF BOATING

MAN BEHAVIOR

E ART OF SEWING

E OLD WEST

E EMERGENCE OF MAN

E AMERICAN WILDERNESS

HE TIME-LIFE ENCYCLOPEDIA OF GARDENING

FE LIBRARY OF PHOTOGRAPHY

HIS FABULOUS CENTURY

FOODS OF THE WORLD

TIME-LIFE LIBRARY OF AMERICA

TIME-LIFE LIBRARY OF ART

GREAT AGES OF MAN

LIFE SCIENCE LIBRARY

THE LIFE HISTORY OF THE UNITED STATES

TIME READING PROGRAM

LIFE NATURE LIBRARY

LIFE WORLD LIBRARY

FAMILY LIBRARY:

- HOW THINGS WORK IN YOUR HOME
- THE TIME-LIFE BOOK OF THE FAMILY CAR
- THE TIME-LIFE FAMILY LEGAL GUIDE
- THE TIME-LIFE BOOK OF FAMILY FINANCE

TIM
LI
BOO
®

WO

HO

TH

HU

TH

TH

TH

TH

T

L

T

NATURE/SCIENCE

1977 NATURE/SCIENCE ANNUAL EDITION

TIME-LIFE BOOKS, NEW YORK

First printing.
Published simultaneously in Canada.
Library of Congress catalogue card number 76-25346.
School and library distribution by Silver Burdett Company, Morristown, New Jersey.

ON THE COVER

Possessing a halo of down and brown plumage that will later turn slate gray, a six-week-old Peale's peregrine falcon belongs to a generation of falcons bred in captivity—a feat considered impossible until recently. The breeding program aims at repopulating eyries in the eastern United States, where peregrines were wiped out by the insecticide DDT.

Valuable assistance in preparing this book was provided by the following departments and individuals of Time Inc.: Editorial Production, Norman Airey; Library, Benjamin Lightman; Picture Collection, Doris O'Neil; Photographic Laboratory, George Karas; TIME-LIFE News Service, Murray J. Gart; Correspondents Maria Vincenza Aloisi and Josephine du Brusle (Paris), Margot Hapgood and Dorothy Bacon (London), Elisabeth Kraemer (Bonn), Ann Natanson (Rome), Marilyn Balamaci (Caracas), Benjamin Defensor (Manila), Bernard Diederich (Mexico City), John Dunn (Melbourne), Marti Haymaker (Los Angeles), Douglas Lockwood (Port Moresby), Eric Robins and Ann Turner (Nairobi) and Bing Wong (Hong Kong).

Contents

Great Reef: Saved or Not?

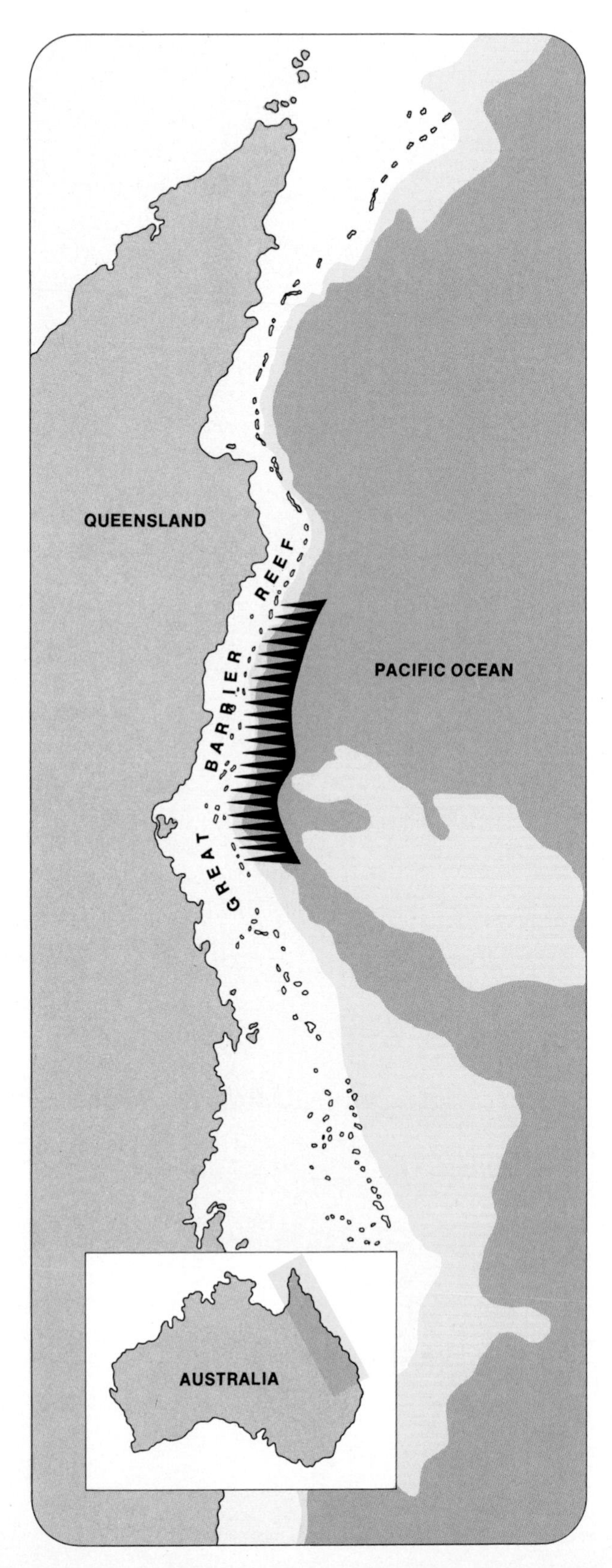

In the early 1960s, marine biologists began to take uneasy note of a creature that seemed to threaten one of nature's greatest wonders: the Great Barrier Reef, a 1,260-mile-long chain of coral reefs and islands fringing the coast of Queensland, in northeastern Australia. They reported that some areas of this vast rampart against the Pacific's surge were under attack by a species of starfish that fed voraciously on live coral polyps, whose limestone skeletons are the main building blocks of the reef.

The polyps' predator was perfectly cast as a villain: known as the Crown-of-Thorns starfish *(Acanthaster planci),* it bristles with toxic spines, grows as large as two feet across, and has from nine to 21 arms. By the decade's end, the Crown-of-Thorns had infested more than 300 miles of the reef's central section. An underwater photographer, observing a ravaged area strewn with coral skeletons, was reminded of "a great forest consumed by fire."

In 1976, this silent undersea warfare lay at the center of a scientific controversy that was anything but muted. After four years of examining the situation, a government-sponsored research team in March 1976 issued a report that seemed almost too good to be true: Starfish infestations, said the report, are a periodic phenomenon, and the wounds inflicted by the current plague are already rapidly healing. The government committee immediately found itself lambasted by conservationists who have long believed that water pollution and other tampering with the reef environment are responsible for a highly favorable starfish environment; in their view, the reef is doomed unless remedial steps are taken. So far, the two sides seem able to agree on only one point: that the Great Barrier Reef's intricately balanced ecology is far from understood—and that intensive research should go on.

Hardest hit by the starfish plague is the area shown by the ridge of arrows. Darker blues indicate deeper seas beyond the 80,000 square miles embraced by the reef.

Crown-of-Thorns starfish blanket a coral bed off Queensland. Infestations have been reported on reefs as far afield as Guam, Hawaii and even the Red Sea.

The Life Style of a Coral-Killer

A dorsal view (top) of an Acanthaster planci shows 16 arms—the number usually found on the Barrier Reef starfish—and the inch-long spines that earn it the name Crown-of-Thorns. The orange, tube-like feet along the underside of the arms (bottom) are tipped with suckers, which are useful for gripping prey.

One universally welcomed result of the government's study of the Great Barrier Reef was a wealth of new information about the strange starfish swarming over the coral. The female Crown-of-Thorns, marine biologists found, releases up to 20 million eggs into the sea each year to be fertilized by the sperm of the male and develop into larvae. The starfish larvae settle on the reef, where vast numbers of them fall prey to the very coral polyps that form the staple diet of young and adult Crown-of-Thorns; normally, only a few survive the six months or so it takes to become a fast-growing starfish with an insatiable appetite for its former predator.

Precisely what upsets the usually high mortality rate of larvae, permitting large numbers to survive and fuel a population explosion, is still uncertain. According to Australian biologist John Lucas, who is studying the possible effects of environmental changes on larvae survival, even a slight change in such factors as water salinity, temperature, or the supply of algae on which the larvae feed could cause their number to multiply dramatically.

Better understood than why the Crown-of-Thorns has spread are its ravenous feeding habits. The starfish, embracing the self-secreted cup of limestone in which a coral polyp lives, extrudes its stomach membrane through its mouth, draping it over the polyp like a collapsed parachute. The stomach's digestive juices then dissolve the polyp into a semifluid that the starfish absorbs. In this manner, a single Crown-of-Thorns can consume as much as a square foot a day of the hard corals that make up about 70 per cent of the reef's coral cover. And when thousands of the starfish congregate on an area of the reef, a slow-motion feeding frenzy infects the horde, driving them to strip the living coral from large areas with remarkable efficiency.

The underside of a starfish arm reveals a brilliant red sensory spot at its tip. The spines bristling on Acanthaster's upper surface can cause pain and nausea if touched.

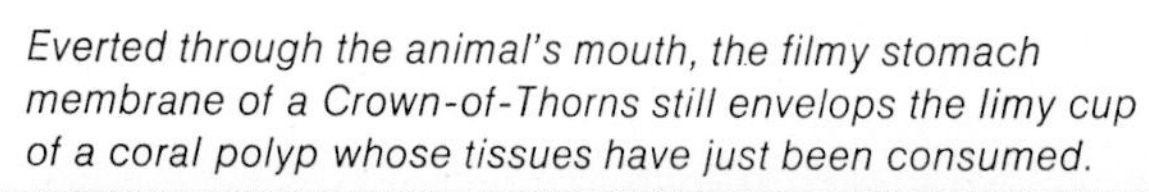

Everted through the animal's mouth, the filmy stomach membrane of a Crown-of-Thorns still envelops the limy cup of a coral polyp whose tissues have just been consumed.

A Crown-of-Thorns moves off a piece of coral on which it has feasted, leaving behind a stark white skeleton of limestone.

Queensland biologist Richard Kenchington removes gonads from a Crown-of-Thorns starfish. Gonads taken early in the breeding season tell if a starfish is mature enough to spawn; later samples reveal when a mature animal has bred.

Looking for signs of past mass starfish attacks on the Barrier Reef, Edgar Frankel of Sydney University takes samplings from the reef's coral-sand floor with a suction device. At several levels dating from a few hundred to 3,300 years ago, he found Acanthaster fossils in abundance.

A giant triton—the chief natural foe of mature Crown-of-Thorns—uses its muscular foot to grip its starfish prey. The mollusk will slit the Crown-of-Thorns open, tear it to shreds and digest the pieces. Some investigators believe that man's relentless collection of the giant triton for its handsome spiral shell may help account for the starfish infestation.

Lowly Builders of the Colossal Rampart

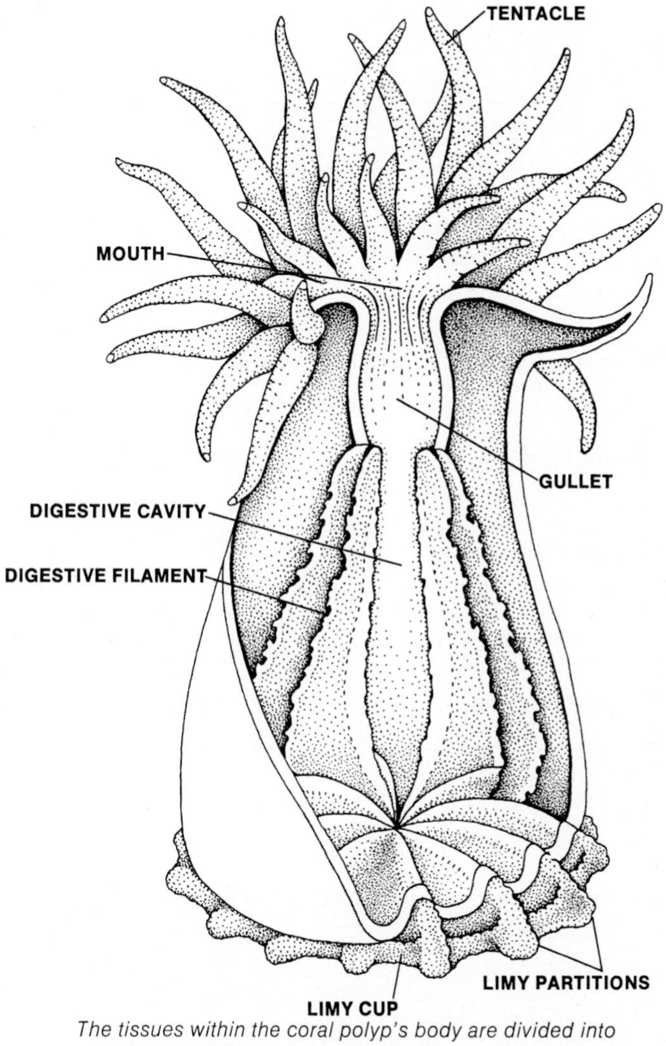

TENTACLE
MOUTH
GULLET
DIGESTIVE CAVITY
DIGESTIVE FILAMENT
LIMY PARTITIONS
LIMY CUP

The tissues within the coral polyp's body are divided into partitions edged with digestive filaments, and are the dwelling place of algae living symbiotically with their host. Outside the saclike body, radiating ridges of the polyp's limy cup grow between and parallel to the inner partitions.

The Great Barrier Reef, the largest structure on earth built by living creatures, is mainly the work of a minute but mighty architect: the stony coral polyp, a primitive, soft-bodied animal usually only one tenth to one half an inch long.

The secret of this coral's building prowess is its ability to manufacture limestone out of the calcium it ingests from the sea. When a free-swimming polyp larva settles down on the reef and becomes a full-fledged polyp, it uses this secretion to surround its base with a stony cup in which the animal anchors itself for life. Once firmly established, the polyp then puts out a bud to create another and identical polyp; as the budding process goes on, a densely populated coral colony is eventually formed, each individual encased in its own self-made shelter. When the colony dies, these casings will add another layer to the reef's foundation.

Protected in its stony cup, a polyp's body is little more than a sac of diaphanous, jellylike tissue, with a mouth fringed with filmy tentacles at the top. This delicate appearance is deceptive, however: The polyp is in fact a ravenous carnivore, its tentacles ever ready to capture any tiny animal that drifts within reach. But while a predator by nature, the polyp plays willing host to swarms of single-celled plants called zooxanthellae. Many biologists think that without the presence of these microscopic plants living within its body cavity, the polyp and others of its kind could never have produced a coral reef. From the polyp the algae gain protection, among other benefits, and in return they consume the animal's waste products that otherwise would retard its growth. So thorough are the algae as rubbish collectors that they permit the polyp to concentrate all its energies on constructing the stonelike casing that is the chief building block of the Reef.

Fragile in appearance but ferocious in intent, a coral polyp extends stinger-studded tentacles to ensnare and paralyze unwary prey. Hairlike cilia lining the animal's gullet will then sweep captured morsels into the digestive cavity, where juices will dissolve them into a nourishing broth.

Branched stony coral

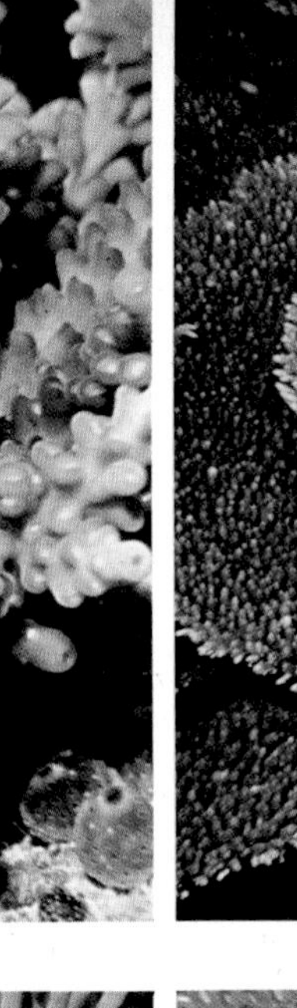

Plate-shaped stony coral

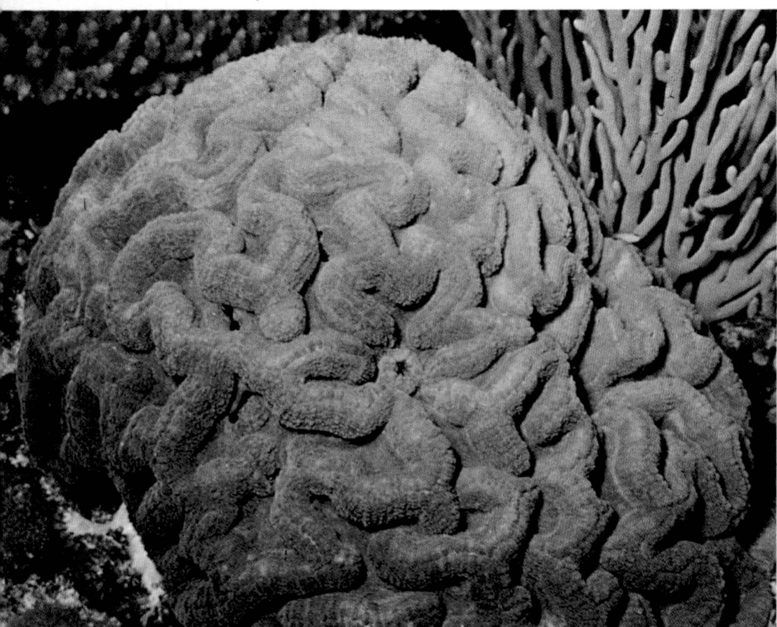

Brainlike stony coral

Horny gorgonian coral

Soft coral colony

Folded stony coral

Soft coral polyps

Lobed stony coral

Feeding stony coral

A Spectacular Garden of Living Skeletons

Naturalists struggle for words when they try to describe the rich, strange beauty of the Barrier Reef's coral kingdom. They have likened the overall effect, for example, to a multicolored marine jungle or to some sort of fantastic garden where the flowers are living animals. And the shapes of individual sections of coral have inspired comparisons with everything from trees and mushrooms to giant brains and even tiered Chinese temples.

The almost incredible profusion and diversity of the reef's coral is the product of an ideal environment—waters that are warm, clear and shallow. Most of the 350 or so species that flourish here can live only where the water temperature never goes below 70° F. and where there is little or no sediment to suffocate the delicate polyps. The most abundant species belong to the genus *Acropora,* whose cuplike limestone skeletons—cemented together by algae, calcareous plants and animal debris—form the reef's main bulwark. These species, in particular, need water shallow and clear enough to transmit adequate light for photosynthesis by zooxanthellae, the one-celled plants living within their polyps and from which they appear to derive the energy they need for growth.

But large-scale limestone construction is not practiced by all the corals. The abundant soft corals of the order Alcyonacea secrete limestone only in microscopic spicules scattered throughout their fleshy bodies to provide a measure of structural strength. Still other corals, called gorgonians and shaped like fans, whips and plumes, also secrete small amounts of limestone but stiffen their flexible skeletal structure with gorgonin, a horny substance. These nonconformists dwell in the deep waters at the outer edge of the reef *(map, page 6),* where they often provide tough, secure anchors for sponges, crustaceans and other marine animals.

Teeming Tenants of the Undersea Maze

No area of the undersea world is more densely crammed with animal life than the Great Barrier Reef. In addition to corals, more than 1,400 species of fish and countless thousands of invertebrates—bizarre and often beautiful creatures of every imaginable shape and color—populate this marine megalopolis, making homes in its caves and crevices and open spaces.

The reef dwellers have developed an extraordinary array of methods for food-getting and defense. Some of the less aggressive creatures, such as the featherstar and the featherduster worm, feed by extending many-branched appendages that filter plankton from the water. Or, like the sea anemone, they trap and stun their prey with stinging tentacles.

Alliances, too, may prove useful: One reef creature immune to the anemone's sting is the clownfish; itself a predator, the clownfish eludes its enemies by darting among the anemone's tentacles, apparently protected by the slime secreted by its skin. Still other denizens of the reef rely on camouflage as a meal ticket. The stonefish, for example, is a near-perfect replica of a rock; but when an unsuspecting small fish nears, the ersatz rock suddenly opens its mouth, creating a current that sweeps the victim into its jaws.

The defensive weaponry of the reef creatures is wonderfully varied. An arsenal of blunt spines, so hard they can be used to write on slate, protects the aptly named slate-pencil sea urchin. And some of the most virulent venom in the world comes from the sharp spines of marine animals like the stonefish and the feathery-finned lionfish. Their poisonous spines can even deter assault by such ferocious predators as the moray eel, which grows to a length of as much as 10 feet and possesses powerful jaws filled with knife-sharp teeth.

Featherduster worm

Stonefish

Slate-pencil sea urchin

Orange clownfish and sea anemone

Featherstar

Blue sea star

Lionfish

Giant clam

Moray eel

In the glass-clear shallows toward the southern end of the Great Barrier Reef—a section untouched by the ravages of the Crown-of-Thorns starfish—an outcrop of Acropora coral serves as a gathering place for banded blue-tangs, silvery black-striped humbugs, and pale blue damselfish.

Forecasting the Earth's Convulsions

CHINA SHOWS THE WAY

by Leon Jaroff

It was cold and blustery on February 4, 1975, in Manchuria's southernmost province of Liaoning. In Haicheng, where the party committee was convened in emergency session, the temperature stood at —4°F., and only a handful of the city's 100,000 people could be seen on the streets. But frostbite was not the greatest threat to the people of Haicheng that day. The committee had just been warned by seismologists that a large earthquake might soon occur in the area between Haicheng and the port city of Yingkow, 30 miles away on the Yellow Sea.

At 2 p.m., the committee made a momentous decision: The earthquake threat was real, they concluded, and emergency measures had to be taken—including the evacuation of all buildings. Within a few hours, the alert had been sounded in southern Liaoning Province. In Yingkow, the military commander of the Kuanteng Commune made a radio broadcast, warning that "there probably will be a strong earthquake tonight. We require all to leave their own homes and animals to leave the fold. There are four movies to be shown outdoors at the city square tonight."

Shops and businesses immediately closed down in Yingkow and Haicheng. Gas mains were turned off, hearth fires were extinguished and

Ruins of a rural Catholic church, 20 miles northwest of Guatemala City, testify to the fury of a 7.5 magnitude earthquake that struck Guatemala without warning on February 4, 1976, leaving 22,833 dead and 77,060 injured. Ironically, the disaster occurred one year to the day after the Chinese had forecast a major quake, evacuated a million people and saved tens of thousands of lives.

families left their homes to take up residence in tents and straw shelters, which sprouted in open fields. Patients were moved from hospital buildings and old or seriously ill people, along with pregnant women, were placed aboard trains heading out of the threatened area. Livestock was led out of barns, cars and trucks were removed from garages and valuable machinery was taken from buildings.

Then at 7:36 p.m., while many of the three million people in the area were in their makeshift shelters or huddled outdoors watching specially set up movies, the earthquake struck. Centered about 20 miles southeast of Haicheng, the quake measured a shattering 7.3 on the Richter scale and was recorded as far away as Peking, 320 miles to the west, and Kyushu, Japan, some 600 miles southeast of the epicenter.

Residents of the Teng Family Brigade, a rural commune that was completely leveled, reported seeing great sheets of light flashing from the earth. Northwest of the city on the low plain of the Liao Ho River, geysers of sand and water spouted into the air, reaching heights of 15 feet. In Haicheng, there was almost total destruction; a Chinese official who visited the city two days after the quake called it "unrecognizable." Multistory buildings had collapsed into the streets. Bridges were twisted, with some of their sections knocked off their piers, and roads were made impassable by rubble and huge cracks. In rural areas, entire villages were leveled, and a train carrying evacuees was derailed and wrecked.

Kenneth Whitham, a geophysicist who headed a delegation of Canadian scientists that toured the area, could still see evidence of the tremendous damage nine months after the quake. "Had they not moved people out of their houses," he said, "the casualty figure could well have been high. They undoubtedly saved tens of thousands of lives." Western visitors place the actual death toll near 300.

The Chinese certainly have every reason to be brimming with pride at their accomplishment in Liaoning Province. It was the latest in a string of as many as 10 successful earthquake predictions and the first of a major temblor. It was also the first forecast in history to have been issued early

To educate the public on the signs and hazards of quakes, the Chinese government publishes an illustrated pamphlet, excerpted here. The pages at right illustrate Mercalli scale values used to measure local effects of quakes. At degree 3 (roughly equal to 3 on the Richter scale, which measures earthquake magnitudes at their source), humans barely feel tremors. Between degrees 4 and 5 (Richter 4), a quake causes ceiling lamps to swing. At degree 6 (Richter 5), objects fall from shelves and buildings are slightly damaged. Between degrees 7 and 8 (Richter 6), there is severe damage to buildings and cracks appear in the earth. At degrees 9 and 10 (Richter 7), houses crumble. Between 11 and 12 (Richter 8), destruction is almost total.

An earthquake precursor that receives much attention from the Chinese is the erratic behavior of animals. In this farm scene, some of the signs to watch for are described in verse: "When cattle, sheep or horses refuse to get into the corral; when rats run out from their hiding places; when chickens fly up to the trees and pigs break out from their pens; when ducks refuse to go to the water and dogs bark for no obvious reason; when snakes come out from their winter hibernation; when pigeons are frightened and will not return to their nests; when rabbits with their ears standing jump up or crash into things; when fish jump out of the water as if frightened."

Over the centuries, the Chinese have devised many instruments to detect earthquakes. The earliest, seen at upper left on these pages from the educational pamphlet, was an animistic apparatus invented in 132 A.D.; when shaken during an earthquake, the dragons on the urn spit out pearls that supposedly dropped into the mouths of the frogs below. The two instruments at lower left are modern seismographic equipment used in Chinese observatories to measure quakes. On the right are two simple detectors that can be built by almost anyone; a tremor will topple the bottle or dislodge the ball on these devices, closing electrical circuits and causing the doorbells to ring.

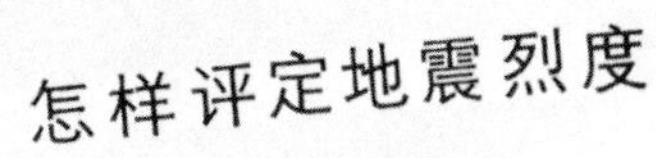

怎样评定地震烈度？

7°-8°

9°-10°

11°-12°

利用动物搞预报　简便易行好办到

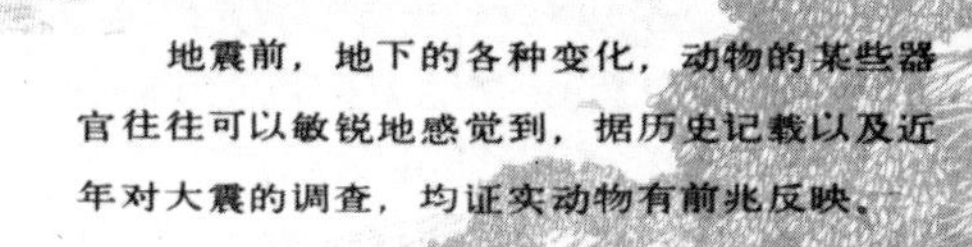

地震前，地下的各种变化，动物的某些器官往往可以敏锐地感觉到，据历史记载以及近年对大震的调查，均证实动物有前兆反映。

震前动物有前兆，　牛羊骡马不进圈，　鸡飞上树猪拱圈

家家户户都观察，

人民战争要打好。

世界上最早的地震仪

测量地震的仪器叫地震仪。公元１３２年东汉时，我国古代科学家张衡，创造了世界上第一台地震仪——地动仪。公元１３８年甘肃发生大地震，震波传到京城洛阳，地动仪西北方向的龙吐一珠，开创了人类用仪器观测地震的历史。

目前，地震台使用我国制造的地震仪，可以测定出发生地震的时间、地点和震级。

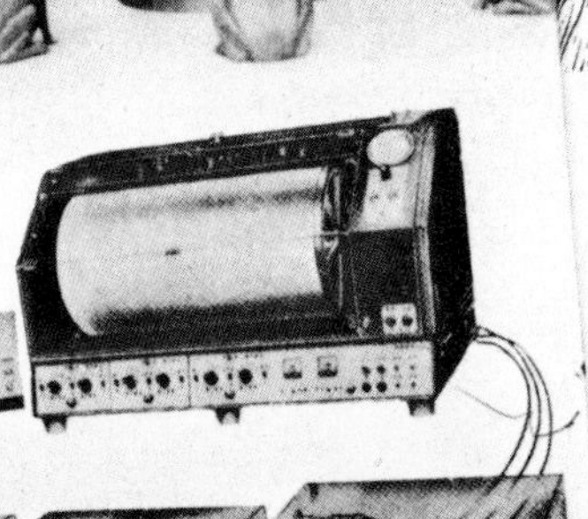

土地震报警器

"人民群众有无限的创造力"。地震区群众土法上马，创造了很多观测地震的土方法、土仪器，对于监视地震，坚持"抓革命，促生产"起到一定作用。

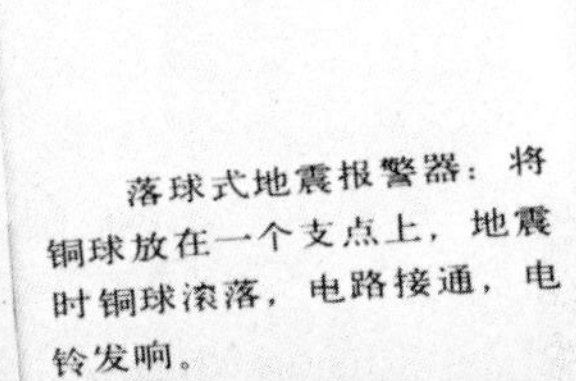

倒立瓶地震报警器：将瓶子倒立，地震时瓶被晃倒，电路接通，发出警报。

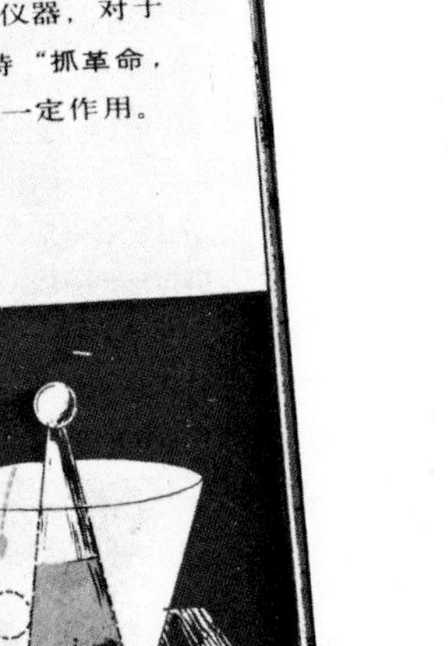

落球式地震报警器：将铜球放在一个支点上，地震时铜球滚落，电路接通，电铃发响。

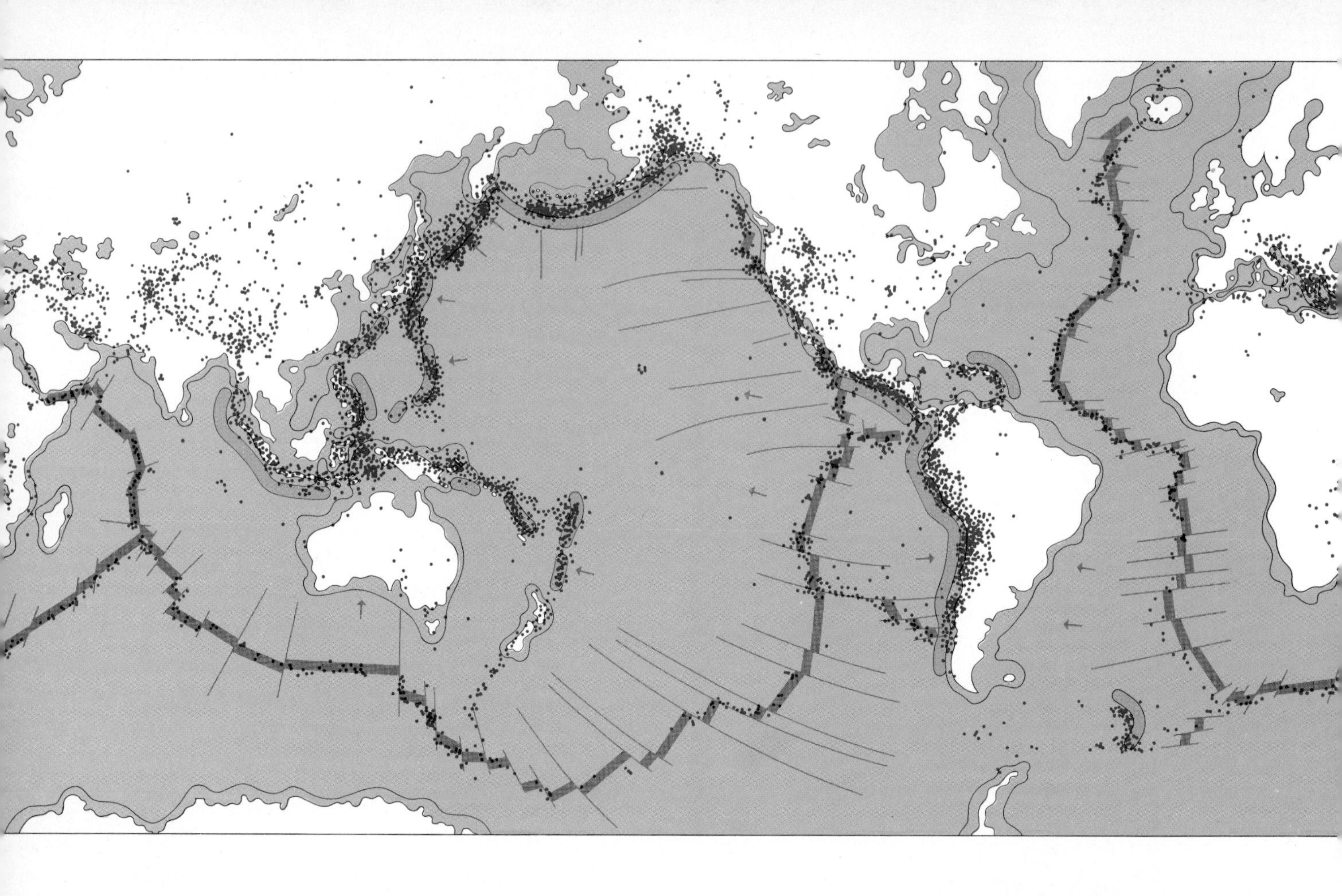

and accurately enough to permit effective precautionary efforts. The extraordinary feat served notice that man is at long last learning how he can cope with a nightmarish phenomenon that has held him subject to its mercy ever since he appeared on this planet and has cost tens of millions of fatalities.

The Chinese cannot take sole credit for the achievement; many of the forecasting techniques they used were developed by scientists in the Soviet Union, the United States and Japan. Still, it was highly appropriate that the landmark prediction was made in China, a country that has suffered more from earthquakes than any other.

Since the first recorded earthquake in China in 1831 B.C., millions of Chinese have perished, most of them in the wreckage of adobe-type, tiled-roof homes that collapse during even moderate tremors. By far the worst quake in history occurred in 1556, near the old capital city of Sian in Shensi Province: Some 830,000 people (all of whose names are recorded in the annals of the Ming Dynasty) were killed. Another catastrophe occurred in 1920, when an earthquake in Kansu Province killed almost 200,000 people. All told, Chinese records document more than 9,000 earthquakes since the Second Millennium B.C., listing the locations of epicenters and the magnitudes of more than 1,300 of them.

It has only been during the past several years, however, that the Chinese have made progress in understanding and anticipating the tremblings of the earth. As recently as March 1966, when two large tremors struck Hsing t'ai, a Hopeh Province town 230 miles southwest of Peking, only a handful of top Chinese scientists were involved in earthquake research; much of their effort was confined to highly theoretical geophysics and the preparation of seismic risk maps to guide officials in choosing relatively safe industrial sites. The Hsing t'ai earthquakes, which apparently caused considerable damage and a large number of deaths, brought about an abrupt change in the government's philosophy regarding such research. Premier Chou En-lai, shocked by the destruction he saw during a visit to the

Earthquakes that occurred around the world between 1961 and 1968 are represented by red dots on this map, reprinted from Nature/Science Annual 1970. Most quakes take place along the boundaries of the dozen or so 40-mile-thick plates of rock that comprise the surface of the earth. Slowly drifting on the planet's mantle, the plates meet head on—one pushing under the other—or they slide sideways past each other. Earthquakes result when adjacent plates move abruptly after long periods of immobility.

stricken community, declared the "People's War on Earthquakes," which made earthquake prediction one of the nation's top priority goals.

In its execution, the program meshed perfectly with Chairman Mao Tse-tung's stipulation that science must not only serve the masses but also must "walk on two legs"—that is, use professionals with the assistance of the masses. When a delegation of U.S. scientists headed by M.I.T. geophysicist Frank Press toured Chinese earthquake research centers in October 1974, they were astonished to learn that the country had 10,000 earthquake researchers—all professionals—(compared to less than a tenth of that number in the United States) operating in 17 major centers; the professionals receive data from hundreds of regional seismic stations and thousands of observation points manned by amateurs. The contingent of amateurs, the Chinese say, now numbers more than 100,000 and includes "workers, peasants, teachers and students, telephone operators, broadcasters, meteorological workers, animal feeders, etc."

With this far-flung network and the cataloguing of their historical records, says Frank Press, the Chinese have already accumulated an enormous amount of earthquake data. They currently look for a wide variety of earthquake warning signs that foreign scientists have discovered. These quake precursors include changes in tilt of the ground, in the speed of seismic waves, in the local magnetic field, in the electrical resistance of the earth, as well as changes in groundwater's content of a radioactive gas called radon.

They also look for several additional kinds of evidence that were first associated with impending earthquakes by Chinese peasants. Among them are sudden changes in the level, temperature, color and smell of well water; underground noises; and—strangest of all to U.S. scientists—erratic animal behavior. The Chinese make much, for example, of strange animal behavior in Tientsin in the summer of 1969 just before an earthquake. According to one of the keepers at a local zoo, swans abruptly left the water, a Manchurian tiger stopped pacing in his cage, a Tibetan yak collapsed and a panda held its head in its paws and moaned.

To acquaint the public with these and other signs, Chinese authorities spell them out in versifying pamphlets. The mass education has paid off handsomely, according to the Chinese delegation to a UNESCO conference on earthquakes held in Paris in February 1976. The delegates reported that the "experiences and manifold discoveries [of the amateurs] have provided professional workers with a rich source for scientific research. For example, in Hsing t'ai district, it was discovered by the masses first that preceding a strong earthquake, there were plenty of perceptible tremors, followed by an interval of quiet and then a violent shock. This phenomenon is summed up as: 'concentration-quiet-violent shock'. . . and has been proved and applied in Haicheng district."

In their successful forecast of the Haicheng quake in 1975, the Chinese made use of virtually all known prediction techniques. As early as 1970, a national earthquake conference decided that Liaoning Province, because of its past susceptibility to quakes and its dense population and heavy industry, should be one of the areas picked for earthquake monitoring. A team of professional seismologists dispatched to the area began studying geological formations and compiling historical data. They turned up plenty of ominous news. Ever since the 1966 Hsing t'ai earthquake in Hopeh Province, they noted, the epicenters of large earthquakes seemed to be migrating toward the northeast, that is, toward Liaoning Province. Also, the seismologists discovered that the province was simultaneously sinking in the southeastern part and rising in the northwestern part.

By early 1974, reports from both professional and amateur observers verified that the change in land elevation and tilt was increasing in southern Liaoning and that the strength of the local magnetic field and the water level in the nearby Bohai Gulf were both rising. Moreover, the number of small earthquakes in the area was rapidly increasing. As the precursors multiplied, more professional seismologists were sent to southern Liaoning, where they traveled around visiting factories and farms, giving earthquake lectures, passing out pamphlets and recruiting amateurs. Civil engineers began strengthening the harbor facilities in the county of Yingkow and reinforcing buildings and bridges.

In mid-December 1974, amateur observers began noticing strange animal behavior. Others reported that well water in four communes had begun to change. Several observation points detected a marked increase in the radon content of groundwater. Seismological stations reported large tilt changes. These signs were followed by a 4.8 magnitude earthquake, strong enough to make buildings tremble. By mid-January 1975, a nationwide earthquake conference was told that there would be an earthquake of magnitude 5.5 to 6.0 in the area around Yingkow during the first half of 1975. Efforts were stepped up to reach every household with information about earthquake preparedness.

At the beginning of February, reports regarding the strange behavior of cows, horses, dogs and pigs, and of changes in the levels of groundwater began to pour into major observation centers, first from southernmost Liaoning Province, then from locations closer and closer to the

An aerial photograph of an orange grove in California's Imperial Valley reveals the earth's shift during a shattering quake in May 1940. In one violent lurch, meticulously aligned rows of trees were displaced by 10 feet—showing the exact southern end of the San Andreas Fault.

Yingkow-Haicheng area. The flow of water was interrupted three times at a nearby hot springs resort, and geysers of gas-filled water shot through the ice in a commune pool. Then the Yingkow Seismological Station began recording a series of small shocks, all in a small region about a dozen miles away. These, in conjunction with the rest of the signs, were interpreted as the foreshocks of an imminent, large earthquake and were reported to the province party committee along with a warning that the quake might strike in the Yingkow-Haicheng area within two days. The alert was sounded, and the historic evacuation order followed.

Despite the accomplishments of the Chinese program, Western scientists feel that it has some failings that stand in the way of developing a truly reliable earthquake forecast system. Says Frank Press: "The Chinese are trying everything that has been suggested without discrimination, in the belief that by examining each possible technique they will find the formula for prediction. It is as if one embarked on a cancer research program in which every chemical agent was tested to determine if it would work in terms of chemotherapy, without having a conceptual model in mind and without employing the recent discoveries of molecular biology." The Chinese manfully admit that they have made some mistaken forecasts; six weeks before the Haicheng quake, for example, residents of the area were evacuated from their houses and spent two nights outside in the snow—only to find that it had been a false alarm.

Scientists in the West, under less pressure than their Chinese colleagues to make successful predictions, have placed more stress on basic research, and they have fashioned an explanation of why and how earthquakes occur. If it proves to be correct and applicable to all types of quakes, it might very well pave the way to earthquake prediction more reliable than today's weather forecasting.

Underlying the current thinking about earthquakes is a theory called "plate tectonics" that has effectively revolutionized the study of geology in the past decade *(Nature/Science Annual 1970, pages 98-111).* Geologists now believe that the surface of the earth consists of a dozen or more giant, 40-mile-thick rock plates floating on the planet's mantle: a 200- to 400-mile-thick layer of hot, semiplastic rock. Driven by immense geophysical forces still not totally understood, the plates are in constant motion. When they meet head on, one plate may slide under the other, pushing it up and forming mountains. Sometimes the plates slide alongside each other—as at the San Andreas Fault, a 700-mile fracture in the earth running through California roughly parallel to the coast. There, the North American plate, carrying most of the state of California in a westward direction, meets the Pacific plate, which is moving the coastal sliver that includes Los Angeles to the northwest.

STICKY PLATES CAUSE QUAKES

In these confrontations between the plates, the motion is not continuous. It is a frictional process called stick-slip by scientists and characterized by a series of rapid jerks interrupted by periods of sticking. Because there is no movement during these periods, the forces driving the plates continue building up stresses in any of the areas that are locked by friction. Finally the stresses become too great, and the rock fractures, allowing the plates to resume their motion. That sudden release of pent-up energy produces earthquakes, and—not surprisingly—almost all earthquakes seem to occur along or near plate boundaries *(map, page 24).*

Back in 1910, a Johns Hopkins University geologist named Harry Reid suggested that it should be possible to predict earthquakes by measuring the buildup of stresses along a fault. But he was years ahead of his time, and his proposal drew little attention. In fact, not much thought was given to earthquake prediction until 1949, when a destructive quake in the Garm region of Tadzhikistan in the Soviet Union caused a rock slide that buried the village of Khait, killing 12,000 people.

Stunned by the disaster, the Soviets resolved to learn how to forecast earthquakes. Before the actual tremor, they reasoned, there must be some geological changes that would, in effect, be early warning signals. To discover the nature of these signals, they organized a seismological expedition to Tadzhikistan, and settled scientists and their families in remote houses in earthquake-active areas. Each house and a nearby group of instruments constituted an observation station; every week, the station received supplies by a truck, which also picked up the recorded data. But nature does not often unlock her secrets easily, and two decades passed before the expedition reported to Moscow that it had finally found a reliable, easily read earthquake omen.

The world learned of the Russian success at a 1971 international scientific meeting in Moscow. There, the Soviet scientists revealed that the most recognizable sign of an impending earthquake was a change in the velocity of seismic waves passing through the earth's crust below the threatened area. These waves—actually vibrations that radiate outward from earth tremors, mining blasts or underground nuclear test explosions—travel in two different forms, which seismologists know as P (pressure) waves and S (shear) waves. The P waves, like a pulse that moves along a Slinky toy, expand and contract rock in the direction in which they are traveling, while S waves, like the vibrations of a taut string, shake the rock in a direction that is perpendicular to their path.

When an underground shock occurs, P waves, which ordinarily travel 1.75 times as fast as S waves, reach distant seismographs first. But by meticulously checking seismograph records before and after Tadzhikistan quakes, the Soviet scientists found that the ratio of P- to S-wave velocity began to decrease in the period before a quake, dropping to about 1.6. Then, shortly before the tremor struck, the ratio mysteriously returned to 1.75 again.

Further study showed that the longer the period of abnormal wave velocity before a quake, the larger the tremor was likely to be. The changes apparently begin as long as 10 years before a magnitude-8 quake, one year before a 7-pointer and a few months before a magnitude-6 (each additional point represents a 30-fold increase in the energy released). Thus the telltale P and S waves could be utilized to forecast not only the approximate time and area of the impending earthquake but the magnitude of the quake as well.

The Russian announcement about wave velocities sent U.S. seismologists scurrying to their records. Scientists at the Columbia University Lamont-Doherty Geological Observatory knew just where to look; they had set up a network of seismographs in the Adirondack Mountains of upper New York State, where tiny tremors occur frequently. Lynn Sykes, head of the observatory's seismology group, promptly assigned a graduate student, Yash Aggarwal, to see if there had been any change in seismic-wave velocities prior to a small series of earthquakes that had taken place in the mountain region around the time of the Moscow meeting. Aggarwal soon reported back that, before each of the Adirondack quakes, there had indeed been a distinct drop in the ratio of P- to S-wave velocities, then a return to normal before the tremor.

Out on the West Coast, a trio of Caltech geophysicists—James Whitcomb, Jan Garmany and Don Anderson—reexamined their records from another instrumented area around San Fernando, where a good-sized earthquake had killed 65 people in February 1971. The three scientists discovered that P waves passing through the area had slowed down significantly in 1967, some three and a half years before the quake. This was followed by a return to normal speed a few months before the earthquake hit.

S WAVES DISCOUNTED

The Caltech researchers also determined a significant fact that the Russian scientists had missed: It was primarily the velocity of P waves, not S waves, that changed before an earthquake. That information had important implications for future quake forecasting. During periods when there are few natural tremors, scientists are able to set off small explosions—by detonating a stick of dynamite in a quarry, for instance—to generate the seismic waves they must have in order to make their predictions. The P waves created by these small explosions are easy to record, but the S waves are less distinct. Now the scientists at Caltech had shown that the S-wave velocity was not important for quake forecasting.

Even with this prediction tool in hand, earth-

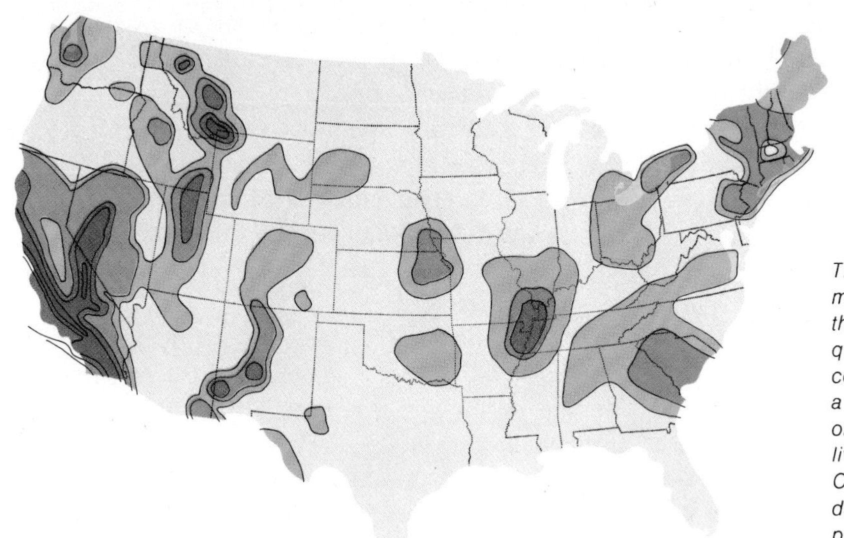

This map identifies the areas of the country most likely to be hit by earthquakes over the next 50 years and indicates probable quake intensities by progressively darker colors. For example, citizens of Maine—in a light yellow section—will probably endure only moderately severe quakes; people living in the deep-orange areas, delineating California's major faults, are in the gravest danger. The map is based on one prepared by the U.S. Geological Survey as a guide to the structural strength that is necessary for buildings.

quake researchers were not satisfied. Although seismic waves showed great promise for predictions, researchers could hardly rest on their laurels until they discovered why the waves —and other earthquake precursors—behave the way they do. Answers were not long in coming.

The key was a discovery made in the late 19th Century by Osborne Reynolds, an Anglo-Irish engineer and physicist. Reynolds discovered that granular materials expand in volume when their shapes or structures are changed under stress —a phenomenon that he named "dilatancy." Little attention was paid to Reynolds' work until the mid-1960s, when a team of researchers under M.I.T. geologist William Brace began a study of the reaction of rocks under great mechanical strains. The team discovered that just before rock reaches its breaking point, countless tiny cracks open in it, resulting in the increase in volume observed by Reynolds. Brace found that dilatancy also caused strange changes in the properties of the rock: its electrical resistance went up and the speed of sound waves passing through it dropped off.

Dilatancy remained a matter of merely academic interest until the Russian discoveries were announced. Almost immediately, two former students of Brace—geophysicists Amos Nur at Stanford University and Christopher Scholz at Lamont-Doherty—realized that the effects observed by the Russian seismologists were the result of dilatancy.

In separate papers, first Nur and then a Columbia University team headed by Scholz presented almost identical explanations. They reasoned that when dilatancy cracks first open in the rock and increase its volume, the pressure of water in already-existing voids of the rock drops, temporarily strengthening the rock. This may well be the reason that, prior to a large quake, the number of small tremors sharply diminishes. The opening of cracks also causes seismic waves to slow down, since they cannot travel as fast through the new openings as they do through solid rock. But groundwater eventually begins to seep into the cracks. Then, because seismic waves travel through water almost as fast as they travel through rock, the seismic-wave velocity quickly returns to normal. The water also increases the fluid pressure, which weakens the rock until it suddenly gives way, causing the earthquake.

Dilatancy may also account for most of the other phenomena observed before an earthquake. As cracks open in the rock, electrical resistance goes up because the air in the cracks is not a good conductor of electricity; the resistance goes down again as the groundwater seeps in. The increase in the volume of rock also may cause the crustal uplift and tilting that precedes many earthquakes. In addition, because the tiny cracks increase the surface area of rock exposed to water, the water comes in contact with more of the radioactive material that is present in many rocks and absorbs more radon—which would account for the increased radon in groundwater prior to a quake.

The connection between dilatancy and prequake changes in the local magnetic field is a little more vague; scientists speculate that the field is influenced by increasing stress on the rock or by the changes in the rock's electrical resistance. Strange animal behavior is still more difficult to rationalize, although Western scientists are keeping an open mind on the subject. Some speculate that the animals can perceive foreshocks too slight for human senses to detect, or perhaps can hear high-frequency noises, inaudible to humans, that are generated by fracturing rock. Also, some animals may have the ability to sense changes that occur in the local magnetic field.

Armed with knowledge of the precursors and the dilatancy theory, U.S. scientists have quietly begun to make successful earthquake predictions. The first came in 1973 when, after studying data from seven portable seismographs in the Adirondack region, Columbia University's Yash Aggarwal forecast a local earthquake of magnitude 2.5 to 3 within the next few days. Two days later, as he was sitting down to dinner at his Blue Mountain Lake encampment, the earth rumbled under his feet. "I could feel the waves passing by," he said, "and I was jubilant."

The year before, Caltech's James Whitcomb had begun monitoring P-wave velocities in the rock near Riverside, California. "We saw that P waves started slowing down in 1972 and stayed that way through most of 1973," he recalled. "In November 1973, the velocity began to increase again and so, in December, we predicted that a 5.5 quake would occur within the next three months." On January 30, a 4.1 tremor hit the Riverside area.

Though Whitcomb's estimate of the magnitude was off, the fact that the timing of a quake could be predicted in that particular locale was significant. Previous forecasts had involved quakes along "thrust" faults, where rock on one side of the fault is pushing directly against rock on the other. But the Riverside quake jolted an area around a so-called strike-slip fault, where the adjoining sides are sliding past each other. The Riverside forecast thus indicated that predictions could be made for the quakes caused by the biggest rift in the United States: California's San Andreas Fault.

In November 1974, Malcolm Johnston, a seismologist with the U.S. Geological Survey, helped to make the first successful San Andreas prediction. Reviewing a year's worth of accumulated data from monitoring stations set up along the fault near Hollister, California, he noticed that the strength of the local magnetic field between two of the stations had gradually risen over a period of a week and then gradually subsided. During the same interval, the surface of the earth in the area had undergone measurable although slight changes in tilt. Reporting these readings to a gathering of geologists and seismologists on November 27, Johnston pointed out that they were just "the sort of thing one would expect to see before a quake."

Another U.S. Geological Survey scientist, John Healy, was even more positive. It looked to him as if the Hollister area would experience a moderate earthquake. When? "Maybe tomorrow," said Healy, half in jest. The next afternoon a 5.2 quake rocked Hollister. Afterward, checking data stored in the USGS regional computer, the scientists discovered that seismographs had also recorded P-wave velocity changes in the Hollister area before the earthquake.

FORECASTING WHEN AS WELL AS WHERE

Dilatancy actually provides two warnings of an impending quake. If the monitors detect changes in P-wave velocities, electrical resistance and other dilatancy effects over a wide area, a large quake can be expected; but not for many months, or even years. If the signs show up only in a small area, the quake will be minor but will occur soon. The return of the dilatancy effects to normal is the second warning. It indicates that the quake will happen in about one tenth the period of time during which the dilatancy effects were measur-

Major Quakes That Caught China Unawares

The Chinese earthquake prediction system, so successful in Liaoning Province (Southern Manchuria) in 1975, apparently failed the second time around. In July 1976, two great earthquakes—8.2 and 7.9 on the Richter scale, respectively—struck within a 16-hour period in an area about 100 miles southeast of Peking. Based on magnetic field changes, an early warning that a great quake would occur in the Peking-Tientsin area before the 1980s had been issued by Chinese seismologists in 1975. In spite of their own warning, the seismologists evidently failed to detect any other signs just before the temblors.

As a result, no public evacuation order was given and great numbers of people were reported killed. Most of these people were in Tangshan, an industrial city with a population of one million. The city, located near the epicenters, was virtually leveled by the quakes.

able. Therefore, if the changes suddenly return to normal after being recorded for 10 months, then the earthquake should occur in approximately one month.

Despite the rapid progress being made in earthquake prediction techniques, the United States is still far behind China in establishing a comprehensive forecasting system. Small networks of monitoring stations equipped with seismographs—and some with magnetometers and tiltmeters—have been set up in California's Bear Valley, upper New York State and the Charleston, South Carolina area (where 60 were killed during a major earthquake in 1886). But the networks are far from complete and lack adequate computer facilities. Vast areas of California and other earthquake-prone regions in the United States are unprotected by any detection systems and are unlikely to get any help soon.

The danger of an earthquake seems especially grave in California—even though the region has not experienced a great quake since the 1906 San Francisco disaster, which claimed 700 lives. Along the San Andreas Fault, several sections of the Pacific and North American plates have been locked together for years, while other parts of the plates have slid as much as 30 feet past each other. Sooner or later, these locked segments will have to catch up with the inexorable movements of the opposing plates. If they suddenly let go—moving 10, 20 or even 30 feet in a few seconds—the resulting earthquakes, probably in the 7- or 8-magnitude range, would cause tremendous destruction for miles around.

In February 1976, the U.S. Geological Survey revealed that a 4,500-square-mile area along a 120-mile stretch of the fault centered at Palmdale (just 35 miles north of downtown Los Angeles) has risen nearly 10 inches since about 1960. This development seems particularly ominous to seismologists because the Palmdale section of the fault has not shifted since 1857, when a major earthquake rocked the then lightly populated area.

The USGS, worried that the so-called Palmdale bulge may be the result of dilatancy and thus a precursor of a major earthquake, appealed to President Gerald Ford for funds that will permit further monitoring of the area. The President promptly added $2.6 million to the USGS budget for fiscal 1977—two million dollars of it earmarked for studying the bulge. Less than two months later, after studying changes in seismic-wave velocity, a dramatic announcement was made by Caltech's Whitcomb. Sometime before April 1977, he stated, a quake measuring between 5.5 and 6.5 on the Richter scale might well occur in the vicinity of the bulge. It was the first public prediction of an earthquake made by a reputable scientist in the United States and, coming from the man who had privately forecast the 1974 Riverside quake, it seemed cause for real concern. According to a recent study made by the Federal Office of Emergency Preparedness, if a somewhat larger quake were to hit without warning near Los Angeles today, as many as 21,000 would be killed and more than 700,000 injured.

As the Chinese proved so dramatically in Liaoning Province, such casualty figures could be greatly reduced by an accurate forecast of the earthquake and by sensible precautionary moves before it struck. But the United States, unlike China, is almost totally lacking in contingency plans to carry out an orderly evacuation of an endangered area.

Both nations could probably gain much from a cooperative earthquake research program. The Chinese could make good use of some of the sophisticated instruments and advanced computers employed by seismologists in the United States. Their program also lacks U.S. expertise in rock mechanics and other sciences that would enable them to improve their prediction techniques. U.S. scientists, in turn, could derive useful information from both the 2,500-year-old Chinese earthquake catalogue and from the great volume of earthquake data currently being collected in quake-prone China.

Frank Press, who headed the delegation of U.S. seismologists that visited China in 1974, stresses the importance of this cooperation. "If a pooling of the knowledge and expertise of international scientific communities could be accomplished," he says, "there is little doubt that reliable earthquake prediction would become a reality in the foreseeable future."

Scientists already have a goal even beyond reliable earthquake forecasts. They hope someday to be able to control or at least moderate large quakes. That startling possibility arose in 1966 when David Evans, a Denver geologist, reported that small earthquakes—rare in the Denver area—seemed to occur whenever poisonous chemical wastes from the U.S. Army's nearby Rocky Mountain Arsenal were pumped out of harm's way down a two-mile-deep well *(Nature/Science Annual 1971, pages 63-64).* The dilatancy theory had not yet been advanced, and Evans suggested that the fluid chemicals might be acting as a lubricant to allow movement along small faults (the explanation probably is that the increased fluid pressure weakened the stressed rock, causing it to fracture).

After setting up seismographs and confirming that the quakes had indeed been set off by the fluid, USGS scientists in 1969 were given permission to conduct an experiment at the Chevron Oil Company's Rangely oil field in Colorado. There, Chevron was injecting water under high pressure into less productive wells to recover more oil—and in the process was generating small quakes.

If forcing water into the earth started quakes, the scientists reasoned, pumping water out of the same wells might stop the tremors. In November 1972, they injected water into four Chevron wells, setting off a series of small quakes, and then pumped it out again. The reduced fluid pressure strengthened the rock, and the tremors stopped almost immediately. For the first time, man had controlled earthquakes.

Inspired by the Rangely tests, two USGS geophysicists, C. Barry Raleigh and James Dieterich, proposed a daring experiment in 1974. They suggested drilling three deep holes at intervals of 500 yards along a section of the San Andreas Fault. By pumping water from the two outer holes, they would be able to strengthen the rock around each. Then they would inject water into the center hole, weakening the surrounding rock until it failed. This would produce a quake that, in theory at any rate, would be contained between the two strengthened sections of rock and would thus be relatively minor. If all went well, the next step would be to drill about 300 three-mile-deep holes along strategic sections of the San Andreas Fault and then use the three-hole technique to successively unlock segments of the great plates. The estimated cost of the huge project would be more than a billion dollars, but the adjacent plates would be kept moving and California spared from the disastrous earthquakes that otherwise will almost certainly come.

Los Angeles residents are reminded of the ever-present threat of earthquakes by a three-stories-high mural painted on a Santa Monica Boulevard building by local artists. The mordant fantasy depicts remnants of an expressway overpass destroyed by an earthquake.

Blythe
U.S.
MAIL

Breakthrough in Ceramics

Man's oldest manufacturing process, relegated for millennia to the making of pots, bricks and glass, has become a new bonanza; what metallurgy was to the Industrial Revolution, ceramics engineering promises to be for the Atomic Age.

The impetus is twofold. The industrial world is using up its metals almost as fast as its fossil fuels. At the same time, an increasingly sophisticated technology is demanding more of its materials—more strength, more durability, more resistance to heat. In answer, metallurgists have developed many versatile alloys; but with each new advance, the cost rises—and so does the incentive to find non-metallic substitutes.

Ceramic materials have always been attractive in price: their basic ingredients are heat-fused sand, clay and other limitlessly abundant earthy substances. They also happen to be harder than most metals, less subject to chemical attack and more heat resistant. In the past, however, there has been one crucial catch; the very hardness of ceramics made them brittle, and under mechanical and thermal stress, they broke.

No longer need that be the case. Today, scientists are finding ways to make ceramics do everything metal can do—and some things it cannot. For instance, turbine engines, a promising alternative to the gas-guzzling piston engine in today's automobiles, run most efficiently at temperatures that would oxidize or soften existing metal alloys. So the Ford Motor Company, among others, is testing turbines with rotors made of silicon nitride, derived from sand and nitrogen. Other novel ceramic products in the testing stage or actually in production include garbage-disposal blades, ceramic foam that absorbs intense heat without cracking and xenon-gas light bulbs whose ceramic-encased electrical arcs produce more light for less power than a tungsten filament.

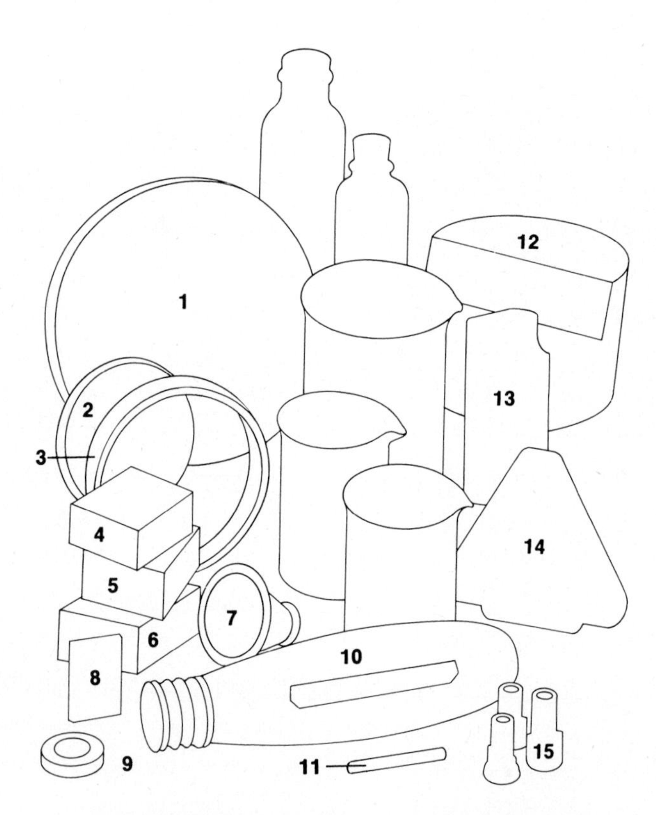

1. Honeycombed heat exchanger
2. Catalytic converter part
3. Garbage-disposal blade
4. Insulating foam
5. Insulating foam
6. Insulating foam
7. Rocket-engine cone
8. Machinable silica
9. Chain-saw sprocket
10. Light-bulb arc case
11. Laser rod
12. Insulating foam
13. Turbine vane
14. Furnace rack
15. Sand-blast nozzles

A variety of new ceramic products, having properties once thought impossible to achieve in the material, surround beakers and bottles holding the common earthy stuff from which they were fired. The key at left identifies them.

900 ml
±5%
800

Tailor-made Toughness

To strengthen most ceramics, scientists adjust the recipe so that the molecules take on as homogeneous a crystalline structure as possible, since any irregularities may become cracks under stress. They create this molecular orderliness by using chemical additives, keeping impurities to less than one part per billion and controlling temperatures to 1/1000 of a degree.

Glass, however, normally cools so rapidly during manufacture that its molecules are randomly arranged. As a result, it calls for special fortifying measures. The lens and sheet glass at right are chemically strengthened by immersion in a molten salt bath. There, sodium chloride molecules react with the glass and meld with its outer layers. When cool, this extra layer resists stresses that would shatter ordinary glass.

Yet even glass can be endowed with an orderly structure if it is seeded with nuclei of special metallic oxides around which crystals form and is subjected to heat under exacting controls. The result is an opaque, fine-grained material called glass-ceramic that can rival steel in strength, withstand extreme thermal shock *(right)*, or be shaped by ordinary metal-working tools as shown below.

Without cracking or chipping, a glass-ceramic core is turned on a metal-working lathe. This adaptability to machine tooling allows ceramics to be used for a wide range of products—including ball bearings and gaskets —that formerly could be fabricated only with metal.

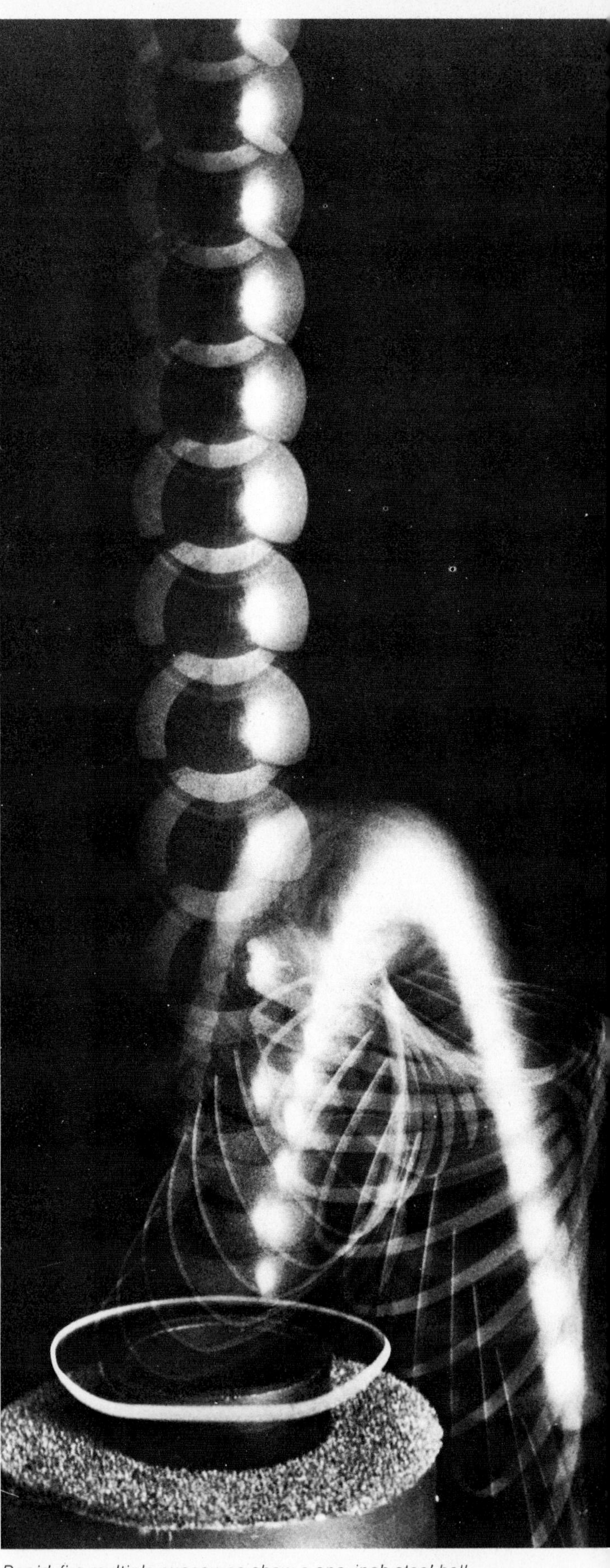

Rapid-fire multiple exposures show a one-inch steel ball dropping from a height of 10 feet onto an eyeglass lens. The ball bounces off, and the lens, which is made of chemically strengthened glass, remains intact.

With one end imbedded in a block of ice and the other licked by flame, a glass-ceramic dish nonetheless fails to crack, owing to its tendency not to expand when heated. Such dishes can be popped directly from the freezer into the oven.

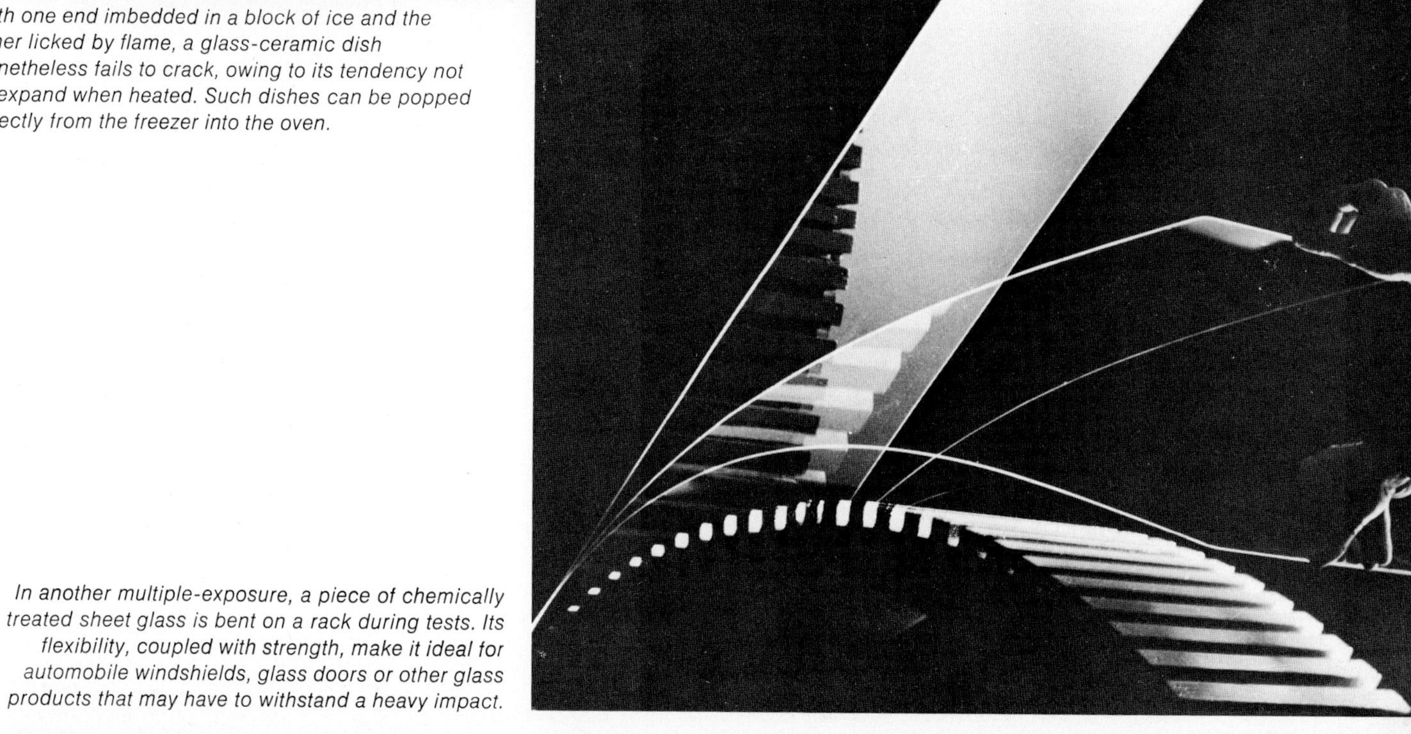

In another multiple-exposure, a piece of chemically treated sheet glass is bent on a rack during tests. Its flexibility, coupled with strength, make it ideal for automobile windshields, glass doors or other glass products that may have to withstand a heavy impact.

Special Jobs for Special Materials

It is a long way from the clay-pigeon that shatters when hit by a few pellets of shot to the bulletproof vest at right—but both are composed of ceramics. Boron carbide, the stuff of which the vest is made, is only one of several tough, lightweight ceramic materials that may serve as armor for tomorrow's combat forces.

Such surprising applications have become routine in the field of ceramics engineering. In recent years, many an appliance-buyer has been startled to discover the existence of stove-tops made of glass-ceramic. The unique molecular structure of the stove-top allows radiant heat to pass upward from metal coils beneath it without cracking while preventing heat from traveling sideways; as a result, the stove-top remains cool to the touch centimeters away from the coil area.

Pure science, too, owes a lot to the new ceramics. For instance, the 144-inch-diameter telescope mirror at right, recently installed on a mountaintop in Chile, is made of an extremely pure glass with a dense and regular molecular structure. Because changes of temperature have virtually no effect on the shape of the mirror, astronomers can now photograph the heavens with less distortion than ever before.

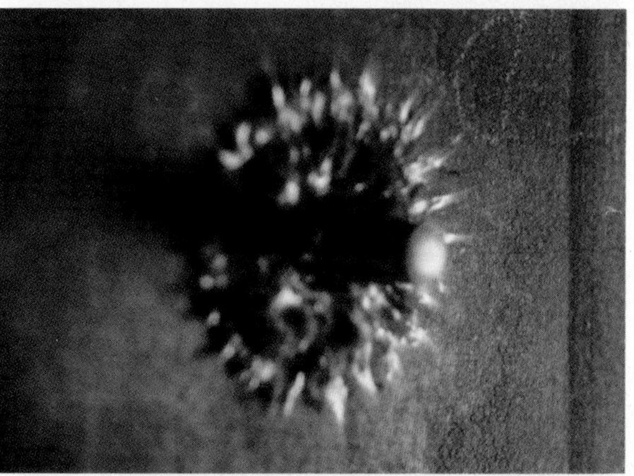

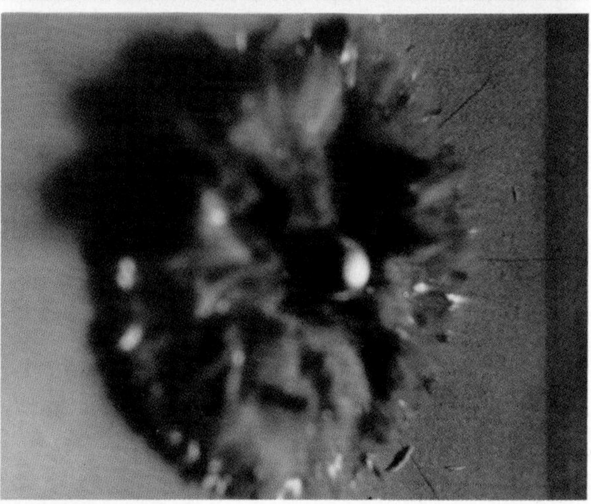

High-speed photography freezes the effects of a bullet striking a protective vest of boron carbide: Penetrating only the outer layer, the bullet breaks into fragments that spray outward along with ceramic powder.

Whisking a sauce on an electric range overlayed with a flat glass-ceramic top, a cook need not worry about spilling. A mere swipe of a rag suffices to mop up any mess.

As scientists check progress, a disc of fused silica—98.95 per cent pure—is ground to a tolerance of one millionth of an inch. When finished, it will be coated with reflective aluminum to become a giant parabolic mirror for a telescope.

TOP
TOP
TOP

Glass Fibers that Carry Messages of Light

Like so many other metals that have been mainstays of modern technology, copper, the basis of telephone wire, is becoming scarce and expensive. At the same time the demand for home and public communication channels is growing exponentially. Again, a ceramic product promises an answer—and an improvement. The system diagrammed at right uses glass fibers to carry voice messages that are coded into pulses of laser light rather than of electricity. Because of the extreme high frequency of light waves, up to 10,000 times as much information can be sent through these so-called optical fibers as through copper conductors of comparable size.

The governing principle is simple. The transparent core of a fiber carries the light, while an outer layer—called cladding—acts as a reflective wall, containing the rays. A rough analogy would be a golf ball driven into a serpentine pipe; clanging and ricocheting from side to side, it would follow the course of the pipe as long as its momentum lasted.

The efficiency of an optical fiber depends on the clarity of the core and the reflective quality of the cladding. The Corning Glass Works has developed a method of making a glass fiber so clear that if it were sea water one could see to the bottom of the deepest ocean trench. The cladding, also glass but of a different composition, refracts, or bends, straying light waves back into the core.

Heated to the melting point, both glass and cladding can be drawn out together into a single flexible filament. Gathered in bundles, the filaments become communications cables *(right)* that will soon replace bulky copper channels in major metropolitan phone systems. In addition to their enormous information-carrying capacity, such optical cables will be free from disruption by stray electrical charges, lightning or the sort of cross-talk that sometimes afflicts adjacent copper wires.

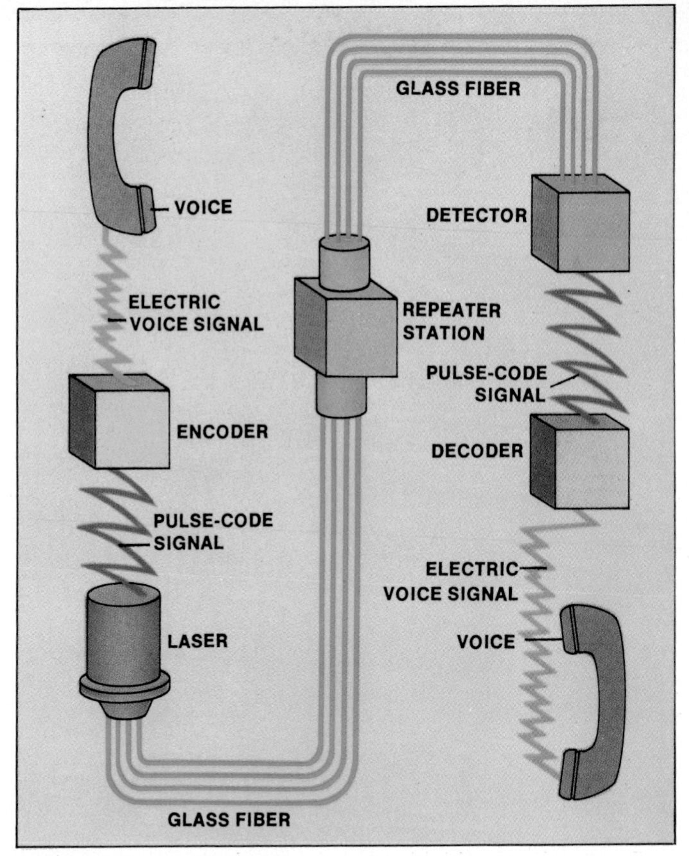

From voice to ear, sound transmitted through an optical fiber system undergoes a series of physical changes. The speaking element in the telephone turns voice into electric signals. These travel to an encoder linked to a miniaturized laser, and the laser emits light pulses into the fiber. Just as in a conventional telephone system, this signal must be boosted at intervals—although less frequently than with copper wires. At the other end of the line, a light-detecting device turns the pulses back into electricity, and another device deciphers the pattern to form a voice signal.

The polyurethane matrix of an optical cable is peeled back to show the internal elements: six fibers—called wave-guides—which are flanked by two nylon cords that add strength. The whole cable, no bigger around than a pencil, is flexible enough to form a circle with a one-inch radius.

In a darkened lab, a helium-neon laser pumps light into a 328-foot-long experimental fiber of fused silica wound on a drum. The fiber conducts the light through its core and projects it onto a screen, where it appears as a red spot.

Better Mileage with Ceramic Turbines

All engines that use heat to produce power are subject to a law of thermodynamics that states: the higher the temperature, the greater the efficiency. Turbines—sophisticated pinwheels driven by hot gases—are particularly well-suited to take advantage of this law. Unlike the piston engines in today's cars, their parts fit together loosely enough to sustain heat expansion without damage. To realize their advantage in efficiency, however, they would have to operate at temperatures beyond 1,900° F., the softening point of alloy steel. Ceramics, of course, can sustain that temperature and engineers have been trying to build a ceramic turbine since early in this century. The results have always been the same: The brittle ceramic breaks up inside the engine and comes spitting out the exhaust.

Now, tough new ceramics have manufacturers hot on the trail of a 2,500° automobile turbine. The key materials, silicon carbide and silicon nitride, have shown great promise in laboratory tests. Fashioning them into delicate half-pound rotors that can spin at 64,000 rpm's is another matter. Ford Motor Company has turned out some 1,000 rotors of various ceramic compositions, and all have cracked during long usage. But Ford is so confident of success that it has accepted a government contract to produce a ceramic turbine to run at 2,500° for 200 hours by 1978. Such an engine, offering dramatically better gas mileage than present-day power plants, could be ready for full-scale production by 1985.

At the Ford Gas Turbine Laboratory in Dearborn, Michigan, an engineer fits an experimental turbine engine with a silicon nitride stator. Stators are fixed members that direct hot gases against the rotor blades at the proper angle.

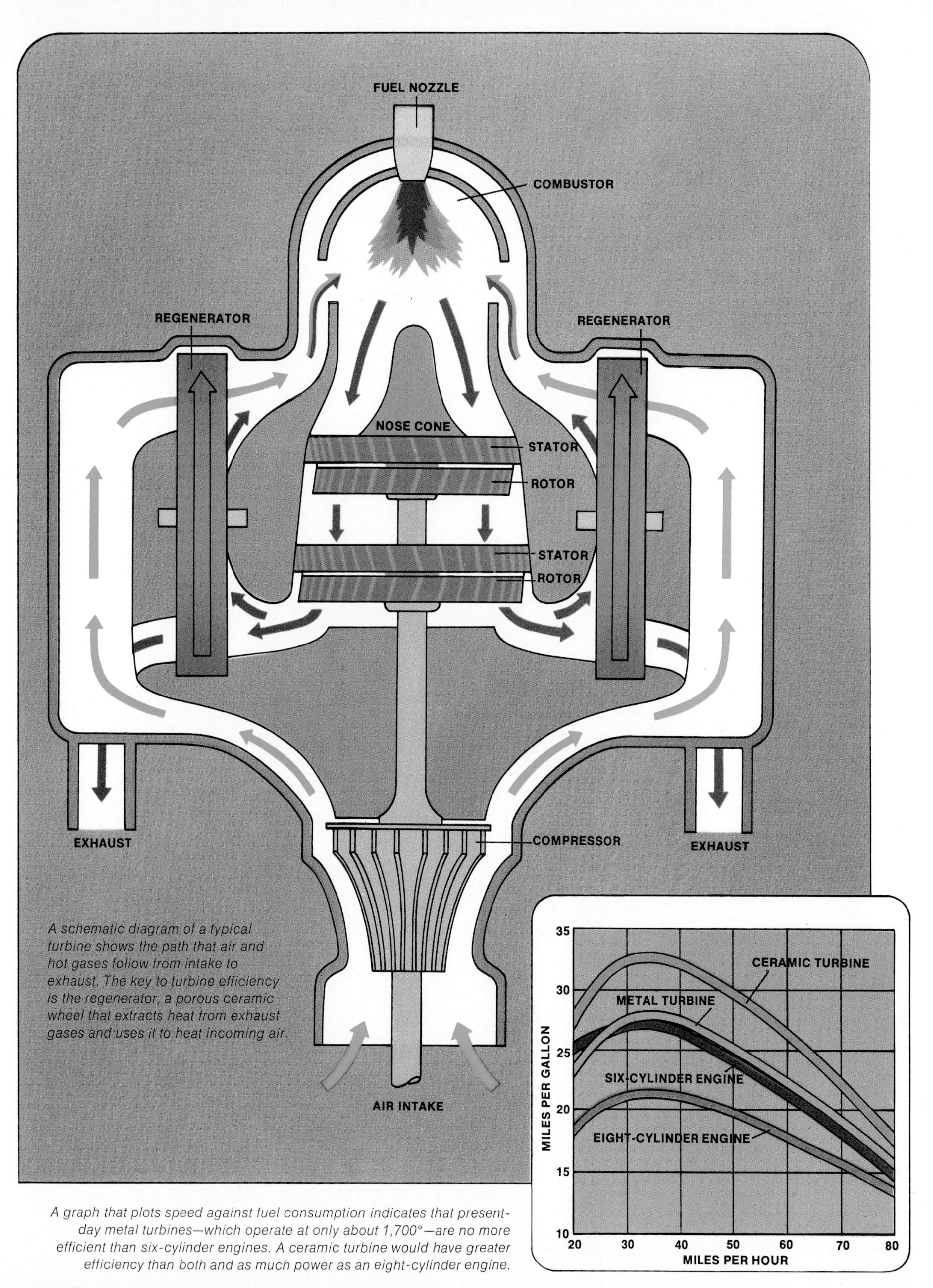

A schematic diagram of a typical turbine shows the path that air and hot gases follow from intake to exhaust. The key to turbine efficiency is the regenerator, a porous ceramic wheel that extracts heat from exhaust gases and uses it to heat incoming air.

A graph that plots speed against fuel consumption indicates that present-day metal turbines—which operate at only about 1,700°—are no more efficient than six-cylinder engines. A ceramic turbine would have greater efficiency than both and as much power as an eight-cylinder engine.

While a technician checks the temperature with an optical instrument, a new turbine's combustor—the engine chamber in which fuel burns—is subjected to a blast of heat.

A silicon nitride stator, raised to 2,500° F. by an oxygen-gas flame, glows but does not soften. Automotive engineers hope to eventually produce ceramic turbines that will operate at 3,000°—and will use half as much fuel as equivalent engines of today.

Momentous New Science

A BLOCKBUSTER BOOK UPDATES DARWIN ON SOCIAL BEHAVIOR

by Maitland A. Edey

Rarely has the world been offered such a splendid stepping stone to the exciting future of a new science." With these words, a leading scientific magazine greeted the appearance last year of a book that, in many respects, deserves to be compared with Charles Darwin's *Origin of Species,* published more than a century ago.

Unlike Darwin's epochal proclamation of the theory of evolution, this new work by Edward O. Wilson of Harvard does not break new scientific ground. Its title—*Sociobiology, the New Synthesis*—is an open acknowledgment of a heavy debt to others, notably Darwin himself. Nonetheless, the accomplishment is stunning. Wilson has clarified some chronic trouble spots in evolutionary theory; at the same time, he has offered an instrument for bridging a gap that has long existed in the study of man—the gap between social scientists, who tend to ignore evolution theory in their investigations, and biologists, who accept it as the cornerstone of everything they do.

By almost any measure, Wilson's book is a big one. It is oversized (having an unusual square format of 10 by 10½ inches) and overweight (nearly three pounds). It is 697 pages long. Its bibliography lists 2,560 separate scientific volumes or papers as its sources, and its range of subject matter is stupefying. Wilson is a formidably erudite man who seems to be as much at home talking about the digestive peculiarities of termites as he is talking about herding among dinosaurs, the schooling of herrings, cooperative

Ring-billed gulls, like these shown on an island in Lake Erie, nest in crowded colonies—a form of inherited behavior that improves their survival chances in three ways. It stimulates sexual activity; it provides a protective cover of flying birds at all times; and it helps preserve superior genes, because the strongest gulls get nesting sites at the center of the colony—where their chicks are safest.

Wild dogs operate in a pack on Tanzania's Serengeti plains to pull down a zebra, something that a single dog could not do because of its much smaller size. Since they are not overly speedy, dogs will usually pick out victims that are young or ailing, and they relentlessly chase their prey to exhaustion before finally closing in for the kill.

nest-building by South American parrots, child-rearing among baboons, conversation among dolphins and the evolutionary future of man.

The link that holds these diverse subjects together is social behavior. Termite, parrot, dolphin and man are all social creatures. They live together in mutually supportive groups. Togetherness has affected their behavior.

The purpose of Wilson's book is to examine as great a diversity of social behavior as he can in an effort to find its biological base: i.e., how much of it is hereditary. In the case of humankind, this subject is a veritable mine field of strongly held —and, in some cases, diametrically opposed— views. At one extreme are men like Robert Ardrey, a persuasive popularizer of paleoanthropology. He has termed man the killer ape, suggesting that there is a human genetic streak that explains man's long history as a hunter, a murderer, a fierce defender of his territory, and that his climb up from apehood and his development of a culture can be explained in terms of that genetic killer instinct. Boiling Ardrey's thesis down and swallowing it whole, one can argue that man is the cruel creature he is because his genes have made him that way for millions of years. From this it follows that he will not change his killer ways unless he changes his genes.

At the opposite pole stand men like the behavioral psychologist B. F. Skinner of Harvard. Skinner argues that any creature capable of learning can have that learning shaped by rewarding "good" responses. According to this argument—and again simplifying it—if a monkey gets a banana every time it pats its brother, brotherhood among monkeys can be encouraged, regardless of genes.

The implications of these two positions, as far as the future evolution of man and his culture are concerned, are, obviously, very strong. Developments in genetics, along with the discovery of DNA and its role as the master blueprint of the individual, suggest that before too long man will begin to have the capability to shape himself and his destiny by deliberately controlling his genes —*if* his genes do indeed play a significant role in his behavior. According to Ardrey's extreme view of evolution, the genetic component of behavior could be overwhelming. According to the Skinnerian view, it could be negligible.

Is social behavior genetic? Yes, says Wilson, some of it is—but the reasons that this is so are not always obvious. If one is willing to think like a sociobiologist, he points out, one must begin by discarding a basic human prejudice that the individual is important.

A SUITCASE FOR GENES

In genetics the individual counts for nothing. What matters is the preservation and change of the genes in response to environmental change and challenge—the process Darwin called natural selection. From the point of view of the gene, a body is simply a convenient suitcase for protecting the gene until it can produce more genes; as Samuel Butler once put it: "A hen is only an egg's way of making another egg." Looked at in this way, a population of human beings or a colony of ants becomes not so much a group of individuals as a collection of genes, most of them alike, but with enough variability in them to enable the selection process to work. Such a collection is known as a gene pool.

Wilson's book examines sociality throughout the animal kingdom and shows that, on balance, it proves to be uncontestably adaptive—that is, designed to improve the survival chances of genes within the gene pools. Social behavior is just another device serving the ends of survival and reproduction, basically no different from limbs, hearts and digestive enzymes. This is true for extremely primitive marine creatures like corals, whose colonies exist in a togetherness so tight that they are physically attached to one another. It is also true for a great number of higher animals including antelopes, dogs, lions and apes—and men.

To nail this down, it is necessary to tick off only a few examples of the advantages conferred by sociality. Mutual defense is an obvious one; a troop of baboons is a formidable adversary to a prowling leopard, whereas a single baboon would provide an easy meal. Less obvious is the tendency of certain songbirds to converge into tight flocks during flight when attacked by a falcon. It would appear that if the birds scattered, each trying to get away by itself, all might escape, and all but one certainly would.

What is the advantage of jamming together? Apparently the genes that program jamming have been selected through countless generations of fatal experience demonstrating that single birds do not escape the faster-flying falcon, and that the chance of being marked down and killed is reduced when a bird becomes just one of a mass of bodies. What makes the massing adaptive, and thus turns it into a truly useful evolutionary behavioral trait, seems to be that the diving falcon has all its killing power concentrated in its talons. The rest of its body is rather light and fragile. Therefore, while it may indeed succeed in striking and killing one bird with its talons, it may at the same time strike others with its body. Inasmuch as falcons sometimes dive at speeds in excess of 200 miles per hour, such accidental collisions could prove fatal to the attackers and could make them more prudent about diving into massed flocks of small birds.

Cooperative hunting also turns out to be more productive than solo efforts. A lioness hunting alone enjoys not much more than half the success that two or three enjoy when acting together. For one thing, the familiar tactic of driving prey in the direction of a hidden partner is impossible for a single lion. Another example: wild dogs, although weighing only about 50 pounds each, are able, in packs, to hunt down and kill antelopes that weigh up to 10 times as much as they do. This would be far beyond the capability of a single dog.

Breeding success is also improved through sociality. Studies of gull colonies show that not only does sexual activity increase under the mutual stimulation of hundreds or thousands of like-minded gulls in close proximity with one another, but also that the continuous presence of numerous adult gulls, either sitting on their nests or flying over the rookery, tends to discourage cruising avian egg- and chick-eaters, such as skuas. Among wildebeests, mating takes place during a period of great activity over a short time. The result is that the calves are all dropped within a few days of one another. And although all the lions and leopards and hyenas and wild dogs in the region feast on young wildebeests for a few days, the mass of births simply overwhelms the predators, and most of the calves survive their first critical hour of helplessness.

The survival value of certain kinds of behavior was apparent to Charles Darwin when he formulated his theory of evolution in 1859. But the significance of other sorts of behavior remained utterly baffling to evolutionists until sociobiology came to the rescue. Ant society is a prime example, and it receives a long, careful examination in Wilson's book—partly to illustrate the insights attainable by the new science, and partly because social insects are Wilson's specialty. He knows as much about them as any man alive.

Ants—along with other social insects such as termites and certain bees and wasps—have developed togetherness to an extraordinary degree. An ant colony does not consist of one kind of ant, but usually three: queen, worker and male. Some species of ants have a fourth form called a soldier. Each of the forms is physically different from the others, and each performs specialized tasks that the others do not. A worker ant can never become a queen, nor can a queen ever become a worker.

Queens are nothing but oversized egg-laying machines, pouring out eggs around the clock to maintain the population of the colony. Other ants in the community are usually incapable of reproduction: the males exist solely for the purpose of fertilizing the queen; the workers and soldiers are sterile females, only rarely laying eggs. The workers take care of all the chores but one—defense. That is the responsibility of the soldiers, which have larger heads and stronger jaws than workers. Soldiers are designed to fight, and they rush to repel any threat to the colony, either taking defensive positions in a breach of the fortifications, or actively attacking an invader.

What stumped Darwin was the existence of sterile workers and soldiers. For in thinking about them in terms of natural-selection theory, he ran headlong into a paradox: how could these castes of insect societies have evolved if they leave no offspring?

Wilson takes a hard look at that paradox, and also at a second and related one: the evolution of altruistic behavior. Wilson defines altruism as an act that occurs "when a person (or animal) in-

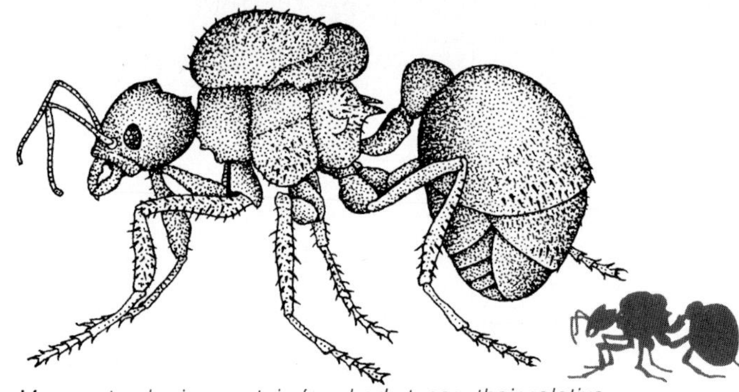

Many ant colonies contain four body types, their relative sizes shown by the figures at the right of each drawing. Largest is the queen, whose sole function is to lay eggs.

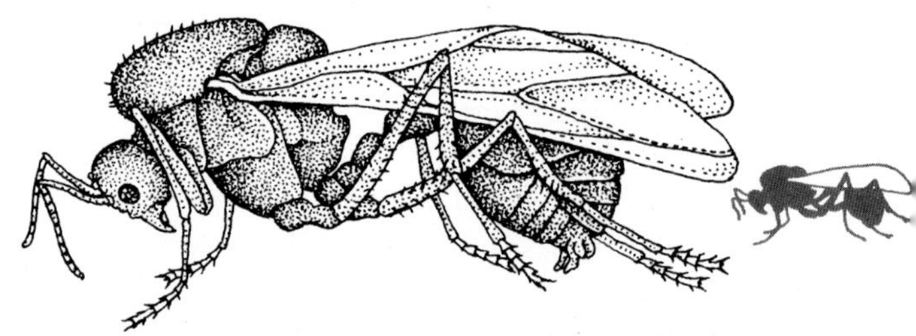

Males, like queens, are produced periodically, and both grow wings and fly off to start new colonies. During the nuptial flight, males will fertilize each virgin queen.

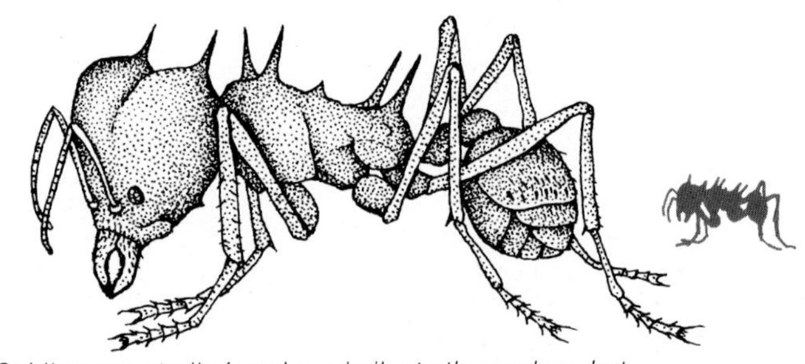

Soldiers are sterile females, similar to the workers but usually with larger bodies and much larger heads and jaws to aid them in their major task: defending the colony.

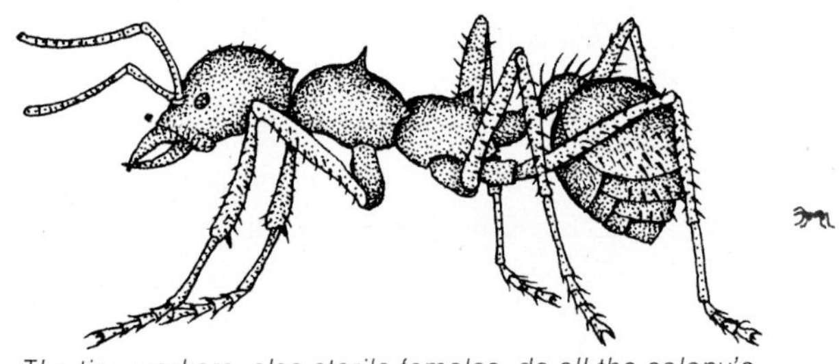

The tiny workers, also sterile females, do all the colony's housework, from tending infants to gathering food. These four drawings are of a species of leaf-cutter ants.

Inside a leaf-cutter colony, workers scramble to care for pupae—the white forms with developed legs and black eyespots—from which new ants hatch. Both the pupae and larvae—an earlier, legless stage—are fed a fruitlike fungus by-product that is grown on leaf mulch in the colony.

creases the fitness of another at the expense of his own fitness." By the terms of that definition, a soldier ant that gives up its life for the benefit of its fellows is acting altruistically. And by the same logic that makes the evolution of insect castes a mystery, equally mysterious is the development of such self-sacrifice among ants. How can the trait ever manage to concentrate itself in the genes in significant amounts if the behavior itself frequently leads to the death of the ant? In short, is not altruism self-destroying?

Wilson's review of this knotty problem is absolutely fascinating. He starts out by observing that Darwin himself arrived by logic at a general understanding of its solution. Darwin suggested that such things as castes and altruism could evolve if they were of overall benefit to the family of the self-sacrificer, since selection could theoretically work at the family level just as well as it could at the level of the individual. He cited the example of a particularly fine vegetable that is harvested and eaten by the farmer before it can produce seeds of its own, but is nevertheless not lost in the genetic sense, because the farmer takes the trouble to save the seeds from other vegetables of the same fine stock; in due course the farmer sows these seeds and thereby preserves fineness.

According to Wilson, Darwin was right. But he did not understand how the process worked, since that depends on an understanding of genetics, and Darwin had never heard of genes; they would not be discovered until the next century. As a result, the twin problems of caste and altruism continued to plague evolutionary biologists until 1963, when a solution was proposed by a young British entomologist and geneticist, William D. Hamilton.

Hamilton pointed out that ants—like most other social insects—determine sex in an unusual way. They use the so-called haplodiploid mode, which simply means that unfertilized eggs produce males and fertilized eggs produce females. Since the queen is the only producer of eggs in the colony, it follows that all the other females (the sterile workers and soldiers that are the daughters of the queen) will be sisters. These sisters have about 75 per cent of their genes in common. In other words, one soldier ant is very close genetically to another soldier ant. So, when the soldier sacrifices its life to save the lives of all the others in the colony, it is actually saving a great many of its own genes—more, in fact, than it would save if it were not sterile, but mated and had offspring of its own. In that case the offspring would have only half of the soldier-mother's genes, the other half having been donated by a male with a set of quite different genes.

The apparent elimination of certain genes by the suicidal behavior of an altruistic ant therefore turns out to be the preservation of the same genes in all the other ants. A fine thing all around; for not only does it help protect the ants from present danger, but it also helps perpetuate altruism, and thus the future of the colony, by helping to ensure that future generations of equally altruistic soldiers will be on hand to make their own sacrifices for the colony when the appropriate time comes.

The success of any sort of social behavior can be measured by the ability of a species to survive, to increase its numbers, to spread out in its environment, or, by evolution, to occupy more and more niches in an environment. By these definitions of success, the ant version of sociality is an unparalleled triumph. At the present moment about 8,000 different species of ants are known. At the rate new ones are being discovered, it is estimated that the total number of known species will ultimately rise to 12,000. "There are more species of ants," says Wilson, "in one square kilometer of Brazilian forest than all the species of primates in the world, more workers in a single colony of driver ants than all the lions and elephants in Africa." The backyard of any suburbanite in temperate North America may have a hundred or a thousand times as many ants in it as his town has people.

THE EVOLUTION OF ALTRUISM

For all its usefulness to ants, altruism is not an evolutionary panacea. In a survey of social traits from the lowest creatures on up, Wilson finds that altruism generally decreases the higher one looks on the evolutionary scale. He lists four main groups of social animals:

1) Colonial marine forms like corals, bryozoans and syphanophores. Within a colony of bryozoans, specialization is so extreme that the individual members have virtually lost their identity. The colony itself becomes the organism, and the individual members begin to play the role of specialized cells within it. Some are for digestion, others for surface protection, and so on. They reproduce by growing buds, which assures that their genetic overlap is 100 per cent. They are physically attached to one another, and no individual can survive without all the others. Therefore, their altruism is also 100 per cent. In Wilson's words, "They have come close to producing perfect societies."

2) Social insects. These are less nearly perfect than colonial marine species in that their genetic overlap is only 75 per cent, and their altruism is correspondingly reduced. Notwithstanding the important factor that they have evolved castes of sterile workers, the society is not quite ideal. Things sometimes go wrong in an anthill. Signals get messed up. Female workers occasionally sneak eggs of their own into the brood cells. In fact, says Wilson, there is evidence that "in some species of ants, bees and wasps a low-keyed struggle continually takes place between queens and workers for the opportunity to produce sons." In addition, some ants are just plain lazy. They become a drag on the colony as a whole, doing very little work but living as long as the others and enjoying the benefits of the others' harder work.

3) Vertebrates, including mammals. Here there are no castes; the genetic overlap is only 50 per cent, and altruism is reduced nearly to zero. With the exception of mother-infant care, selfishness rules the roost, and all that keeps the social groups of higher animals from flying apart from inner destructiveness is a wide variety of behavioral inhibitors and motivators that space populations out in an area, prevent fighting, control numbers, and so on.

Nevertheless, the adaptive push toward sociality is very strong, and the trait is correspondingly widespread among vertebrates. The reason, Wilson suggests, is that mammals are far more intelligent and can exploit sociality in far more complicated ways. "Each member of the vertebrate society," he says, "can continue to behave selfishly as dictated by the lower degree of kinship. But it can also afford to cooperate more by deftly picking its way through the conflicts and hierarchies of the society with a minimum expenditure of personal genetic altruism."

Such behavior is based on the ability of individual mammals to recognize one another, something that is beyond the grasp of an ant. The best that an ant can do is to recognize a fellow-member of its own colony by its smell. A thousand or a million, they all smell the same, and which is which no ant can tell. But a chimpanzee not only knows all the other members of its troop personally, it also knows how, for its own peace of mind and bodily security, to behave toward each one. Furthermore, it can observe and remember the success or failure of certain acts, not only with respect to its own fortunes but also to the fortunes of the entire troop.

4) Humans. Wilson puts man in a separate category from the other vertebrates because of the extreme degree to which he has carried the "vertebrate traits while adding unique ones of his own. In so doing he has achieved an extraordinary degree of cooperation with little or no sacrifice of personal survival and reproduction."

MAN: THE ULTIMATE ALTRUIST

In a sense, man appears to have rediscovered altruism—or at least reversed the downward trend displayed by other vertebrates. Unlike other mammals, he is an inveterate sharer. He is constantly giving things away, not so much out of the goodness of his heart as because he is the only animal intelligent enough to look ahead and see the validity of the proposition: I'll help you now, you help me later. All barter, all commerce is built on that proposition. So is the invention of money. So, ultimately, is culture, and finally the post-industrial technological behemoth that we have forged for our current dwelling place. Altruism, however one cares to look at it philosophically (that is to say, morally), turns out to be an indispensable component for the survival of intelligent beings who are designed to live in groups—as men are.

Wilson goes much further than simply looking at humans in terms of their altruism. However, he proceeds cautiously, well aware that sociologists and many psychologists are uncomfortable with ideas that base the complexities of human behavior on genes. There is every reason for such discomfort.

Soon after Darwin's theory of natural selection was enunciated, it began to be distorted by people who did not fully understand it but who, at the same time, were not above using it to bolster their own social or political ideas. Social Darwinism emerged. This was the belief that the survival of the fittest was not the survival of populations but the survival of individuals, of *rugged* individuals who survived at the expense of others. "Nature red in fang and claw"—as the poet Alfred Lord Tennyson phrased it—became the byword of Social Darwinism, and it was used to justify the heartless inequities of the class system in England, accentuated by the onset of the Industrial Revolution. The poor were poor because they deserved to be; they were genetically unfit and demonstrated their unfitness by their poverty—a neatly circular argument. The same argument was used to justify the subjugation of other peoples throughout the world by the British during the build-up of their empire.

Modern sociobiology is in many ways the opposite of the old Social Darwinism. It sees competition as only one of the processes at work within societies, and stresses the roles of cooperation and altruism. Sociobiologists also acknowledge the overriding importance of experi-

ence and culture in shaping the fine details of human behavior. Nevertheless, Wilson would still search for human behavioral attributes that are universal. These, properly understood, should provide a steady base for analyzing the more changeful and enigmatic behavior that results.

The problem, then, is to identify traits so ingrained in human behavior that we may not even recognize them for what they are: evolved patterns of action critical to our survival. Since man is a primate, he shares some of these traits with apes and monkeys. Others, which explain why he is a man and not an ape, he has to himself. In the first category, Wilson lists the following:

- Aggressive dominance systems, with males dominant over females.
- Scaling of responses, especially in aggressive reactions. This simply means that facial and other behavioral signals change and become more emphatic as the tension rises. When the boss raises his eyebrow, he does not mean the same thing as when his face gets purple and he bangs his desk with his fist. Woe to the clerk who does not understand this.
- Prolonged maternal care, accompanied by pronounced socialization among the young. Care is widespread in the animal world. Even ants are solicitous of their eggs and larvae, but they have no adolescence as we understand it. An ant never plays; it does not need to. Only the higher animals with larger brains do that. Among these higher species, socialization is a critical tool for teaching youngsters how to get along in the complicated society they are about to join—how to interpret the boss's frown, for example.
- Matrilineal organizations. Despite the dominance hierarchies that males work out among themselves, the real glue that holds many primate societies together, including many human ones, is the ties between females—sisters and their offspring.

Wilson then lists four traits peculiar to humans:

- True language and elaborate culture.
- Sexual activity continuous throughout the menstrual cycle. Among other mammals, females are sexually attractive to males only when in heat.
- Formalized incest taboos and rules for marriage exchange. This complex subject goes back again to genes. In a small population where inbreeding is the norm (or forced because of the population's isolation, on an island, for example), evolution will tend to be more rapid and specialization more pronounced because the gene pool will have little variety. What traits there are in it will double up and become increasingly concentrated through inbreeding of close relatives. Some of those traits are potentially harmful. If carried singly in the recessive state by an individual, they do not express themselves, and he goes happily through life without ever realizing he has them. But if he marries someone with a bad trait like his own, it could double up and appear damagingly in his children.

With a show of fangs, a dominant male gelada baboon in Ethiopia sends a subordinate scurrying (upper left). Such threat behavior and the organization of dominance hierarchies are needed by higher animals to avoid bloodshed—altruism is not well developed among them.

A strong case can be made for man's instinctive loathing of incest as an evolved behavioral device for avoiding too close inbreeding. The trait would have developed early in man's evolutionary history, long before he had any understanding of what he was doing—any more than gibbons have when they throw adolescents out of the family to seek mates elsewhere in the forest, or a female mouse has when, confronted with a choice of mates, she selects the one that smells the least like her father.

- Cooperative division of labor between adult males and females. The degree and complexity to which this developed in humans has no parallel among animals. Ants, bees and wasps divide labor, but they do not do it along sexual lines, since both workers and soldiers are females.

MAN'S HUNTER-GATHERER HERITAGE

In considering the deep-set characteristics of human behavior, it should be emphasized that they have evolved over a tremendously long period of time during which man's way of life did not really change much. He remained a scavenger and a hunter-gatherer, living in small bands, aggressive, fiercely loyal, suspicious of strangers but aware of distant relationships, able to devise ways of outbreeding for his young. So he has continued through thousands of generations, his instincts shaped to serve his way of life.

Now he finds himself suddenly confronted with a way of life that the old traits may not be suited to. No matter that he created that new way himself, no matter that he has shown a good deal of flexibility in adapting to it. He still has to live in it with an old set of instincts, which appear to be increasingly anachronistic in dealing with the new problems of overpopulation, habitat destruction, exhaustion of natural resources, greater and greater imbalances in standards of living throughout the world—and a technology now so potent that he can wipe himself out overnight if the old angers and suspicions prove so strong in a crisis that they affect his decisions.

Sociobiology carries with it the clear implication that somewhere in its future lies the necessity for some intelligent social engineering in humans. This will not be accomplished, says Wilson, by designing the kind of perfect cultural environments that Skinner would have. For all the conditioning Skinner would give us, some of our genes may not accept that environment. Under sufficient stress, they may react by burning it down or blowing it up.

Nor is man simply a killer ape, the victim of his genes. In fact, and despite Robert Ardrey, he is not really much of a killer at all compared to many other animals. Hyenas, for example, habitually practice cannibalism: cubs feeding on an animal carcass must be guarded by their mothers lest they be eaten by other members of the hyena clan. Lions and monkeys sometimes fight to the death. Says Wilson: "We are among the more pacific mammals as measured by serious assaults or murders per individual per unit time, even when our episodic wars are averaged in."

What makes man appear so bloodthirsty is that he is so good at killing. When he decides to do it, he kills more efficiently and more intelligently and on a larger scale than any other creature known, just as he does nearly everything else more efficiently and more intelligently. Therein lies his greatest power and his greatest peril.

As possessors of a culture, we have learned how to do many things superlatively well. We are also unique in the animal world in being able to think about the consequences of what we do, and to make elaborate plans for the future. In that planning, sociobiology seems to be telling us, let us not forget our genes. They just may be fatally ill-designed for the new world we are creating. As Wilson puts it: "Social evolution has locked us onto a particular course which the early hominids still within us may not welcome."

If so, we had better get on with the job of thinking more like sociobiologists in order to find out more about our deep-set behaviors, how to analyze them, how to control them, how to change them. That will take time, and time is running out. Technologically we are moving at breakneck speed; biologically we are moving at an imperceptible crawl. If we are to survive as a species, we had better do something about ourselves before the gap created by those different speeds becomes too great. According to Wilson, we have about a hundred years.

In a herd of wildebeests grazing in East Africa, the light-brown youngsters are all the same size, indicating that they were born within a few days of one another. This birth synchronization effectively swamps hungry predators and thus ensures the survival of most of the newborn.

S. CHWAST

Science vs. Astrology

A BLUE-RIBBON COMMITTEE TRIES FOR A KNOCKOUT

by Robert Wallace

In terms of the brain power involved, the biggest bomb last year was the blockbuster dropped on astrology by 186 prominent scientists, including 18 winners of the Nobel Prize. Most of the distinguished group had long considered it beneath professional dignity to comment on "the pretentious claims of astrological charlatans." But now, in a statement headed "Objections to Astrology," they let fly. "One would imagine, in this day of widespread enlightenment and education, that it would be unnecessary to debunk beliefs based on magic and superstition. Yet, acceptance of astrology pervades modern society. We are especially disturbed by the continued uncritical dissemination of astrological charts, forecasts and horoscopes by . . . otherwise reputable newspapers, magazines and book publishers. This can only contribute to the growth of irrationalism and obscurantism."

The scientists' statement, which appeared in the intellectual magazine *Humanist,* was drafted by Bart J. Bok, a past president of the American Astronomical Society. The magazine also carried two lengthy articles—one by Bok himself, the other by an engineer and science writer, Lawrence Jerome—that were calculated to demolish astrology for all time. This "pseudoscience," noted the articles, makes some extraordinarily ambitious claims. It holds that the personality of an individual is shaped by the positions of the sun, moon and planets in relation to various constellations of stars at the very instant of his birth. His nature may turn out to be saturnine, perhaps, or martial or mercurial, depending on the planet that most influences him. Furthermore, as he goes through life, his particular nature will be affected in predictable ways by the constantly

In a lighthearted look at one of the longest-running—and least-availing—battles waged in the name of science, a besieged astronomer flails out against the superstition of astrology, represented by the 12 signs of the zodiac.

changing configuration of the heavens, and he can improve his lot or steer clear of trouble if he heeds the prevailing celestial conditions.

The scientific mind finds these notions to be entirely without merit. As far as is known, a distant celestial body can make itself felt on earth only by gravitational, magnetic or radiative forces—and because of the distances involved, says Bok, such forces are "unbelievably, vanishingly small." In fact, he adds, "the gravitational forces at birth produced by the doctor and nurse and by the furniture in the delivery room far outweigh the celestial forces."

Some defenders of astrology, seeking refuge in pure speculation, have proposed that each planet gives off a unique and still-undetected radiation or "vibration." To this, Bok replies: "If there is one thing we have learned over the past 50 years, it is that the sun, moon, planets and stars are all made of the same stuff, varieties and combinations of atomic particles and molecules, all governed by uniform laws of physics. . . . It does not make sense to suppose that the various planets and the moon, all with rather similar physical properties, could manage to affect human affairs in totally dissimilar fashions." And in any case, why should astrologers insist that "the precise moment of birth is the critical instant in a person's life? Is the instant of conception not basically a more drastic event?"

The scientists' attack appeared not to faze astrologers and believers in the least. A Gallup poll revealed no falling-off in the number of Americans—a thumping 22 per cent of the adult population—who admit to having a hunch that stars and planets may influence people's lives and foretell events. Some 1,250 of the nation's 1,500 daily papers continued to print astrology columns, which were read regularly by as many as 35 million people. Nor did the editors of these otherwise reputable publications appear to feel any embarrassment. An editorial in the Washington *Star* called the antiastrology statement "the most futile broadside of recent memory" and concluded sourly, "we hope it made the scientists feel better."

Neither did the scientists get much help from their cousins in psychiatry. Said Dr. Stephen Appelbaum of the Menninger Foundation: "It's just as easy to believe in astrology today as it is to believe in the government. Astrology's been around a lot longer than the government and it's done a lot less harm." Then, in a backhanded swipe at the scientists, he went on: "I'd tie the growing interest in astrology to a tendency to reject the crushing influence of a technology that allows us to go to the moon, yet does little to help our minds or produce a feeling of security."

Another psychiatrist, Dr. Alan Rosenberg of New York, said he thought American interest in astrology would increase. "People are confused. They want help in making decisions involving finance, personal relationships and employment. Religion isn't meeting the need as it once did and psychiatry has its limitations. So . . . in an attempt to attach themselves to something that appears to have scientific possibility [they] have turned in growing numbers to astrology."

The fact that there is no scientific support whatever for astrology has never, for more than a twinkling, disturbed true believers. When astrology was developed in Babylonia 4,000 years ago, as a means of foretelling the fate of kings, there were undoubtedly men of rational mind who opposed it—to no avail. When astrology spread to Greece, the scientist Aristarchus of Samos (c. 250 B.C.), famous as the first scholar to maintain that the earth moves around the sun, did his best to halt the nonsense—with no success. In Rome, Cicero spoke out against it, observing that "Superstition . . . has usurped nearly everyone's wits and scored over human silliness." In Renaissance Italy, the philosopher Pico della Mirandola growled that "astrology stands first among those superstitions of which she is both mother and foster-child." In France, Voltaire snapped at "this idle fancy of astrology," and in Switzerland John Calvin denounced it as "a devilish superstition." But then poor Calvin was obliged to add, "And yet at this day it hath got the upper hand."

Astrology, alas, hath often got the upper hand in its encounters with men of intelligence, many of whom *need* a convenient superstition and cannot be forced to give it up by mere logic or scorn. Victory over astrology—or at any rate over an individual astrologer—requires a different strategy, first demonstrated by England's great satirist Jonathan Swift.

In Swift's day, the foremost astrologer in London was an overweening quack named John Partridge, who had grown rich publishing an almanac of vague, equivocal predictions. To attack him, Swift wrote his own almanac, a pamphlet titled *Predictions for the Year 1708* and attributed to the pen of a certain Isaac Bickerstaff, Esq. In it, the fictional Bickerstaff, claiming to be a truly skilled reader of the stars, derided other astrologers as bumblers and, as evidence of his own talent, wrote: "My first prediction is but a trifle, yet I mention it to show how ignorant these sottish pretenders to astrology are in their own concerns: it refers to Partridge the almanac-maker. I have consulted the star of his nativity by my own rules, and find that he will infallibly die upon the 29th of March next about eleven at night of a raging fever. Therefore I advise him to consider of it and settle his affairs in time."

On the morning of March 30, 1708, there appeared a printed *Elegy* announcing the death of the unfortunate (and, of course, still living) Partridge, exactly as Bickerstaff had predicted. After a few days, Swift published another pamphlet, *The Accomplishment of the First of Mr. Bickerstaff's Predictions,* set forth by a supposedly disinterested observer. Partridge had indeed died on the right day, wrote the observer with his tongue firmly in his cheek, but at five minutes past seven in the evening, not at 11, "by which it is clear that Mr. Bickerstaff was mistaken almost four hours in his calculation."

Hoping to save the world from predicted destruction, Hindu priests throw sacrificial butterfat into a ritual fire. Indian astrologers had prophesied that a global holocaust would occur on February 3, 1962, because of a rare conjunction of eight planets in the sign of Capricorn.

Subsequently, as the wits of London nudged one another in delight, there appeared a dozen pamphlets by various authors, some defending and some attacking Bickerstaff. The finest of them was written by Swift himself, probably in collaboration with his playwright friend, William Congreve. Titled *Squire Bickerstaff Detected,* it told of the sufferings astrologer Partridge had endured because of the villainous Bickerstaff. Churchbells had been tolled for poor Partridge; he had found a crapehanger in his own house, measuring the walls for the black drapes that were to be put up; the sexton had called, and then the undertaker. As a crowning indignity, he had been dunned for the expenses of his own funeral. "I could not stir out of doors for three months after this," the astrologer allegedly complained, "but presently one comes up to me in the street, 'Mr. Partridge, that coffin you was buried in last, I have not yet been paid for.' "

Partridge might have survived as an astrologer if the affair had remained in the realm of satire. But it did not remain there. As though all the gravitational, magnetic and radiative forces of the stars and planets were furiously at work, it somehow crossed over into the real world. Perhaps because they were sick of Partridge or sick of astrology, the Company of Stationers, a guild of publishers, struck his name from their rolls and claimed all rights of publication of *Partridge's Almanac.* When Partridge appealed, he was overruled by the Lord Chancellor. He was dead in effect if not in fact, and had to take up a new career. Abandoning astrology, he set himself up as a physician, and only God knows how many patients perished at his hands.

The lesson of this, if one may presume to point out such a thing to 186 eminent scientists, including 18 winners of the Nobel Prize, is: spend no more time denouncing astrologers. It has never been any use. Just announce their demise, then sit back and watch fact follow fiction.

More Foods for Mankind

Quail eggs for breakfast? Possum for lunch? Oryx for supper? Bizarre meals like these, seemingly of interest only to a wilderness adventurer or an insatiably curious gourmet, may someday be common. Such, at least, is the aim of a number of programs designed to expand the list of animal species that supply mankind's food.

Some of the fastest-moving of these new programs are propelled by the profit motive. A major growth industry in Louisiana, for example, involves the cultivation of crawfish—delicious freshwater cousins of lobsters that can be raised by the ton in any shallow pond. Louisiana farmers have also discovered that rice fields make an excellent crawfish habitat; stocking and harvesting of the crustaceans can be done at times that do not interfere with rice cultivation and the profits per acre increase by about 25 per cent.

Global malnutrition is another motive force for novel animal-breeding efforts. Much of the world now suffers from serious protein deficiency, in part because populations are soaring, and also because farmland is widely misused. African herders, for example, devote their rangeland to cattle, even though the animals feed on only a few of the local plants and, in consequence, are undersized and give very little milk. By contrast, antelopes—among them the oryx and eland—thrive on the vegetation and require comparatively little water. Efforts are now underway to measure their potential for ranching, and agronomists are also giving thought to the possible domestication of another well-adapted creature—the African buffalo. Such efforts seem long overdue: Out of a total of 4,500 mammal species, humankind has domesticated a mere 16.

Afloat on a 250-acre pond in Louisiana, a worker hauls up a wire-mesh trap full of crawfish. Three thousand such traps, sunk in the pond and baited with fish heads, yield 30 tons of crawfish a year. The harvest is mostly consumed locally, but some shipments go as far afield as Boston and Paris.

The Catfish: Goblin into Protein

Even more than the crawfish, the catfish is on its way to becoming a staple food in Mississippi, Arkansas and Louisiana. The number of fish farms has risen dramatically in the last decade, and while only 55,000 acres are devoted to catfish ponds, the annual yield is up to 80 million pounds —1,500 pounds an acre as opposed to a cattle-ranching ratio of 150 pounds of beef an acre.

Unfortunately, consumption outside the South and parts of the Midwest has been discouraged by the appearance of the fish, which has a bulbous head and a spray of fleshy whiskers that the catfish use to feel their way while bottom feeding. But the delicious fish does not lack for enthusiasts abroad. The U.S. now exports fry to catfish farms in South America, Europe and the Philippines; and this fall, frozen catfish by the ton will be shipped to the fish-loving Japanese.

At a catfish breeding pond in Greenville, Mississippi, a netted scoop called a brailer dips into a seine net and lifts a load of two-year-old catfish weighing up to two pounds apiece. A handful of newly launched breeding programs in the South and Midwest aim at developing catfish that will grow faster and reach maturity at a uniform size.

An Arkansas state fish hatchery contains carefully diked and watered ponds, each an acre in size. The fish grown here are used to stock public waters throughout the state.

Channel catfish—the only species raised commercially—feed in an Arkansas pond. Not only is its flesh firm and tasty, but the channel cat is especially efficient at converting its diet of fishmeal pellets into meat.

A brailer, loaded with fish from the Greenville pond, is hoisted from the seine net by a long crane mounted on a flatbed truck. The catfish will be lowered into vats of water in the second flatbed truck on the dike and delivered alive and fresh to nearby markets or to local processing plants for freezing and distribution to other parts of the U.S.

Odd Birds, Possums and Outsized Rodents

Chickens, domesticated in 2000 B.C. in the Indus Valley, provide fully a fifth of the world's meat. But when it comes to laying eggs, quail—according to experimental breeders in Pennsylvania—are better. Quail begin to lay eggs in a third the time it takes a chicken to get started and a healthy quail hen will lay an egg almost every day for the next year. The layers can be kept in small, inexpensive pens and they eat much less than chickens, making the net cost per pound of eggs lower. In terms of meat, however, the quail is no great shakes: The average quail weighs only half a pound.

By contrast, the cassowary of New Guinea, also a target of experimental breeding, weighs up to 150 pounds. A cassowary is a flightless bird that lives in deep forests and has been raised for millennia by natives for its meat and feathers. The New Guinea government is capitalizing on the local knowledge of cassowary husbandry by setting up wildlife preserves and paying natives $5.00 each for eggs and chicks to stock a new 10-acre breeding farm in the southern highlands. Eventually, this will improve the local protein supply, but no one expects cassowaries to become a big export item.

Possums, on the other hand, may go far—if the visions of an Alabaman named Frank Basil Clark hold up. Clark insists that possums taste good and cost almost nothing to raise. His Big C Possum Ranch is now breeding the hardy marsupials, and he promotes them tirelessly with an International Possum Show and bumper stickers that read "Eat More Possum."

A somewhat surer bet as a significant food source is the capybara, the world's largest rodent. Capybaras live in herds in Venezuela and reach a weight of 100 pounds on a diet of grass; moreover, they produce six young a year. One ranch in Venezuela already has 60,000 of the outsized rodents and crops them regularly for an eager Venezuelan market.

Frank Basil Clark, America's number one possum breeder and promoter, displays his registered champion buck, Stonewall IV. Possums produce at least a dozen young a year, live on cheap animal food, and yield meat that is low in calories, high in protein and—according to Clark—"cleans out the arteries like a Roto-Rooter."

The quail selected by agronomists for an experimental breeding program in Emmaus, Pennsylvania, is a fast-growing species, Corturnix, that matures in approximately two months. Compared to chickens, it saves a pound of feed for every pound of eggs it produces.

Stout legs make the cassowary of New Guinea a speedy bird. The hard horny crest enables it to lower its head and run full tilt through thick brush without harming itself.

A group of stolid, heavy-lidded capybaras sits on the edge of a river on the El Frio Ranch in Venezuela. Capybaras move slowly, tend to stay in one place and are easily rounded up for slaughter. Their meat is then dried and salted for local use. So far, no U.S. consumption.

The Art of Antelope Ranching

A wild oryx is chased down by a bush vehicle. When it becomes winded and stops to face its pursuers, the ranchers will jump down out of the car, grab its horns and wrestle it to the ground. Total elapsed time for capture: a mere two or three minutes.

Masai ranch hands tie the wild oryx's legs and blindfold it to quiet the animal. It will then be transferred to a dark pen with thick straw sides, where it gets used to captivity.

Over the centuries domestic cattle have worked their way into much of Africa—and some experts consider their introduction into the drier areas a disaster. They move in dense herds, ruin the land, and, because of their water needs and their susceptibility to tsetse fly and other diseases, produce a low return of meat per acre of range. The oryx, on the other hand, has been adapted to East Africa's drier areas for tens of thousands of years. This handsome black-and-buff-faced antelope is immune to local diseases, eats a wide variety of vegetation, leaves the land in good condition, grows sleek in places that might starve cattle and needs less than five quarts of water a day, compared to a cow's 42 quarts.

Today, the Washington-based African Wildlife Leadership Foundation is experimenting at the Galana Game Ranch in southern Kenya with a herd of 75 oryxes, built up from wild animals. The oryxes appear to be tractable enough for local-style ranching: they are herded by Masai ranch hands during the day, then put into corrals at night to protect them from lions and other predators.

Corrals are provided for oryxes at night to protect them from predators. Penning of oryxes during the dangerous hours of darkness is possible because, unlike much other wild game in hot climates, they eat during the day.

Domesticated elands mingle with goats at Kenya's Galana Game Ranch. The eland—as big as a cow—is superior to the cow in every

respect but two: it jumps six-foot fences; and because it is sensitive to heat, it feeds at night, making protective penning impossible.

Exotic Victuals from the Plant Kingdom

Exotic plants appear to have as great nutritional potential as exotic animals, according to a report published in March 1976 by the National Academy of Sciences. Under NAS sponsorship, a panel of 83 botanists from around the world reviewed more than 400 obscure tropical plants and concluded that 36 of them could significantly improve the nutrition and economies of poorer tropical countries. The list includes some extraordinarily sturdy species. For example, a cereal called channel millet, native to the Australian desert, needs just a single rainfall to grow to maturity. No less remarkable is the tamarugo, a tree that grows through a crust of salt several feet thick in Chile's Atacama desert; its leaves and pods are such good forage for sheep that salt-ravaged regions—in Pakistan or the Canary Islands, for instance, could stock the animals in numbers competitive with the world's finest forage areas.

Pound for pound, perhaps the most nutritious plant on the list is the winged bean of New Guinea *(right),* which is grown in the backyard vegetable gardens of natives but has never been scientifically cultivated. Almost all of it—leaves, shoots, pods and roots—are high in protein. The shoots can be eaten raw, the pods boiled or fried, the roots baked like a potato, the leaves served as a salad—and anything left over can be fed to animals. Moreover, like other legumes, the winged bean efficiently extracts nitrogen from the atmosphere and could be an important enricher of impoverished tropical soils.

The winged bean has clusters of long edible pods.

Certain other plants win mixed reviews from the NAS panel—in their present form at least. For example, the durian of Southeast Asia *(opposite)* is described in the report as "the most controversial of all fruits," although its nutritional virtues are undeniable. The durian can grow as much as a foot long and weigh up to 40 pounds, and inside are five sections of cream-colored pulp rich in carbohydrates and vitamins. Elephants, tigers and monkeys love durians, as do natives, who build fences around wild durian trees so that they can get the fruit before the animals do. Unfortunately for its general acceptance, the durian has the reputation of being the world's worst-smelling fruit: One decidedly unenthusiastic partaker described its odor as "a mixture of old cheese and onions flavored with turpentine," while another likened the pulp to "custard passed through a sewer."

The panel is nonetheless hopeful about the durian's future. One of the five known species has a considerably milder odor than the rest, and selective breeding may produce strains even more acceptable to a larger market. Meanwhile, a few durian trees have already been introduced to Central America, and their output has very quickly been snapped up —suggesting that the durian's distinctive odor may be less of a problem than has ordinarily been assumed.

Regardless of the durian's fate, the NAS panel entertains no doubts as to the need for a new, exploratory spirit in agriculture. Over the millennia, farmers have tended to concentrate on fewer and fewer crops, and today the majority of the world's population relies on a mere 20 staples for its food supplies. "These plants are the main bulwark between mankind and starvation," states the report, "and it's a very small bastion." And careful, scientific examination of neglected plants can hardly begin too soon. Partly because of displacement by conventional crops, thousands of plant species are in danger of becoming extinct—and the endangered list includes a number of the plants that have been singled out by the panel for their potential as an important food source of the future.

The durian, grown in trees that reach 100 feet or more in height, is enclosed in a thick skin covered with prickles.

Vanquishing Smallpox

A NOVEL PLAN PAYS OFF

by Don Moser

High in the rugged mountains of Ethiopia, a group of determined hunters is systematically tracking down the last survivors of an endangered species. Soon, probably in weeks or months, the species will become extinct, at least in its wild state. Yet its passing will not be mourned by even the most fervent conservationists, for this endangered species is the microbe known as variola—the smallpox virus.

When smallpox disappears from Ethiopia, man will have eradicated a dread disease from the face of the earth for the first time. It is possible, though not likely, that a few infectious cases will still exist elsewhere, and thus health officials will watch and wait for two years before claiming global victory. At the same time, researchers will continue to investigate a pair of diseases found in monkeys that might possibly be smallpox in disguise. But if the war against smallpox has truly been won—and most epidemiologists believe it has—the accomplishment will surely be the greatest in the history of preventive medicine.

Smallpox has given up its sinister ghost to a massive 10-year campaign run by the United Nations' World Health Organization. Fifty countries, some of them suspicious of or hostile toward one another, participated and cooperated. Hundreds of thousands of health workers labored under dangerous circumstances as they probed into the outermost corners of the earth to track down the last infectious cases. If the magnitude of the

A World Health Organization helicopter brings smallpox vaccine to Ethiopia's rugged highlands, the last stronghold of the disease. Until helicopters came into use in the campaign against the dreaded virus, health workers trekked to remote villages on muleback or foot.

operation was mind-boggling, the benefits are even more so, for the campaign will result in the eradication of a disease that has killed countless millions. Indeed, it has been estimated that before the advent of vaccination, smallpox killed 8 to 9 per cent of all the humans on earth.

GRIM FATALISM

Smallpox has always been one of the four apocalyptic scourges of mankind, and in comparison to the other three—yellow fever, bubonic plague and cholera—it has the capacity to strike terror into the heart. Victims of smallpox suffer horribly and die hard, and those who survive are frequently left blind or disfigured. Over the centuries the malady has inspired a kind of grim fatalism, an acceptance of misery, for there was—and still is—nothing a doctor could do to prevent the disease from running its course.

To understand the battle between man and smallpox, it is necessary to understand something about the disease and how it works. A smallpox virus is a tiny, brick-shaped organism that consists of a protein envelope surrounding particles of DNA—the genetic material that organizes and directs the activities of a cell.

The variola virus is usually transferred from man to man through the air. When inhaled, it is intercepted by the tonsils, adenoids, or other lymph tissues around the back of the nose and throat. These tissues normally manufacture antibodies to destroy foreign substances; but, in this case, before they have time to act, the virus attaches itself to a living cell, into which it injects some of its own DNA. The virus's DNA orders the cell to stop fulfilling its normal functions and instead to direct its energy toward manufacturing more viruses. Soon, the subverted cell starts turning out replicas of its attacker.

After several days of multiplying, the viruses suddenly burst from the host cells and spill into the bloodstream. The body's reticulo-endothelial system, consisting of the lymph nodes and parts of the spleen, bone marrow and other lymph tissues, recognizes the viruses as hostile intruders and tries to filter them from the blood. But the viruses simply attack the reticulo-endothelial system itself, multiplying until they spill again into the blood in such numbers that the natural defense system is overwhelmed. Millions of viruses travel all over the body, infecting new cells. At this point—perhaps 10 days after the initial intake of the virus—the victim begins to feel ill, with flulike symptoms. A week or two later a rash appears on the victim's body—the first outward manifestation of smallpox. From this point onward, a grim lottery has begun. The victim may live or die, and there is no way of telling which. Even in a modern hospital, doctors can do nothing but try to prevent such complications as pneumonia, infection through the skin or dehydration. The victim may die within a couple of days; more commonly, a week or two passes as pus-filled lesions spread over the body. These lesions are areas of combat between viruses and the body's defense system. In some cases, the lesions merge into broad, pus-filled envelopes, until the victim is hardly recognizable. The horrible appearance only suggests the victim's suffering, for similar lesions form inside the body, on the surface of the throat, for example.

No one knows just how the virus kills. Usually the victim dies of what is called overwhelming viremia—but those words are simply medical shorthand to signify a poisoning process that is imperfectly understood. What is certain is that of those victims who contract variola major, the more virulent strain of the virus, from 20 to 50 per cent die. Of those who contract a milder strain, variola minor, death takes only about 1 or 2 per cent. But many survivors are permanently blinded as a result of lesions forming in the eyes. Most victims are disfigured by scars.

Such scars appear on the face of the 3,000-year-old mummy of Pharaoh Ramses V of Egypt, and indeed, there is evidence that smallpox existed in both Africa and Asia in the millennium before Christ. Because smallpox was often confused with chicken pox or syphilis, its record in Europe is confused, but the virus certainly existed there by the 10th Century. It has been estimated that by the 18th Century, one child out of every five born in Europe died of smallpox, and countless numbers were blinded.

The virus was even more murderous in the New World. Spanish troops brought smallpox to

During a smallpox epidemic at the turn of the century, hospital ships were moored in the Thames near London to isolate patients. Though smallpox vaccine was discovered by an English doctor, Edward Jenner, his country was one of the last in Europe to use compulsory vaccination; smallpox was not eradicated there until the 1930s.

Mexico in 1520, where it subsequently killed 3.5 million Indians. In the United States, fatalities among affected Indians sometimes reached 90 per cent. It is all too clear that the whites sometimes used the virus as a biological warfare agent. In 1763, the commander of British forces in the Alleghenies instructed subordinates to infect the Indians with smallpox. Soon after, one of the officers wrote in his journal: "Out of our regard for them [two Indian chiefs] we gave them two blankets and a handkerchief out of the smallpox hospital. I hope it will have the desired effect." It did: a few months later smallpox was raging among the tribes of the Ohio Valley.

Man's attempts to defend himself from smallpox are as old as the disease itself. Many early techniques were misguided and even destructive. Bleeding was common, as was the practice of wrapping victims in scarlet cloth. American Indians put victims in sauna-like sweathouses, and since they usually suffered from dehydration, such treatment boosted the death toll.

One of the oldest methods of combating the virus, which may have been practiced 3,000 years ago in Africa and Asia, was a process known as variolation. A physician would take pus or scab material from a smallpox victim and rub it into a scratch on the arm of someone who had not yet contracted the disease. Occasionally the person thus inoculated got smallpox and died; sometimes he infected others. But surprisingly, the technique was often successful. For reasons that are still not clearly understood, when inoculated in this way the body was able to arrange its defenses for efficient combat. White corpuscles contained the virus in the immediate area of the scratch, while the body began to produce antibodies as a barrier against further spread. The variolated person grew mildly ill, but he recovered, and the antibodies now in his bloodstream immunized him against subsequent attacks of smallpox. Thus, thousands of years ago, men had discovered—without knowing just why it worked—the basic principles underlying vaccination.

But variolation remained a risky process that exacted its own death toll. A chance observation in 1796 by the British naturalist and physician Edward Jenner changed all that. Jenner observed that British milkmaids, who often came down with a minor pox disease they acquired from the udders of cows, very rarely caught smallpox. On the assumption that there was some relationship between the milkmaid's disease, known as cowpox, and human smallpox, Jenner inoculated an eight-year-old boy with pus from a milkmaid's cowpox lesion. Seven weeks later he inoculated the boy with human smallpox virus. The child showed no reaction—he was immune.

Jenner called his discovery vaccination, after the Latin word *vacca,* for "cow." Although vaccination was initally controversial, it caught hold soon in both Europe and America. As scientists refined the vaccine and the process of administering it, they began to bring the old scourge under control. In the decade after World War II, health workers fought smallpox to a standstill in country after country. By the early 1960s variola had disappeared from the developed world, but it remained endemic in 30 countries in Africa, Asia and Latin America, afflicting some 2.5 million people a year.

Ironically, the final assault on smallpox was nearly scuttled by schemes for a war on a different and far less deadly disease—measles. After repeated requests from new African nations, the U.S. Agency for International Development (AID) decided in 1965 to attempt a measles-eradication campaign in West and Central Africa, and asked for technical support from the Center for Disease Control (CDC) in Atlanta. The CDC—the disease-fighting arm of the U.S. Public Health Service—was wary of getting involved. For a number of technical reasons, its officials believed that measles eradication was virtually impossible in developing tropical countries, and at that time they were particularly wary of finding themselves in a losing battle.

Public health specialists throughout the world were still reeling from the abysmal failure of a costly international campaign against malaria. After spectacular early successes it became clear that the program would never succeed. Malaria was too pervasive, mosquitoes were growing resistant to DDT, and the malaria parasite itself was becoming resistant to the new drugs. (Today malaria is increasing at an alarming rate in many parts of the world.) "We were in a state of depression about malaria," says Dr. Donald Millar, an early head of the CDC's smallpox task force. "We figured if we got committed to something like measles eradication, which we thought was impossible, we'd get another black eye. But smallpox looked like a winner."

THE DECISION TO LAUNCH A WAR

Epidemiologists had several reasons for wanting to tackle smallpox head on. It seemed vulnerable in ways that other diseases were not. It passed only between humans, and there were no insect transmitters or reservoirs of infection in animal populations. Unlike such diseases as typhus, the virus had no hard-to-detect carrier state; victims soon became obviously very sick. It was conspicuous: If someone in a village had it, everyone else knew the disease was present. Finally, smallpox was fairly easy to diagnose.

Also, technological advances gave health officials a new edge. A modern freeze-drying technique made it possible to keep smallpox vaccine indefinitely in the tropics even without refrigeration. And the U.S. Army had developed a jet-injector gun with which a vaccinator could inoculate 1,000 people an hour, thus making immunization possible on a vast scale.

There was one other factor in deciding to launch a war against smallpox. It was clear that Americans were in greater danger from vaccination than from smallpox itself. The last North American victim of smallpox was stricken in 1949. But each year since, from seven to nine people, most of them children, had died from adverse reactions to smallpox vaccine. The CDC wanted to stop vaccinating Americans, and the best way to do that was to eradicate the disease.

AID and CDC debated over which campaign to carry out. Finally they agreed to a compromise: CDC would run the measles-control campaign, but AID would pay for a smallpox-eradication program to ride piggyback, as it were—and Africans would be immunized against both diseases at the same time.

Just as the American program was getting underway in 1966, the World Health Organization (WHO) declared its own war on smallpox and committed itself to eliminating the disease from the earth within 10 years. The global attack started on several fronts. The CDC, working with local health authorities, managed the campaign in the 16 countries of West and Central Africa where smallpox was endemic. WHO fielded multinational teams in 19 other endemic countries of Asia, Africa and Latin America.

When the campaign began, most epidemiologists believed that smallpox was a highly contagious, rapidly spreading, predominantly urban disease. Thus the smallpox fighters adopted a strategy of mass vaccination. Teams of vaccinators would sweep through each country, concentrating on urban areas and vaccinating as many people as possible. According to generally accepted mathematical theory, once they had vaccinated four out of every five of the inhabitants of a country—or 80 per cent—the probability of an infectious case transmitting the disease to an unvaccinated person would approach zero. Just as a forest fire will peter out when the density of trees drops below a certain level, the chain of disease transmission would be broken, and smallpox would die out.

But right at the beginning of the program, something very curious happened—something that later would result in a dramatic change of strategy. On December 4, 1966, a smallpox case was reported by a missionary in Ogoja Province in eastern Nigeria. The man in charge of the campaign there was a 30-year-old American epidemiologist and former medical missionary, Dr. William Foege. Foege's vaccines and equipment had just begun to arrive, and he lacked the supplies to start a mass-vaccination program. But Foege is an intense man, devoted to the battle against human suffering, and he reacted like a fireman. Using the missionary radio network to track down other active cases in the area, he and his vaccinating teams set out to inoculate the people in the villages where the outbreaks had occurred. They could not immunize everyone in the province, but they would do what they could.

Ultimately, Foege and his men found 43 smallpox cases in the area. The surprising thing was this: within three weeks from the time Foege went to work, there were no new cases. With limited resources, vaccinating only a small portion of the population, Foege had wiped out the disease in the province. It was, in Foege's words, "a serendipitous event"—an indication, by pure luck, that the mass-vaccination strategy was wrong.

Soon there were other indications. Foege himself organized a textbook mass-vaccination campaign in Abakaliki Province, Nigeria, and managed to vaccinate 88 per cent of the population—comfortably above the theoretical 80 per cent necessary to break the chain of transmission. But three months later there were 37 new cases in the region. Clearly, something was wrong with the mathematical theory.

TOSSING OUT OLD BELIEFS

As work in West Africa progressed, traditional assumptions about smallpox began to seem shaky. For one thing, as health workers pressed farther into the hinterlands, they found more and more smallpox; thus it was not a disease of the city—it had just not been reported from outlying villages. For another, fieldworkers began to find isolated villages where cases turned up over a period of eight or nine months. If the virus were highly contagious, *all* the susceptible individuals should have been stricken in a much shorter period. The new evidence showed that, on the contrary, the disease is usually transmitted through prolonged face-to-face contact.

The sum of this new information began to convince Foege, Millar and other CDC people working in Africa that their approach was wrong. They concluded that their emphasis should not be on mass vaccination, with its 80 per cent magic number. Instead, their effort should be aimed at ferreting out existing smallpox cases and immunizing 100 per cent of the people who might come in contact with each case. Since the disease moved more slowly than had been thought, there should be adequate time to build a social wall of immunity around each case. The difficulty would be in finding all the cases in remote regions, and ensuring that no unvaccinated persons were left in the vicinity of the outbreak.

So in Africa the Americans adopted a new

A rural priest in Ethiopia listens to health workers' pleas for permission to vaccinate villagers. Since smallpox scars are considered a sign of beauty in parts of the country, local leaders sometimes granted their approval only reluctantly.

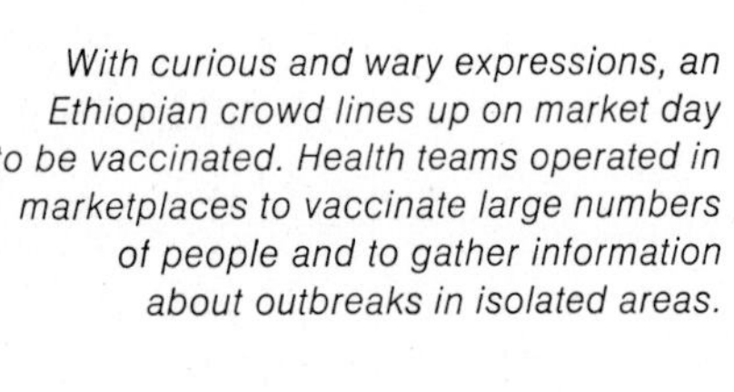

With curious and wary expressions, an Ethiopian crowd lines up on market day to be vaccinated. Health teams operated in marketplaces to vaccinate large numbers of people and to gather information about outbreaks in isolated areas.

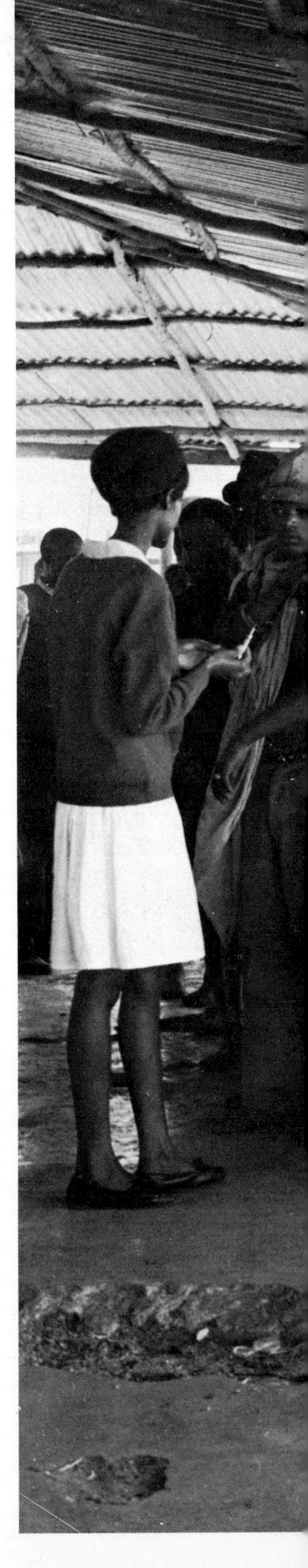

Half-healed scars on a child mark her a lucky survivor of smallpox. The most virulent form of this untreatable disease kills one in three of its victims and blinds many of the rest.

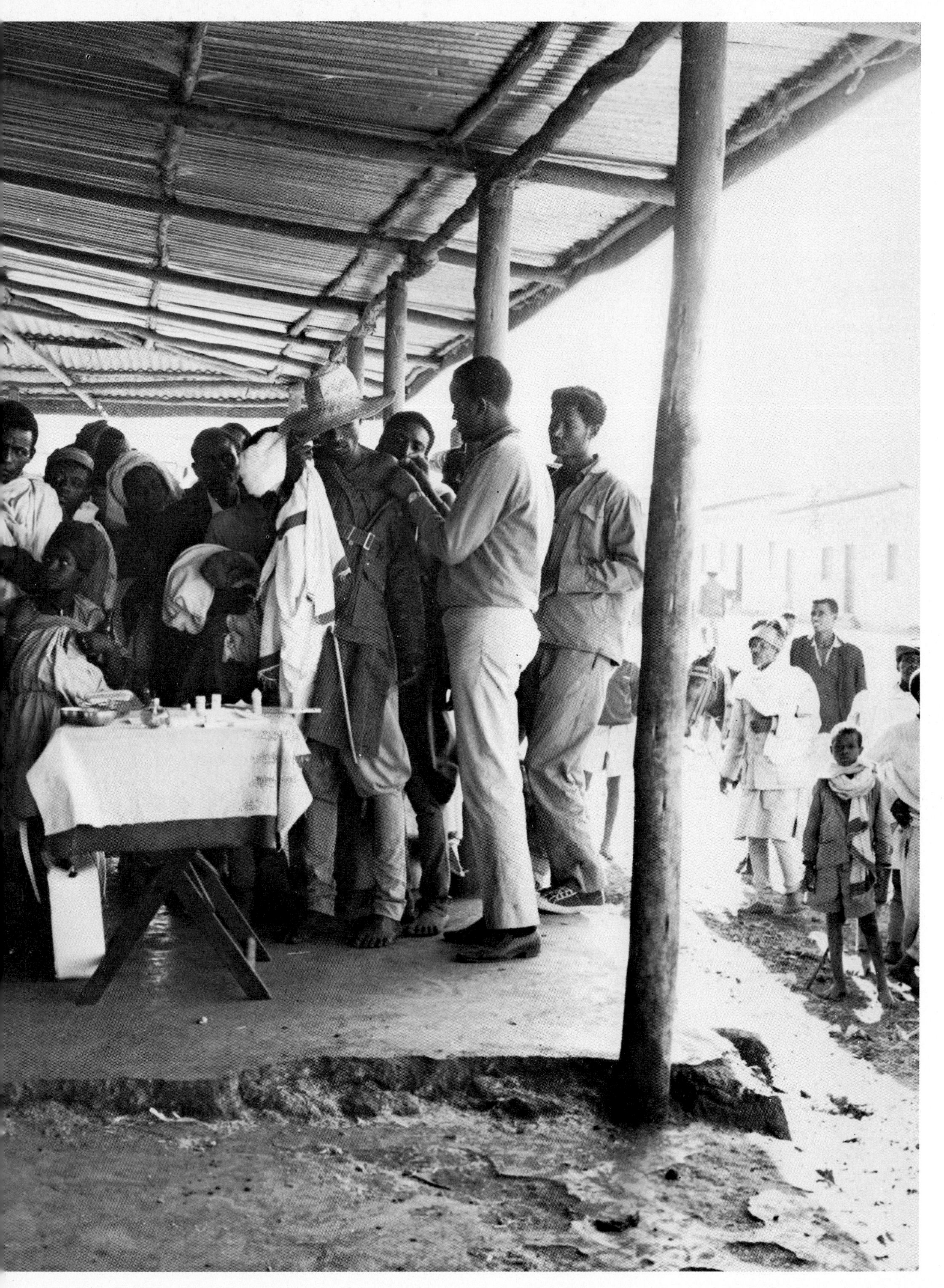

strategy, which they came to call surveillance/containment. The task they faced was enormous. The region was geographically larger than the original 48 states, with a population of 120 million. Since the new approach depended on finding every last case of smallpox, health workers would have to seek out nomadic tribes and reach villages in areas where communications were poor and roads almost nonexistent.

FROM VILLAGE TO OUTPOST

Applying what the participants describe as "shoe-leather epidemiology," teams of African health workers and CDC specialists slogged the bush, interviewing people, tracking down rumors, searching out cases in the most remote corners of the land. When they found a smallpox case, they took a census of the village and then stayed there, for days if necessary, until they had immunized every living soul. They then immunized everyone in other nearby villages, until an unbroken wall of immunity surrounded the victim. Later, the teams made follow-up visits until they were sure that the virus was contained.

Some people feared that such an approach could never work. The teams of vaccinators worked in a period of turbulent political upheaval. There were coups in Sierra Leone, Ghana, Niger and Togo, and in Dahomey the government changed hands so often that there were a number of different ministers of health in one year. But the African health workers on the teams were filled with nationalism, and they tackled the chore enthusiastically. Out in the villages, although some people feared vaccination, the great majority were eager to cooperate.

The success of the new strategy astonished even its most ardent adherents. In eastern Nigeria, with only 750,000 people vaccinated out of a population of 12 million, smallpox disappeared. The elapsed time: five months. By October of 1969, out of the 16 endemic countries, 15 were smallpox-free, and the last one joined the list the following year. Thus smallpox was wiped out in 16 countries within only four years, and at a cost of only $15 million in U.S. aid—just 10 per cent of what the United States had been spending each year on its domestic vaccination program. With the likelihood of a smallpox import diminishing by the week, the United States abandoned routine vaccinations in 1971.

After the Americans' early successes in Africa, WHO reexamined its own approach. The head of WHO's smallpox campaign, Dr. Donald A. Henderson, was a former CDC man himself, and he became an enthusiastic supporter of the new strategy. Brazil, after shifting to surveillance/containment, eradicated smallpox in 1971, and Indonesia followed in 1972. But the Indian subcontinent, with its enormous population, remained a problem. Although Bangladesh had been essentially smallpox-free for years, refugees had brought the disease back from India after the war with West Pakistan, and now it was raging. In India itself, some states had achieved notable success with surveillance/containment; other states, continuing with a mass-vaccination policy, failed. Indeed, as the system for reporting outbreaks was improved, it became clear that in some parts of India, smallpox was as bad as ever—or worse.

Recognizing that something had to be done, Dr. Henderson turned to William Foege, the former medical missionary whose work had been so successful in Africa. Foege and his team of Indian health officers and international WHO workers experienced continual frustrations. In those areas with high infant mortality, it was inevitable that some children would die—of smallpox or some other malady—shortly after vaccination. Simple countryfolk thought there was a cause and effect relationship. Dr. Mary Guinan, on WHO's India team, recalls the strategems she resorted to in order to get around people's fears. "Women would hide their babies. The people in my villages usually had a child every year, and so if there were children in a house, but none under one year old, I'd start searching. I'd usually find a baby hidden in the quilts." To get children to submit to vaccination, Dr. Guinan took to carrying candy as a lure. To convince adults, her interpreter explained that she was a direct emmissary from Shitlamata, the Hindu goddess of smallpox. Since Dr. Guinan is tall, blonde and attractive, she was usually able to pass muster as an assistant goddess.

An Indian health worker uses a poster to describe smallpox symptoms to a class of children. More than 100,000 Indians participated directly in the herculean task of eradicating the disease from their densely populated country. Said one doctor, "It was an impossible dream—but it was finally perceived as being possible, and that made it possible."

The size of the problem was staggering. In Bihar state alone, there were 77,000 villages that had to be searched once each month. But 29 different countries provided people, vaccine or other support for the Indian campaign, and the vast Indian bureaucracy, once it got rolling, was able to commit over 100,000 health workers and other civil servants to the program. The last known case of smallpox in India was reported on May 24, 1975. The last case from Bangladesh came just five months later.

By 1976, the virus had been driven to its last stronghold: the highlands of Ethiopia. There health workers have been hampered by factional warfare and hostile mountain tribesmen. "It is very difficult to persuade the people to accept vaccination," says Dr. Henderson, who visits the country frequently in his role as director of the WHO campaign. "In a village of 500, a team may vaccinate 50 people the first day, and it may take three weeks to persuade the rest, one by one." The tribesmen are well armed and apt to shoot at any outsiders. "We've had one Ethiopian staff member who has been killed," says Dr. Henderson, "and we've had a helicopter blown up by a hand grenade—in this case the tribesmen were Christians who thought the team members were Moslems trying to convert them by vaccination."

In some Ethiopian villages smallpox scars are considered attractive, and thus the people are reluctant to cooperate in eliminating the disease. Yet for all the obstacles, the Ethiopian fieldworkers have pushed the virus steadily back, week by week, to a few remote villages.

Once the last case is reported from Ethiopia, can we be certain that smallpox really is gone? Probably we can, but scientists still have two areas of concern. One of the comforting traditional assumptions about smallpox is that no reservoir of the virus exists in animal populations. But on

September 1, 1970, a nine-month-old boy in a smallpox-free part of Zaire came down with a disease curiously like smallpox. Specimens from the child were sent to a laboratory in Moscow, where researchers concluded that the boy had monkeypox, an illness of some African monkeys.

Monkeypox belongs to the same group of pox virus diseases as cowpox and smallpox, but it had never before been found in humans. Within two weeks of the Zaire outbreak, four more cases of human monkeypox turned up in Liberia, 3,600 miles away. Since then, monkeypox has struck down nearly a score of Africans, and a few of the victims have died. In 1971, even as scientists were beginning to examine monkeypox, a wild chimpanzee captured in Zaire was found to be carrying a virus known as whitepox, indistinguishable from smallpox.

Thus far, it appears that humans can contract monkeypox by close contact with infected monkeys, but probably cannot pass the disease on to other humans; and so far as is known, humans do not catch whitepox from monkeys. But could it be—just possibly—that monkeypox is really a form of smallpox in disguise? Or could smallpox, in the guise of whitepox, have infiltrated populations of nonhuman primates—animal reservoirs from which the virus could reemerge to attack man once again? Most virologists think not, but they're hedging their bets.

"We know that pox viruses do change," says Dr. James Nakano, who is investigating the monkey diseases for the CDC. In fact, "any pox virus in animals which resembles smallpox must be looked at with suspicion. There's a camelpox we're looking into, and even a disease called gerbilpox, which has appeared in gerbils in Dahomey. We don't think any of them present a serious danger to man, but we're going to be conservative and continue our research."

A LAB ESCAPEE

Health workers are also concerned about the possibility of a laboratory escape. Even when the last human outbreak becomes history, the variola virus will not be literally extinct. Cultures of live variola are kept at nine research laboratories in the United States and at an unknown number of laboratories in other countries. Once the world is considered free of natural smallpox, the CDC will ask most United States labs to destroy their cultures. But variola will live on indefinitely in some labs both here and abroad, so that scientists will have a base line for comparison in case of a future pox virus outbreak. Dangerous organisms rarely escape from top laboratories, but it can happen. Recently just such an escape took place —with smallpox—at the London School of Tropical Medicine. The circumstances, reported in a 1974 government white paper, are so bizarre that they bear recounting.

On February 28, 1973, Ann Algeo, a new lab technician at the school, visited an acquaintance named Bruno, a technician who worked in another laboratory in the building. At the time of Miss Algeo's visit, Mr. Bruno was working with live smallpox virus at an open bench. Miss Algeo's supervisor knew that she sometimes visited Bruno's lab to use some equipment stored there, but did not know that Mr. Bruno was working with smallpox. Mr. Bruno's supervisor knew that Bruno was working with smallpox, but did not know that Miss Algeo ever visited the lab.

Eleven days after her visit, Ann Algeo became ill, and on March 16 she was admitted to a London hospital. There doctors at various times diagnosed her illness as meningitis, fungal infection and glandular fever. The doctors contacted Miss Algeo's superior, but he had no reason to think she might have been exposed to smallpox. Mr. Bruno's superior—who might have guessed—was away from his office and missed a critical phone call from the hospital that might have alerted him to Miss Algeo's symptoms. Thus Miss Algeo spent a week in an open ward of a hospital before anyone suspected that she was an infectious smallpox case.

When the first suspicion arose on March 22, hospital officials immediately tried to track down all the other patients who had been in the ward, but because of another error they overlooked a recently discharged arthritis patient, Mrs. Nora Hurley, who had for a time occupied the bed next to Miss Algeo's. Several days passed before the hospital realized its oversight, and two more days were lost because the hospital had made a clerical error in recording Mrs. Hurley's address. On March 28 a health officer finally tracked her down and vaccinated her—but the health officer failed to tell her that she might have been exposed to a lethal disease. Mrs. Hurley thought the vaccination was simply follow-up treatment for her arthritis, and thus saw no reason to tell the health officer that her son Thomas and his wife had visited her in the ward and had passed reading material to Miss Algeo in the next bed.

When both Thomas Hurley and his wife fell ill a couple of days later, neither they nor his mother had any reason to suspect smallpox. On April 1, the two younger Hurleys were admitted to another hospital. Doctors diagnosed their illness as food poisoning.

During a fortuitous discussion with Mrs. Hurley on April 4, a social worker who had heard about the smallpox outbreak put two and two together. The social worker immediately called the younger Hurleys' doctors—but the social worker was too late. Mrs. Hurley's daughter-in-law died just two days later. And on April 15 Thomas Hurley died. Miss Algeo, who had been vaccinated as a child, recovered.

A smallpox scare swept through London. Millions of dollars were spent on vaccinations and in trying to track down suspected cases. There were no more smallpox cases, but only the social worker's alertness had prevented the disease from reaching a third, and probably much larger, generation of victims.

LESSONS LEARNED THE HARD WAY

There are some sobering lessons in this story. For one thing, the tragedy resulted from a series of minor errors. For another, doctors at two major urban hospitals failed repeatedly to recognize the disease. Since the incident, laboratory security has been tightened at the London School of Tropical Medicine, and elsewhere too—but a high level of vigilance will have to be maintained. As we move into a smallpox-free future, fewer and fewer doctors will have had experience in recognizing smallpox symptoms. And with the abandonment of vaccination programs, the world will become more and more susceptible to a viral escapee. With today's methods, a new outbreak could probably be quickly contained, but perhaps only after widespread panic.

After the dramatic success with smallpox, can man now hope to eradicate other dread diseases? The consensus among most epidemiologists is: no. There is no other disease, with the possible exception of a tropical affliction called yaws, so vulnerable to today's technology. While many diseases have been brought to a very low incidence, particularly in the developed world, they probably cannot be entirely eradicated on a global scale. Some, such as yellow fever, have reservoirs in animal populations; others, like malaria, are borne by insect vectors and thus cannot be controlled without massive manipulation of the environment. Still others, such as polio, have carrier states in which infectious cases can be difficult to identify; or, like cholera, they may lack a long-lasting, effective vaccine.

Yet even if variola stands alone as a candidate for extinction, there has been a great deal of positive fallout from the smallpox campaign. WHO has gained prestige, and the organization now plans a frontal assault on six other diseases that, though little known in the developed world, afflict hundreds of millions of people in the tropics. They include malaria, leprosy, schistosomiasis (snail fever), filariasis (river blindness), trypanosomiasis (sleeping sickness) and leishmaniasis (tropical ulcer). Although global eradication is not feasible, WHO does aim to greatly reduce the impact of all six diseases within the next decade.

But to many of the veterans of the war on smallpox, the greatest benefit of the campaign was that it showed that even the least-developed countries of the world, with reasonable outside assistance, could take on a major disease and win. All the countries that fought smallpox within their own borders now have public-health departments and a new sense of confidence that can be directed to other problems. "Smallpox should give us a ray of hope that man can in fact alter these things," says the dedicated William Foege. "Internationally minded humans have shown that they can design a rational, global health order. The benefits from the smallpox campaign will continue to accrue forever—and that's the best cost-benefit ratio you can get."

Television on a Disc

Throughout 1976, the finishing touches were being applied to a remarkable new television product that will turn the viewer into his own programmer. Instead of accepting what the networks offer, he may select a first-run movie, rock concert or ballet; or he may treat himself to a lesson in golf or cooking. These choices and hundreds more will soon be available on shimmering 12-inch discs that play for 30 to 40 minutes per side and cost $2 to $10 each. The discs snap into a player that hooks up to a TV set.

This revolution in home-viewing became possible with the development of techniques for etching a disc with billions of tiny instructions arranged in a spiral track—somewhat like the track of a standard long-playing record but 20 times as thin. The microscopic fineness of the track is necessary because the disc must—like the signal beamed from a television station—feed three million separate instructions per second into the set at home; each picture on the screen consists of about 100,000 dots, and 30 new pictures are required every second to create an illusion of movement. An extra 15,000 directives per second regulate the sound.

The precise nature of the video-disc system of tomorrow is still anybody's guess, since there are several entrants in the field. A European electronics firm, Philips, has joined with the U.S. entertainment conglomerate MCA to produce an innovative laser-operated system, while RCA has developed a more conservative mechanical system. Both produce excellent pictures and sound *(overleaf)*, but they are incompatible: Discs from one cannot be used with players of the other. As a result, cautious consumers must wait to see which is the more successful before risking their money. Zenith, meanwhile, is watching the battle closely and working on prototypes of its own. Perhaps the only agreement is that the video-disc market will be huge—it may total one billion dollars or more within a decade.

An RCA video disc like the one held aloft spins inside the shelf-top player, bringing Arnold Palmer to life on a television screen. The player simply hooks up to the set's antenna, with no special adaptations needed.

RCA
0 5 10 15 20 25 30
Search
Stop
Pause
Play
Power

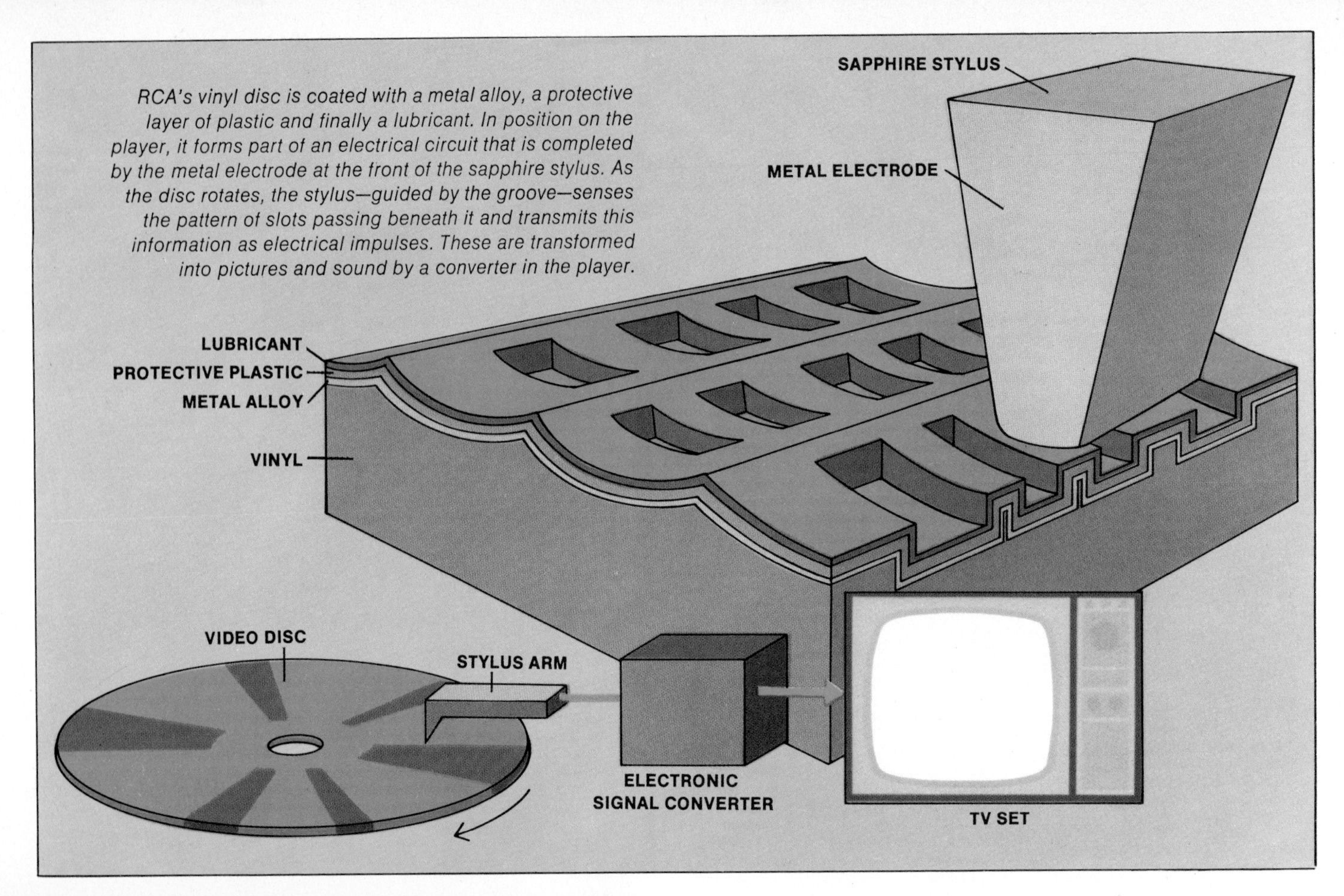

STYLUS AND SLOTS OF AN RCA DISC MAGNIFIED 1,300 TIMES.

The RCA Way

In planning its video-disc system, RCA decided that the surest way to avoid kinks in mass production and home-usage would be to design a player that, as in ordinary phonographs, picks up signals from the disc with a stylus. The video-disc version exerts only about 50 milligrams of pressure on its track, 40 times less than the pressure of most phonograph needles. Even with such a featherlight touch, it wears out after about 400 hours of play since it must travel along six miles of groove on each side of a disc; a new stylus, costing about $10, is easy to insert.

Like competing systems, the RCA player will operate only with its lid closed—a precaution that protects the user as well as the equipment. The disc whirls around 450 times a minute—14 times faster than a long-playing phonograph record. (The Philips-MCA video disc spins even more rapidly—at 1,800 revolutions a minute.)

Though the RCA player is not as versatile as the Philips-MCA, its simplicity, together with its use of existing parts and construction methods, means it can be sold for about $400, making it $100 cheaper than its rival.

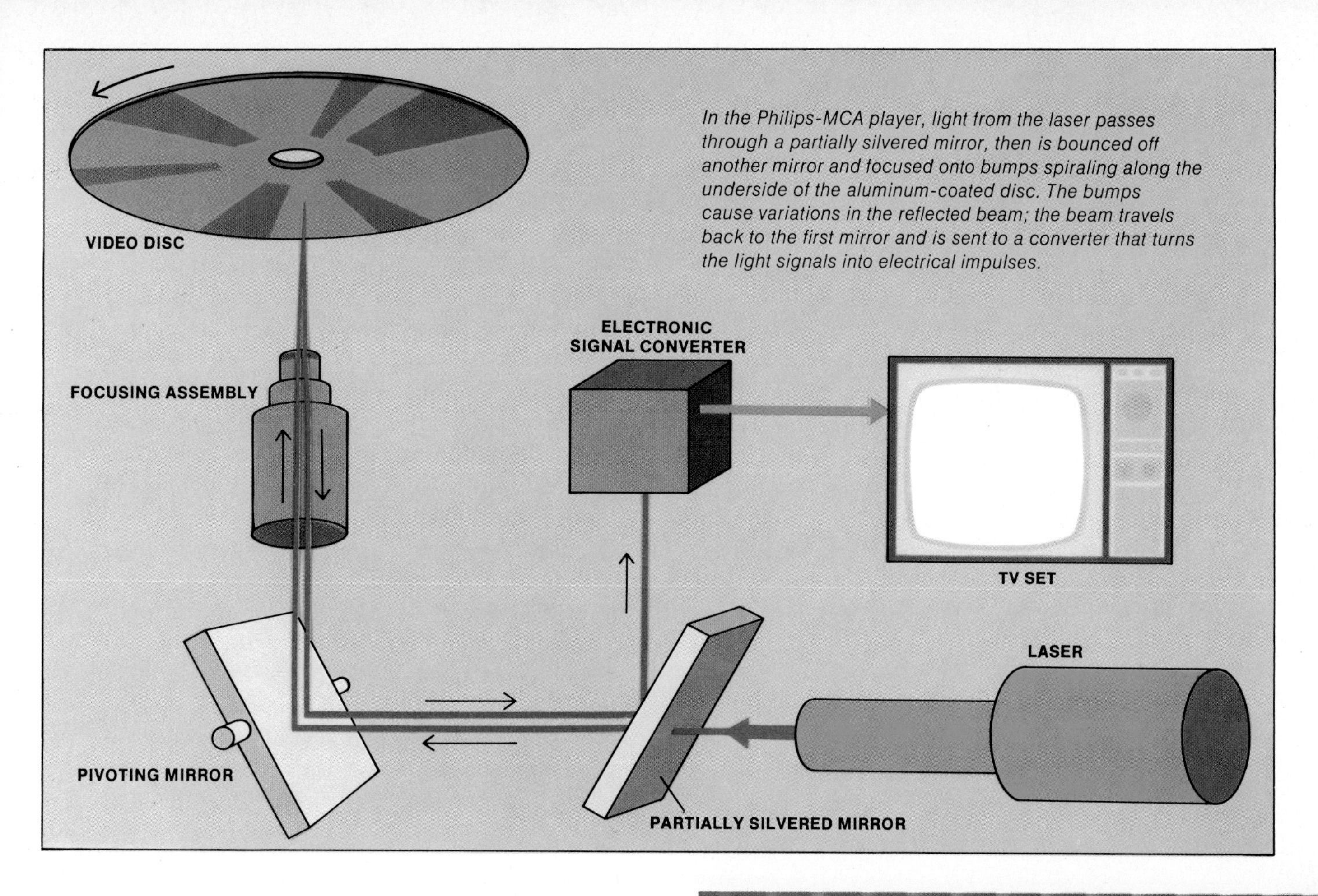

Philips-MCA Method

Instead of employing a stylus, the Philips-MCA player uses a beam of light from a tiny laser to scan bumps on a grooveless disc. Its sponsors are gambling that any problems in the manufacture or maintenance (lasers have never been mass produced for home use before) will be outweighed by the unique performance features of the system.

To guide the laser beam along the continuous spiral of bumps and to compensate for warps in the disc, the player utilizes mechanically controlled mirrors. The mirrors can be made to perform viewing tricks by an optional hand-held device, like a standard remote-control unit for television. For example, since a complete revolution of the disc contains information for just one picture frame, the mirror system can be instructed to read the same circle over and over again, thus stopping the action on the screen. The frames can also be slowed down or reversed. And because each of the 54,000 frames on the disc is coded with a number, the device is able to quickly search out and lock on any frame that the viewer wishes to study.

BUMPS ON A PHILIPS-MCA DISC MAGNIFIED 6,000 TIMES.

Making the Master

Video discs are mass-produced in much the same way phonograph records are: a metal die, made from a master disc, stamps out millions of vinyl replicas of the master's detailed patterns.

In the Philips-MCA process, a plate-glass master disc is first coated with a very thin layer of metal. The intense light of a laser beam, modulated by the film or videotape being transferred to the disc, melts pits of differing lengths and separations in the master's metal coat; the pits become bumps when the vinyl disc is stamped. Zenith's mastering system also relies on a laser, but the Pyrex master is coated with plastic that is light sensitive. The patterns formed by the laser remain invisible until the master is washed in a solvent, leaving holes in the coating.

RCA's process is the most complicated of all. After a spiral groove is mechanically cut in a metal master disc, it is coated with a special plastic. A stream of electrons is then aimed in precisely gauged bursts at the revolving disc, marking a series of rectangular areas in the groove. Next, the disc is submerged in a developer that dissolves the plastic in the exposed areas, creating the pattern of slots that will be read as electronic signals by the stylus.

No matter which company wins out in the marketplace, video discs will have a profound effect on many fields, particularly as further technological advances occur. For example, storage of written information will be revolutionized when —as seems sure to happen—electronics engineers develop television screens that can make fine print legible. It will then be possible to photograph the entire Encyclopaedia Britannica and its supplements, transfer all this knowledge to one side of a video disc, and consult any desired passage in a trice—at a fraction of the cost of microfilm systems currently used by government, industry and scholars.

Bathed in the same red light that is used in photographic darkrooms, an RCA technician puts the light-sensitive master disc on a turntable. The electron tube at left slides on a wheeled platform over the disc to make slots in the prepared groove of the record.

Zenith's mastering laser beam starts at right and travels through various monitoring, directing and focusing devices to the master disc. The oscilloscope at left checks electronic signals, and the TV screen shows the final picture.

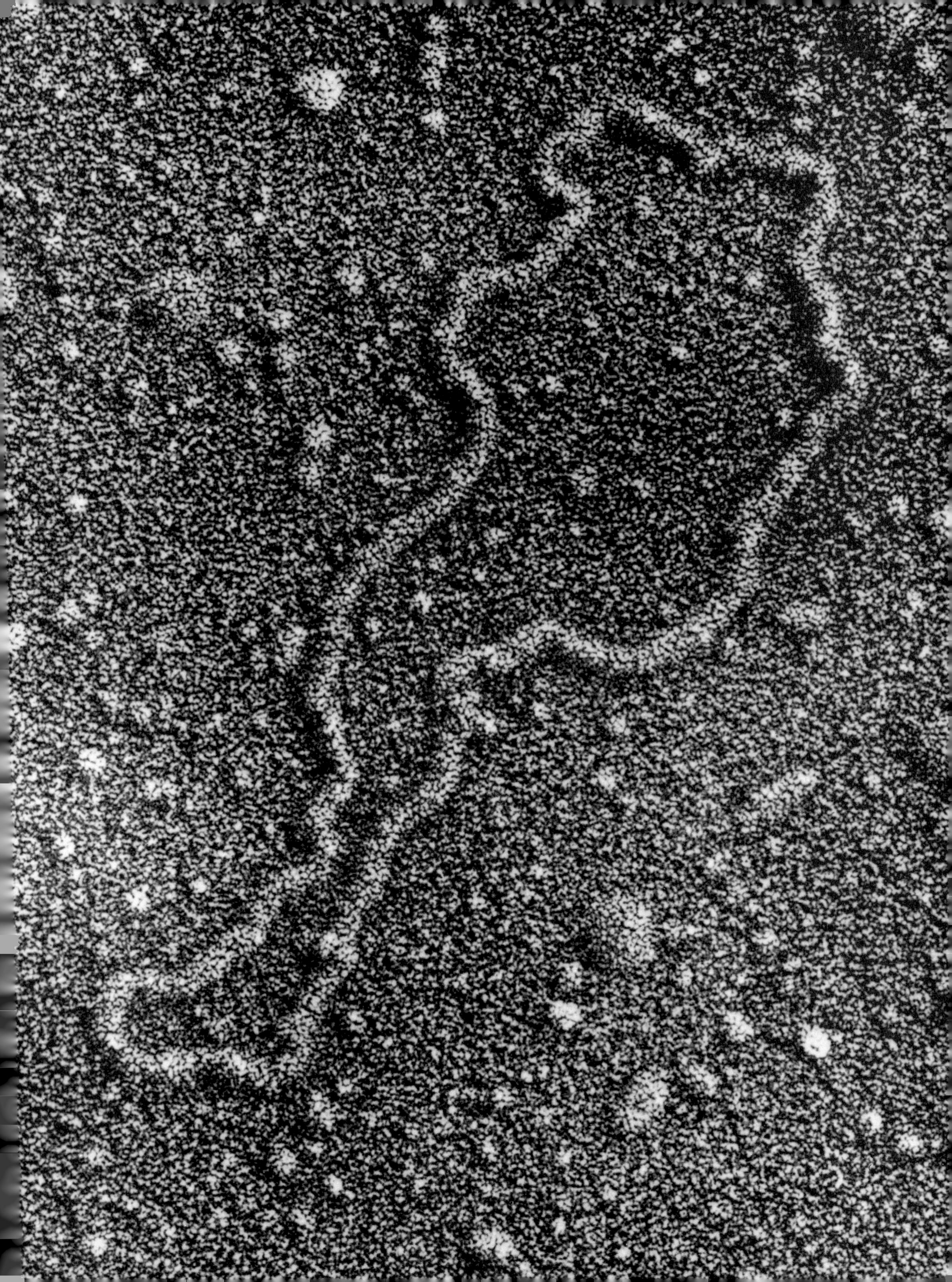

Wonderful Sickly Microbe

A FRAIL BACTERIUM OPENS THE DOOR TO GENETIC MARVELS

by Graham Chedd

Roy Curtiss III began his career as a geneticist by breeding chickens while in high school on Long Island. He was very good at it: At the age of 16, he produced a lusty broiler that was acclaimed as the "Chicken of Tomorrow" by the A & P supermarket chain in its annual awards to young farmers. Curtiss went on to make a tidy income from chickens while he was in his teens, and he majored in poultry science at Cornell University. But in considering which of several attractive graduate-school offers to accept, he concluded that poultry science—while a worthy field—was not exactly on the cutting edge of intellectual advance. So Curtiss decided on a career as a bacterial geneticist, breeding microbes instead of chickens.

Early in 1976, Curtiss added a new microbe—a variety of the common bacterium *Escherichia coli*—to the collection of bacterial strains stored in several large freezers in his laboratory at the University of Alabama Medical Center in Birmingham. Each of the strains sits in its own test tube—rack upon rack of them—condensing the air to a mist whenever the doors of the freezers are opened. The test tubes are labeled with numbers following the Greek letter χ (chi), which is Curtiss' signature as a bacterial geneticist. The microbe that joined the others in 1976 was revolutionary enough to receive a designation Curtiss had been reserving for a very special occasion. It is known as χ1776. Its effect will be to usher in the era of genetic engineering and thereby bring profound—if still unknown—changes to our world. What makes this weighty role so extraordinary is that, unlike those plump and sturdy

A looped molecule of DNA, called a plasmid, supplements the genetic instructions carried on a bacterium's chromosome. This plasmid is a historic specimen: It was the raw material for the first successful introduction of foreign genes into a living organism. The bumps and graininess in this electron micrograph result from the substances used to heighten the plasmid's features.

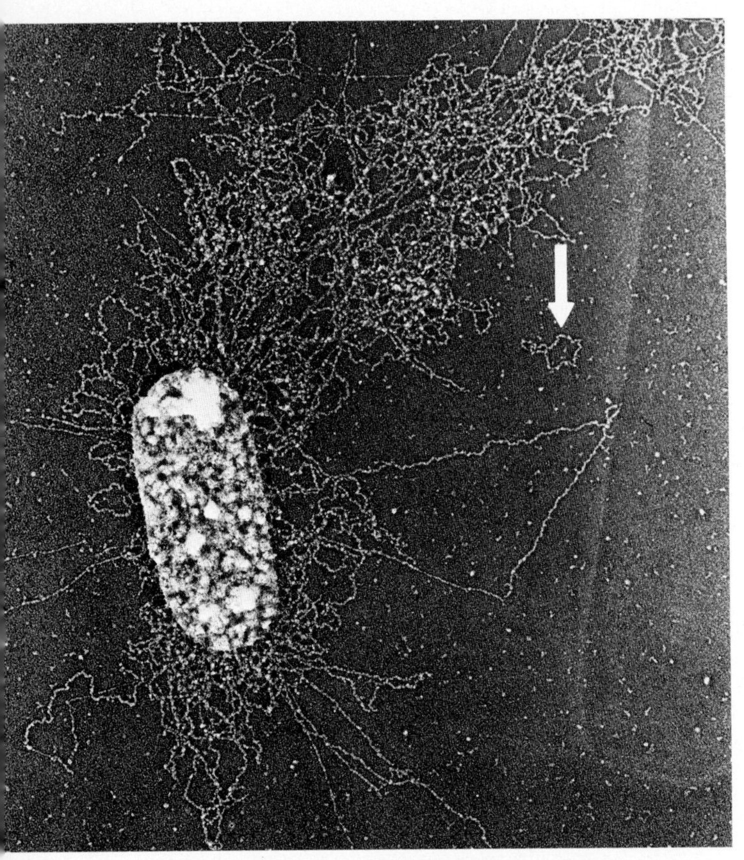

Bathed in a detergent to dissolve its cell wall, an E. coli bacterium yields its chromosome and plasmid (arrow). The shorter length of the plasmid allows it to keep its shape while the longer chromosome spills its coils untidily.

broilers of Curtiss' high school days, χ1776 is undoubtedly the sickliest, most crippled bacterium on the face of the planet.

To understand why such a debilitated bacterium would be of such consequence, it is necessary to go back to 1973, when Stanford University scientists discovered a new way to control the genetic mechanism of evolution. For thousands of years, man has deliberately selected and crossbred individual plants or animals to create desirable traits. But because different species of animals or plants cannot interbreed to produce fertile offspring, the degree to which the genetic cards could be reshuffled was sorely restricted. The genes regulating milk production in cows, for instance, could be improved by crossbreeding with other members of *Bos indicus,* but in no way could a horse gene containing the characteristic of, say, speed afoot, be introduced into a cow.

The Stanford researchers finally broke the species barrier—in one area at least. Although cattle and horses still are unable to successfully interbreed, the scientists figured out a method by which they could accomplish a one-way genetic exchange between certain kinds of microbes and almost any other living creature, including man.

The new experimental technique depends upon the unique capacity of several microbes to pass their genes around among themselves. The genes of all living organisms, with the exception of some viruses, are made up of the precisely coiled molecule deoxyribonucleic acid, or DNA. In bacteria, practically all of the genes—which may number in the thousands—are carried in a single long strand of DNA, called a chromosome. Each gene, in effect, is like a word whose identity and position contribute to the total meaning of a chromosomal sentence. Higher organisms have many chromosomes, and the words from these different sentences can be exchanged and rearranged into new meanings through sexual reproduction. Bacteria, however, do not practice sex, so their ability to generate new and potentially advantageous combinations of genes is theoretically limited.

But many bacteria have evolved a clever way around the problem. In addition to their single chromosome, they possess one or more smaller fragments of DNA, often in the form of a circular loop. This little loop of extra DNA, known as a plasmid, is the equivalent of a few extra genetic words. And while bacteria lack distinct male and female individuals, they do have the ability to pass plasmids to one another by briefly establishing a connecting bridge—a process known as conjugation.

Once a plasmid has crossed the bridge into the host microbe, it can affect the manner in which the microbe functions. The plasmid exchange serves the same purpose as sex in higher organisms, albeit less efficiently: It permits the recombination of genetic words to create new and perhaps useful meanings.

The Stanford scientists managed their penetration of the species barrier by smuggling alien genes into plasmids. They found that, by a series

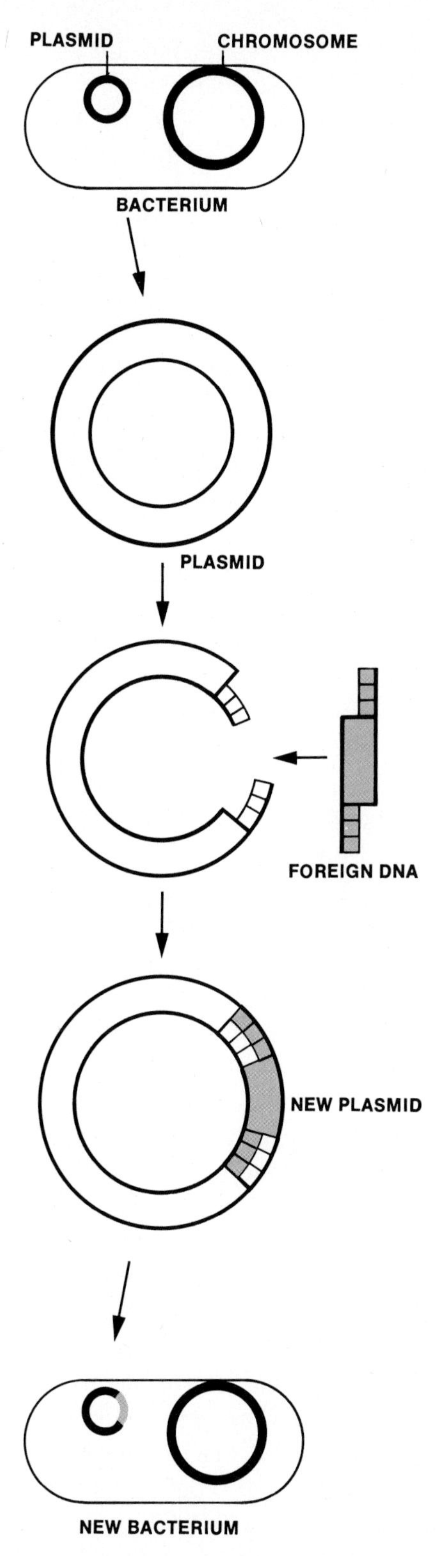

The genetic makeup of an E. coli bacterium is altered by the steps shown above. First, a plasmid is extracted from a microbe. Then it is cleaved with an enzyme, leaving overlapping ends. Next, a strip of foreign DNA, carrying different genes, is spliced into the break, its ends dovetailing neatly with the plasmid's. Finally, the composite plasmid is inserted into another E. coli cell, where its new genes will cause different biochemical behavior.

of complex chemical procedures, a plasmid could be removed from a bacterium and snipped open with the aid of special proteins called enzymes. Once the plasmid ring lay open, extra genes could be slipped into the gap. The plasmid was then repaired, again with the assistance of enzymes, and reincorporated into another microbe. The last step in inducing a microbe to "swallow" a plasmid was accomplished by rapidly cooling the bacterium.

NEW GENES TO SOLVE OLD MYSTERIES

Why should anybody wish to insert the genes of another species into a bacterium? There were —and are—three principal reasons. First, the new technique permits genes that cannot be studied easily in their natural environment to be examined as if they were, in essence, bacterial genes. For example, humans have hundreds of thousands of genes, and trying to work out what each one does and how it does it is almost an impossible task. But putting human genes into a much less complex bacterial host should speed up the analysis of human genes and perhaps answer such questions as whether genes are involved in cancer.

Inserting human genes into bacteria could provide some other medical benefits. Perhaps bacterial cultures can be made to grow such products of human genes as insulin—a vital hormone that is needed for metabolizing sugar and that is in short supply in diabetics. Yet another use of genetic engineering, as this new technique has come to be called, might be the designing of special-purpose microbes that are able to clean up environmental pollutants such as oil spills.

But just as it is easy to speculate upon the potential benefits of genetic engineering, so too can one readily imagine dire consequences, especially when one considers the identity of the microbial host that would be involved in the work. All of the experiments that have been performed to develop genetic-engineering technology—and the great majority of experiments now planned—involve the microbe *Escherichia coli.* The reason is simple: *E. coli* is by far the best understood microbe in the world, having been a favorite of geneticists for three decades because it practices conjugation and is very easy to grow.

The strain traditionally used in laboratory research is derived from, and remains closely related to, *E. coli* microbes that all of us carry in our intestines. And therein lies the rub. What if an engineered *E. coli* escaped from its laboratory birthplace, like some miniature Frankenstein monster, and was somehow able to set up residence in someone's gut? Its new genes might turn out to be involved in cancer, or they might make a dangerous toxin or they might confer resistance to an antibiotic. Even if the escapee were initially deemed harmless, it might eventually generate a new combination of genes with unexpected and perhaps dangerous properties.

UNPRECEDENTED SELF-POLICING

This list of *mights* was so frightening to the scientific community after the Stanford discovery opened the door to genetic engineering that researchers took an unprecedented step in self-policing. In July 1974, a committee of the National Academy of Sciences called for a voluntary ban on any experiments with engineered *E. coli.* One of the many scientists who postponed doing experiments because of the moratorium was Roy Curtiss. He had been planning to study the genes that enable the bacteria of dental plaque to stick to teeth, and his intent had been to transfer the genes to *E. coli,* where their chemical effects would be more easily unraveled. Unlike some of the scientists who, while observing the ban, felt that it was unnecessary and weakened their freedom to conduct research, Curtiss believed that the moratorium was not strict enough. His extensive experience with *E. coli* had taught him a few of its wiles, and he wrote an open letter to the scientific community expressing his doubts.

As a result, he was invited to join a panel charged with examining the whole issue of safety regulations for genetic engineering. The panel's ideas were presented at an international meeting of scientists held at Asilomar, California, in February 1975. At the conference—unique in the history of science—the participants engaged in four days of debate, eventually focusing on the possibilities for ensuring absolute safety in research. Some scientists believed that they should work toward total containment of the microbes. They cited the example of a laboratory at Fort Detrick, Maryland, that had once conducted germ-warfare research and had developed elaborate procedures and devices for preventing microbes from escaping. The devices include air locks, the maintenance of laboratory working areas at a lower pressure than the outside, and the sterilization of all the water and air removed from the laboratory. But the construction of laboratories with such a complete range of safety devices would be extremely expensive; and, in any case, safety devices can malfunction or be subverted by human error.

When the conference reached an impasse, Roy Curtiss proposed (and British geneticist Sydney Brenner eloquently seconded) the brilliant idea of devising biological as well as physical methods of preventing the escape of bacteria. Why not, the two scientists suggested, design strains of *E. coli* that were incapable of living outside the lab? The Asilomar participants eagerly seized on the scheme and recommended in their final statement that the majority of their genetic engineering experiments should await the availability of "disabled" microbes that would die if they ever strayed from their laboratory cradles. Curtiss volunteered for the job of creating the bacterial invalid.

Once he got to work back in Birmingham, he was amazed—despite his intimate knowledge of *E. coli*—at how strongly the strain resisted efforts to cripple it. "Every time we turned around," he ruefully said later, "we discovered that *E. coli* had found a new way to spit in our eye."

Curtiss' specific goal was to develop a strain of *E. coli* whose survival would depend on a nutritional supplement supplied in the lab. His starting point was the idea of introducing a mutation into the gene that makes a component of the microbe's outer coat. This component is diaminopimelic acid, or DAP. In order to produce a microbe with a mutation in its DAP gene (called a DAP-minus mutant) that enabled it to grow and make an intact outer coat for itself, it would be necessary for a kindly biologist to provide it with ready-made DAP. In the presence of DAP in its test tube, DAP-minus *E. coli* could grow normally. But deprived of its DAP, the microbe would simply swell up and burst when it attempted to grow. Any *E. coli* escapee would be hard pressed to find DAP in nature; higher organisms have no use for it, so there is little around.

DAP-minus mutants of *E. coli* were not hard to make. What proved a little more difficult was devising a stable mutant—one that would not revert back to making DAP for itself when supplies were scarce. Curtiss solved this by creating a double-DAP mutant—an *E. coli* with two mutations, each in different genes involved in synthesizing DAP. To revert, such a microbe would have to mutate simultaneously in the two different genes—an unlikely event made even more so because one of the mutations was not just a change of a gene but a complete deletion of the gene from the microbe's chromosome. If the first mutation was like a spelling mistake that rendered a genetic word meaningless, the second was equivalent to the word simply vanishing.

A VERY HARDY MICROBE

About five months of hard work brought these dual alterations to completion. Curtiss now had a strain of *E. coli* that could grow only if it was given a supply of DAP in its test tube and that, if it ever escaped into a sewer or a human being's gut, would promptly pop open and expire as soon as it began to grow. At least, that was the theory. But when the new strain was put in a growth medium lacking DAP, it displayed the uncanny ability to multiply successfully even without its outer coat. Even worse, when the DAP-minus mutant was tested in rats, it flourished in their intestinal tracts.

Curtiss and his colleagues were more than a little chagrined—until they discovered that the bacterium was producing a sticky, mucus-like substance called colanic acid, which it was using as a sort of slimy Band-Aid to hold itself together in the absence of its normal outer coat. The hunt then began for another mutation that would prevent *E. coli* from manufacturing colanic acid. After a frustrating period of testing, such a mutation was successfully incorporated into the double-DAP mutant. Sure enough, the new strain could not survive outside its test tube. And this time there was an unexpected bonus: the mutation blocking colanic-acid synthesis also made the strain inordinately sensitive to ultraviolet light. If the hapless microbe ever escaped its confinement in the laboratory, the ultraviolet wavelengths of ordinary sunlight would have the power to kill it.

Unfortunately, the double-DAP, colanic-acid-deficient *E. coli* still had a few tricks left. The most troublesome was caused by the presence within it of superfluous mutations put there in the course of creating desired alterations. Although these extra mutations decreased *E. coli*'s ability to grow, they contributed a troublesome twist. A microbe that is not growing is not trying to make itself a new outer coat—and so it will be unable to pop and expire. Curtiss therefore had no choice except to clean out the undesirable genetic features.

Even after accomplishing this job, he and his colleagues were not content. A final requirement remained: that the microbe be unable to pass on a plasmid to another bacterium. As Curtiss points out: "*E. coli* can conjugate even when it's dying." So he introduced one last change, in a gene involved in the synthesis of DNA. This mutation makes the microbe dependent upon an external supply of the chemical thymine. Without thymine, the *E. coli's* DNA is so degraded that even in its death throes it cannot pass on its genes to other organisms.

At long last, Roy Curtiss and his colleagues had a strain of *E. coli* so riddled with weaknesses that it could not possibly survive without its special laboratory diet. The microbe χ1776 made its official debut in late April 1976, when it was certified for use in genetic-engineering experiments by a National Institutes of Health committee charged with protecting the public's safety. Curtiss believes that χ1776 is by no means the last word on the subject of disabled microbes. He is anxious for other strains to be devised, "or else we'll have all our eggs in one basket." Nonetheless, the availability of the revolutionary *E. coli* χ1776 has now allowed the age of genetic engineering, with its immense promise, to safely begin at last.

To the Aid of Rare Birds

TRICKS HELP CRANES, HAWKS

by Peter Wood

As Egypt was influenced by the river Nile, life in arid New Mexico cleaves to the Rio Grande. Since prehistory, the river, flowing between dry mesas and mountains of forbidding beauty, has provided a vital north-south corridor for animals and man. The bison and pronghorn antelope that once moved up and down the broad valley are now gone, but each fall formations of wild ducks, geese and other migratory birds—wave after wave from Canada and the northern states—funnel down the valley as they have for millennia. Most of them winter on broad, shallow lakes in northern Mexico, but a portion, finding congenial habitat in the reedy backwaters of the Rio Grande and sufficient gleanings in local grainfields, stay north of the border.

It was to increase the numbers of wintering birds, partly at the behest of gunners, that the U.S. Fish and Wildlife Service in 1939 created a refuge along the river 100 miles south of Albuquerque. Called the Bosque del Apache (Apache Woods)—a name that dates back to an early 19th Century grant from the Mexican government—the refuge covers a 57,000-acre segment of the valley from mountain ridge to mountain ridge. By planting corn, sorghum and alfalfa, irrigating marshes and removing cattle, Bosque managers have created an ideal winter habitat for migratory water birds. From October through January, Canada geese, snow geese, mallards, gadwalls, pintails, shovelers and sandhill cranes are legion in the refuge.

In the fall of 1975, two juvenile birds of a species that had not been seen in the Rio Grande

Flying over sere New Mexico, a rare whooping crane in cinnamon plumage keeps company with sandhill cranes, two of them its foster parents. When full grown, it will be snow white and much larger than the gray sandhills.

Valley for over a century dropped out of the sky onto the Bosque. They were whooping cranes *(Grus americanus),* one of only two crane species found in the New World and a very *rara avis* indeed. For the past 50 years, while its cousin, the sandhill crane *(Grus canadensis),* has by and large held its own against encroaching civilization, the less adaptable whooper has teetered on the brink of extinction. The former range of whooping cranes was roughly centered on the wetland prairies between Iowa and Louisiana, and the plow and the drainage ditch, even more than the shotgun, have hastened their departure.

To anyone familiar with these great white birds' poignant, see-saw battle for survival, the appearance of two of them 600 miles west of their known migratory route might seem nothing less than miraculous. Unless, of course, the observer were aware of a highly unorthodox project now underway to disseminate the species.

During July and August of the same year, juveniles of quite a different feather were sighted at five locations in the eastern United States. These birds were peregrine falcons, swiftest and most explosively lethal of all raptorial—prey-seizing—birds. The summer sightings were the first evidence of peregrines living east of the Rockies in over a decade. These reports, too, were welcomed in ornithological circles with knowing nods.

Two birds more dissimilar than the whooping crane and the peregrine falcon would be hard to find, and, as might be expected, the measures currently being taken to save them have little in common—except ingenuity. The strategy being employed for the whoopers is that in the Ugly Duckling story. Called cross-fostering by biologists, it entails the substitution of the eggs of one bird for those of another, relying on the parent to raise the resulting chick as its own. The peregrine program, on the other hand, seeks to introduce captive-raised fledglings directly into the wild, using techniques from the medieval sport of falconry to ease them through the difficult period of adjustment.

In the highly visible field of ornithology, these two experiments represent a new, active approach to conservation, employing all the science and technology man can muster to restore a situation that has deteriorated beyond the ability of nature to repair. If the peregrine and whooping crane are rescued, their good luck—ours, really—will strengthen the position of those who believe that saving the natural environment will take more than a hands-off policy.

A HISTORIC VISITOR

It was a milestone, then, in the whooping crane program when the first great bird, unnaturally attended by a solicitous pair of adult gray-brown sandhill cranes, arrived at the Bosque refuge late in October 1975. As its long legs reached to touch down and it hung suspended like a parachutist on taffy-colored pinions measuring nearly seven feet from wing tip to wing tip, there was no mistaking its differentness. The bird was already larger and lighter colored than other young cranes that were feeding with their parents in the Bosque fields.

When the whooper assumed its full adult plumage, in about eight more months, it would be snowy white, with jet-black wing tips, a black mask and a scarlet crown of red skin. It would hold its gaudy head nearly five feet high. Its bugle whoop, issuing from a coiled windpipe, would carry on the wind a mile or more.

A whooping crane has piercing yellow eyes and appears disdainful of man. But like all birds, it is susceptible to lead shot and loss of habitat. Never plentiful, it is, in company with the California condor and the ivory-billed woodpecker (possibly already extinct), among the very rarest of North American species. More than the other birds, though—more even than the passenger pigeon or the dodo, or any of the scores of bird and animal species that man has so peremptorily hustled into oblivion—there is something about the whooping crane that causes us to say, "not this one; let us draw the line here."

Perhaps it is the ethereal whiteness of the creature; or the fact that it is a bird of passage, seen and then not seen as it alternates between its normal wintering ground on the Gulf Coast and its nesting ground in the boggy wasteland of northwest Canada. There is this, too: For years, when the sole existing migratory flock numbered less than three dozen birds, they carried with them one of the most intriguing mysteries of the natural world. No one knew exactly where in Canada their nesting ground was.

Whatever the reason, in recent decades the well-being of the whooping crane became a rough barometer of the state of the conservation movement in America. The first significant step to protect the species was taken in 1937, when the federal government created the Aransas Migratory Wildlife Refuge on the Gulf Coast near Austwell, Texas. Most of the whooping cranes then surviving wintered on this 47,261-acre tract. When the refuge manager, James Stevenson, completed the first full census at Aransas, in the winter of 1939-1940, he counted only 22 birds.

Thirteen additional whoopers were known to exist near White Lake in southwest Louisiana—but not for long. A fierce August cloudburst drove the birds out of their retreat, and by the time they regrouped, local hunters had shot, and presumably eaten, six. A seventh wound up in New Orleans' Audubon Park Zoo.

For all vanishing populations of animals, there is an eerie time just before the end when the number of survivors is insufficient to maintain the population, much less increase it; while individuals live on, the group, in effect, is already dead. Apparently, with that August disaster, the threshold was crossed by the Louisiana whoopers. During the next seven years the group dwindled to a single bird, which was then captured and transferred to Aransas in the hope that it might find a mate there. But the bird, which autopsy later showed was a female, never seemed to recover from the trauma of being manhandled, and it died a few months later.

That mishap had lasting repercussions. For decades, crane specialists remained wary of any overt contact with adult whoopers. To this day none of the Aransas population has been color-banded, making it impossible to learn such basic facts as the age at which wild cranes mate.

The Louisiana birds were of particular interest because they were the remnants of a unique population of nonmigratory whoopers. If, as scientists suspected, the instinct to nest and winter in the same locality were part of their genetic heritage, then their loss was an even more terrible blow. Obviously, cranes that would stay put could better be protected than ones that twice yearly braved high-tension wires and hunters' guns in a journey of more than 2,000 miles.

Each spring, from late March to mid-April, in groups of two, three and six birds, the Aransas population would catch a midday thermal and spiral up and up, whooping encouragingly to one another. Finding a favorable wind, they would set their wings and sail off to the north. Their journey, with stops along the way, might last a month or more and would take them across Texas, Oklahoma, Kansas, Nebraska and the Dakotas into central Canada. Then they would disappear. The next time the birds were seen would be in October, somewhere along their southward route.

Anxiously each fall, James Stevenson, the refuge manager, would count the birds as they came in. In a good year they might have with them four to six rust-colored juveniles, looking just like those that landed at Bosque in the fall of 1975. In a bad year, there would be two or three. Nor would all the adults return each year. By the winter of 1942, the population had dwindled to just 15 birds. Nearly all the losses had occurred when the birds were away from Aransas. It was essential to learn where they nested and what happened to them during that critical time.

The last wild whooper nest seen anywhere had been found on May 28, 1922, by a game warden named Fred Bradshaw at Muddy Lake, Saskatchewan. The adult birds had circled Bradshaw on foot, trailing their wings as if hurt, to lure him from the nest. After taking photographs, he heard a "strange piping whistle" nearby. It was a newly hatched whooper, half the size of an adult robin. What happened next was recounted two decades later by Robert Allen, director of research for the National Audubon Society and the first naturalist to study the whooping crane in depth. Seeing the chick, Bradshaw grabbed it and wrung its neck, in order, as Allen noted with bitter sarcasm, "to collect this uttermost nib of surviving offspring and give it immortality in the form of a tag with a number on it." The chick is No. 30393 in Toronto's Royal Ontario Museum.

With the help of the Canadian Wildlife Service,

The product of cross-fostering, an hours-old whooper peers through grass in a sandhill nesting area at Grays Lake, Idaho, 1,200 miles south of Canada's Northwest Territories, where it was conceived.

At seven months, one of four surviving Grays Lake whoopers gleans corn in New Mexico's Rio Grande valley, the traditional sandhill wintering ground. The yellow cylinder on its thigh, marked A 01, indicates that this is the first wild whooper ever to be banded.

A gawky two-month-old whooping crane strikes a threatening pose in a field edging Grays Lake. Rod Drewien, director of the cross-fostering project, had just fetched this juvenile from the water for banding; it was hiding there among the rushes on instructions from its sandhill parents, both of which fled at Drewien's approach.

Robert Allen himself spent many weeks during the summers of 1947 and 1948 peering from the windows of a small plane criss-crossing the trackless wilderness from northern Alberta to the shores of the Arctic Ocean, hoping for a glimpse of white that would be a clue to the nesting site. He never spotted it.

Then in 1954, a fire in Canada's remote Northwest Territories brought foresters by helicopter to an area some 100 miles south of Great Slave Lake. They reported seeing several whoopers, including a pair with one young. The search was over. Best of all, an aerial survey indicated that the nesting ground lay within Wood Buffalo National Park, a preserve larger than Massachusetts, Connecticut, Rhode Island and Delaware combined. When Allen was dropped in by helicopter the next year, he found it a region of bog, muskeg, mosquito and black fly—its rivers hopelessly blocked by log jams. For the time being, at any rate, the cranes appeared to be beyond the molestation of man. Why, then, were they producing so few young each year? Why was the Aransas population in such peril?

During the next two decades—which also saw the untimely death, in 1963, of Robert Allen—these and many more questions have been cautiously answered. Each breeding pair ordinarily produces two buff-and-brown mottled eggs in a moundlike nest of rushes or sedges in one of the innumerable shallow ponds in the park. The eggs are laid about two days apart, and the parents begin incubation when the first egg is laid. The two chicks appear some 30 days later. Young cranes grow rapidly and in about 90 days are ready for their first flights. Several weeks after that, they must head south. Winter comes with awful suddenness just 500 miles below the Arctic Circle.

Wild whoopers are diligent parents, continuing to guard and feed the young as long as 11 months after hatching. They will keep a juvenile close at hand when feeding and preening, and they keep it between them when flying. This family cohesiveness, although common to cranes, is unusual for precocial birds—those in which the young are able to walk away from the nest almost as soon as they are hatched. Yet, in spite of the exceptionally solicitous nurturing traits of the whoopers, twins have made it to the Aransas wintering ground only seven times since records have been kept. What happens to the second chick?

Rod Drewien, a University of Idaho biologist whose work with sandhill cranes during the early 1970s was to have a profound effect on the future of the whooping crane, has speculated on that question. Drewien began his research in 1969, on a grant from the Wildlife Service, studying a population of greater sandhill cranes that nested at Grays Lake National Wildlife Refuge, in Idaho. With the aid of an aircraft landing light mounted on a football helmet, Drewien caught 700 of the sandhills at night and color-marked them with lightweight leg tags and neck collars, visible through a scope at long distances. Once identified, the sandhill cranes could be studied as whoopers have never been. Drewien kept meticulous records of their behavior and was able to follow the population down its migratory route along the Rio Grande, where many wintered on the Bosque del Apache Refuge.

Like whoopers, sandhills lay two-egg clutches. But among the Grays Lake birds, up to 40 per cent of the twins survive in a good year. Drewien watched the nests while the chicks appeared—"mean little buggers almost from the moment they hatch." One would quickly establish dominance over the other and get first call on food from the parents. The chicks of many precocial birds follow the mother—ducks and pheasants, for instance—but feed themselves. Sandhill adults, Drewien noted, actually feed their chicks for many months after hatching, and he presumed that whoopers did the same.

Such food dependency, he surmised, might help account for the fact that so few twins survived to migrate from Wood Buffalo National Park. In several ways, the park appears to be a marginal whooping crane nursery area, probably at the very outer limit of the original whooper range, which once reached from central Mexico into central Canada and from the Great Lakes west to Utah. For one thing, the summer is inconveniently short so close to the Arctic; any delay at all in the reproductive cycle dooms the infants. And not much food is available—not enough in most years, apparently, to feed two chicks. Hence the death of the subdominant chick, and often of the dominant as well.

Despite the terrible mortality rate, during the late 1950s and 1960s, the Aransas population showed a slow progress toward safer numbers. The cause is uncertain, but perhaps the efforts of the U.S. and Canadian Wildlife Services and the Audubon Society to educate hunters along the migration route tipped the delicate balance. One persistent fear, however, has always haunted the whoopers' protectors—that a major oil spill, a hurricane or an epidemic of avian cholera might wipe out the flock in a single stroke.

CAUTIOUS APPROACH TO A CHALLENGE

So the Canadian and the U.S. Wildlife Services agreed that the best insurance against such a catastrophe would be to maintain a flock of captive birds as breeding stock, and to return the offspring to the wild. The task was assigned to the Patuxent Wildlife Research Center at Laurel, Maryland, a branch of the U.S. Fish and Wildlife Service; the program came under the direction of a wildlife biologist named Ray Erickson. That was in 1961. Nearly a decade would pass before the first concrete results appeared. Erickson has been alternately damned and praised for his deliberate caution. It is certainly true that he and his Canadian counterparts approached the challenge with the care of diamond cutters. There was, after all, no room for error.

Their obvious starting point was the all but automatic 50 per cent mortality rate in each wild whooper nest. Erickson reasoned that by removing one egg out of each two-egg clutch and hatching it in an incubator at Patuxent, it should be possible to produce a captive flock without seriously impairing the viability of the wild cranes. But before that was done, all phases of the egg-snatching scheme—transportation, incubation and rearing—would have to be carefully tested on sandhill cranes. If, for instance, sandhill parents deserted the nest after one egg was taken, the plan would be too risky to try on whoopers.

As it turned out, the sandhills appeared to tolerate the interference, and in June 1967, a helicopter-borne Canadian wildlife biologist took one egg from each of six whooper nests. Back in the helicopter the eggs were placed in an insulated suitcase, warmed by water bottles. Riding on Erickson's lap, the case was flown to Fort Smith, Northwest Territories, and thence by commercial jet to Washington. Hours after they left the nest, the eggs were in incubators at the Endangered Wildlife Research station at Patuxent. Five of the eggs hatched, and four of the offspring reached adult plumage a year later.

That same fall, nine young whoopers arrived with the incoming birds at Aransas, only one short of the high count for the past 30 years. The productivity of the wild birds had not been impaired by the removal of the six eggs. Indeed, later evidence would suggest that removing one egg from a clutch actually raised the number of wild chicks, presumably by eliminating destructive sibling rivalry. In 1968 and 1969, more eggs were taken, and by 1970, twelve large white cranes, their black wing tips clipped, were stalking the enclosures at Patuxent.

The first phase, while slow, was a triumph. But it would mean nothing unless the birds could be induced to lay fertile eggs. By 1975, seven Patuxent whoopers had reached what was generally believed to be their minimum breeding age, between five and seven years. A number of birds had shown an inclination to pair—whoopers mate for life—and had been separated into special pens. Courtship dances were observed, but that was all. (Not the least of the problems of raising captive whoopers, which show no obvious sexual variation, is discovering which are male and which female; fortunately, the human ear can tell the difference, although it took the Patuxent biologists a while to identify what sounds to listen for.) That spring, Erickson and his staff were forced to resort to artificial insemination to impregnate one mother, and a live chick was hatched, Patuxent's first. But, after much ballyhoo in the press, the chick, named Dawn, died after just 15 days.

It is one thing to raise pigs and chickens in wire pens. Centuries of animal husbandry have yielded a host of tried-and-true techniques; and, through thousands of generations, stock has been selectively bred for tractability. It is anoth-

Incubator-hatched and daubed with identifying colors, peregrine chicks huddle in a brood pan at Cornell's Hawk Barn. For their first two weeks, they are kept warm in brooders before being returned to their parents.

Tom Cade, chief of the Cornell University falcon-breeding project, holds a tame tundra peregrine on a gauntleted hand. The birds that he is seeking to reestablish in the wild will have only a minimal amount of contact with man.

er thing to breed wild animals, especially when it is the essence of their wildness that must be preserved and when the subjects display highly ritualized courtship behavior and pair for life. Plainly, the breeding program was in trouble.

While Erickson and his associates at Patuxent were wrestling with these problems, another scientist, Tom Cade, professor of ornithology at Cornell University, was having similar problems with peregrine falcons. Unlike the whooper, the peregrine had become an endangered species virtually overnight. The cause was DDT. Peregrines feed almost exclusively on other birds, and that fact was their undoing when DDT entered the ecosystem during and after World War II. By feeding on birds that fed on insects that fed on pesticide-treated plants, the peregrines were ingesting multiple doses of the poison. The result—and American peregrines were not the only avian victims—was thin eggshells, which broke in the nest. Almost before local ornithologists were aware of what was happening, it was too late. By 1960, probably no American peregrines were successfully breeding east of the Mississippi. Final confirmation of the disaster came in the summer of 1975, when 200 former eyries from Maine to South Carolina were examined. Nothing! West of the Rockies, only a remnant population hung on.

In one sense, the plight of this spectacular hunter is not so desperate as that of the whooping crane. The peregrine falcon *(Falco peregrinus)* is represented throughout the world by some 20 recognized subspecies, or races, of which the American peregrine, *F. peregrinus anatum,* is but one. Two other subspecies are found in North America: the tundra peregrine that breeds across the top of the continent from Alaska to Greenland and migrates deep into South America; and Peale's falcon, a bird of limited range that stays close to the Queen Charlotte Islands of British Columbia and the Aleutians. It should be noted, however, that these are taxonomists' distinctions and where boundaries overlap, the profiles get fuzzy.

The American peregrine, though it once hunted in all parts of the United States, was never a common bird. Before DDT took its awful toll, for instance, there probably were no more than 12 active eyries in the state of Massachusetts. These birds, however, belonged to a distinctive eastern population, larger and darker than American peregrines living west of the Rockies. Their loss means that an entire genetic strain, like the nonmigratory Louisiana whoopers, is gone forever.

In 1972, after years of pressure from ecologists, the Environmental Protection Agency finally clamped an almost total ban on the use of DDT throughout the United States. It now became theoretically feasible to restock the eyries of the east, if not with peregrines of the same genetic stock, at least with peregrines. In anticipation of the ban, Cade had been breeding peregrines at Cornell for two years. Hundreds of young birds would be needed, and reliable breeding stock and methods would have to be developed.

It may be asked—and indeed it is asked by some who see the peregrine as a vicious wolf of the sky—why bother? "In truth," says Cade, "it cannot be argued that peregrines are needed to maintain any ecological balance. For me it is simply a matter of esthetics." Cade, who was a falconer before he became a professor, is referring to one of the most exciting sights in nature: a peregrine stooping (the term, like so much about these noble birds, belongs to falconry).

A description of a peregrine "falling in a tremendous stoop" comes from an English naturalist, J. A. Baker: "Coming straight down at me, it had not the shape of a bird. It was like a falling head, a shark's head dropping from the sky. It made a faint sighing that quickly hardened to a shrill whining sound, like the wind harping through high wires. A great black-backed gull obscured the peregrine for a second as it passed over towards the shore. . . . There was a loud slamming bang. The gull buckled like hot metal. Its head jerked and flopped. The falcon had struck it in the neck. The falcon hooked and tore the gull's neck apart with her hind talons." Baker knew the bird to be a female because the females are larger by a third than the males, which falconers call tercels. Baker continues:

"She shivered away from the impact, like a splinter of wood flying from a cut log. Then she curved gently out and up above the water, recovering control. From a hundred feet up the gull slid down quite slowly and emptied itself out upon the shingle. The falcon dropped beside it, and began to feed." It was a remarkable kill. Grèat black-backed gulls weigh up to six pounds, the largest falcons only two to two and a half. What makes such a kill possible is the blow's impact, delivered at up to 200 miles per hour.

In contrast to the situation with the whooping crane, the book on falcons and falconry is an old one: The sport was practiced at least 4,000 years ago in China. At the time Cade began his program, however, little was known about reproduction, since falconers have traditionally obtained their birds by trapping fledglings. There were very few reports of falcons breeding in captivity. In fact, since a wild tercel uses roughly a quarter-mile square of sky in which to perform the spectacular mating flight, it was believed that falcons could not be induced to breed in cages with any consistency.

Cade's cages, however, were decidedly out of the ordinary. The center of his operations at Cornell was a large shed, divided into 38 bedroom-sized lofts with 20-foot ceilings and fitted with one-way-glass windows so that the occupants could be observed without being alarmed. In this facility, known as the Hawk Barn, Cade collected five pairs of tundra and one pair of Peale's falcons. Some of the birds were donated or lent by falconers interested in his project. Some of the paired falcons mated and laid fertile eggs; these eggs were then placed in an incubator to hatch. At first the incubator was set to temperature and humidity levels based on the experience of poultry farmers—there being no other gauge—and nothing happened. Trial and error solved this problem (the falcon eggs required slightly lower temperature and humidity), and the Hawk Barn began producing young peregrines in 1973. The output, in fact, was higher than it would have been in the wild because—like many birds—falcons will produce a second or even third set of eggs as other eggs are taken away.

By the summer of 1975, Cade was ready to send 16 young falcons back to the wild. All of them were tundra birds. Cade had also succeeded in breeding Peale's falcons, but was saving these for future breeding stock, since he considered them the best to replace the eastern *anatum*. The Peale's and *anatum* races are closer in size than the smaller tundra birds, and they are only short-range migrators. If Cade could place tundra birds in a new niche, the Peale's should do even better.

A TECHNIQUE BORROWED FROM FALCONRY

For centuries, sportsmen have been releasing captive-bred game birds such as quail, partridge and pheasant with proven success. But these precocial species are able to feed and forage for themselves almost from the time they are hatched. Wide-ranging birds like falcons take much more exacting care. The critical time is when the young bird, accustomed to being fed, must learn to fend for itself. Here a falconry technique called hacking proved useful.

Falconers ordinarily take young birds from the nest before they have developed their flight muscles. Rather than confine the bird, the falconer chooses a tree stump or a board—the "hack board"—on which he feeds his charge each day. While free to test its wings, the falcon depends for food on its master's handouts, just as in the wild eyrie it would depend on its parents. Eventually the bird learns to kill for itself, an instinctive process that nevertheless takes practice to perfect. At the critical moment, when it has learned to kill but before it is regularly feeding itself, the falconer must recapture the bird; otherwise it will leave for good.

Cade's plan for repopulating the wild was simply to eliminate the final step in hacking. There would have to be some refinements, however. Like most birds, falcons derive certain behavioral traits through association with their parents. Biologists call this process imprinting, and it is critical to normal development. In particular, it seems to govern the mating process. A falcon that has missed the opportunity to imprint on an adult of its own species may seem normal until it is time to mate. Then it may not act as it should. This failure—desirable in birds kept by falconers who do not want them searching for a mate—would doom Cornell's project.

The period during which young falcons are most sensitive to the influence of older birds appears to be their second and third weeks, when they first begin to see and hear acutely. Cade's plan for those critical weeks was to put the birds with adult pairs in flight cages in the Hawk Barn. At four weeks the chicks would be moved to high eyrie-like sites that, it was hoped, they would fix upon when they flew afield—and to which they would return when, after two or three years, the urge to mate came on them. Tiny radios and color bands would be attached to the birds' legs to allow the release teams to follow them.

Three eyries were man-made structures: a 75-foot gun tower at Carroll Island in Chesapeake Bay; a specially built tower in an Audubon sanctuary near Lincoln, Massachusetts; and a platform on a New Jersey coastal island. Two natural sites were also chosen, both on New York State cliffs, one just eight miles from the Hawk Barn.

The whole process of hacking back the 16 tundra falcons took more than a month of constant attention by teams of handlers. In order to prevent the birds from imprinting on the handlers, the humans endeavored to keep out of sight as much as possible, complicating the ordinary job of hacking back manyfold.

Two members of a three-bird clutch were killed by great horned owls at the Ithaca site; the third was recaptured and taken back to the Hawk Barn lest it, too, perish. Another bird at the Massachusetts site disappeared unaccountably. The remaining 12 were alive and hunting for themselves by the end of the summer. After the leg radios went dead, Cade and his staff were forced to rely on chance reports that trickled in through January. One reliable sighting of a juvenile was made at 32nd Street and Park Avenue in Manhattan. This fit an old pattern. In the pre-DDT days, pairs of American peregrines from the Hudson River valley often took up residence in Manhattan's concrete canyons to prey on the inexhaustible supply of pigeons.

Through the winter, other reports came from the Baltimore area and from the Jersey shore. Apparently the birds were behaving the way eastern peregrines used to. Rather than flying off to South America, they were drifting south a bit. Would experience govern their behavior and induce them to return to their hacking sites in the spring? Or would their genes reign, sending them north to the boreal forests and tundra where their parents were from? "Really, it's anybody's guess," says Cade, "but my instinct tells me they won't go above the latitude they were released at, particularly since the birds we freed last summer seem to have acted during the winter like eastern American peregrines should."

Whether the motive force is genetic or environmental, peregrines, even during their first year, are by and large solitary pilgrims. Long before it is time to move south, they have severed all ties with their parents and are off hunting on their own. Not so with young whooping cranes. Not only are they taught how to feed and how to keep out of trouble, but most important of all, they are taught a migration route. The image of that first southward passage with their parents, the wintering site, and perhaps even the return trip is somehow graven on yearling cranes for life. Thus, though the Aransas whooping cranes fly over numerous prime nesting sites to reach Wood Buffalo National Park each spring, their cultural heritage, which may date back thousands of years, compels them to press on to the appointed spot, where, if Rod Drewien is correct, the conditions for rearing young are marginal.

MIGRATION LESSONS

Here was the ultimate challenge for Dr. Erickson and his Patuxent colleagues. If a second population of whoopers were to be established from the Aransas-Wood Buffalo group, it would have to be taught a migration route. The best plan seemed to be cross-fostering the whoopers with sandhill cranes—a proposal first made back in the mid-1950s by Fred G. Bard Jr., a Canadian expert on bird breeding. Eggs from Patuxent birds would be put in the nests of the whooper's close cousin, the sandhill. The sandhill would then raise the whooper and teach it a migration route, ideally a shorter one than the 2,500 miles the Aransas whoopers fly. Eventually—so the scenario goes—they would discover one another, mate and found a new colony.

Someday Patuxent would have to undertake studies to find a population of sandhills that both wintered and nested on protected lands. Meanwhile, Erickson and his staff bore down on the immediate problem of producing viable eggs.

Enter Rod Drewien. Aware of Fred Bard's proposal, it occurred to Drewien that his Idaho sandhill cranes would make ideal foster parents. And if Patuxent was not yet producing viable eggs, why not take the eggs that ordinarily went to Patuxent from Wood Buffalo National Park and send them directly to Grays Lake where they could be substituted for sandhill eggs? Drewien made the proposal to the U.S. Fish and Wildlife Service in 1972. There was a hitch. The Idaho fostering area lay far to the west of the traditional breeding range delineated by Robert Allen in his whooper study. Besides, Drewien's scheme cut Patuxent largely out of the picture. So no one in Maryland became an immediate champion of it.

Three years later, however, Patuxent's continued failure to produce a second generation of whooping cranes was stirring impatience among the birds' boosters, not the least of the heat coming from the Canadian Wildlife Service, which supplied Patuxent with its eggs each spring. Also, Drewien's project at Grays Lake was drawing to a close, and his valuable experience would be lost if the U.S. Fish and Wildlife Service did not act soon. In March of 1975, therefore, with Erickson's wholehearted support, U.S. Fish and Wildlife Service officials gave the go ahead to Drewien's plan for a direct transfer.

On May 28, a team of biologists—led by Ernie Kuyt of the Canadian Wildlife Service and including Erickson—snatched 14 of 31 whooper eggs that had been laid at the Wood Buffalo nesting site. Two of them came from an unusual three-egg clutch. The next day, packed in the incubator suitcase devised by Patuxent, the eggs were flown to Idaho Falls and from there by helicopter to nearby Grays Lake. Drewien was waiting with 14 pairs of carefully chosen nesting sandhills.

"Every bird we used had been color-marked in 1969-70," he says. "We knew their nesting sites, their potential as parents, everything. They were the best we had. My only gripe was that we gave two infertile eggs to two of our best nesting pairs." They were the two eggs from the three-egg clutch. Ernie Kuyt had neglected to tell Drewien that they were suspect.

Within two weeks, nine healthy whooper

chicks hatched (besides three infertile eggs, two were lost to coyotes). By early August, the young whoopers, now down to six, were the size of peacocks, and Drewien began one of the most important steps in the experiment. Working with an assistant and walkie-talkies, he captured, weighed and color-banded five of the six birds.

Scientists had never handled wild whoopers before, but despite concern all went well. "When the parents see you coming," Drewien told a reporter that summer, "they rush into high cover and order their chicks to drop and hide. Those chicks won't move an inch after that. You could drive a truck over them and they wouldn't budge. Meanwhile the parents go away and do a lot of yakking and jabbering to distract you. My job was to spot the chick just before it dropped, then run up and nab him.

"Eventually color banding will enable us to see exactly when the first couples start pairing, and exactly how old they are when they start to nest. We will then know what the normal breeding age is in the wild; then we will know whether the artificial conditions at Patuxent are affecting their birds. Also there is the possibility that the whooping cranes have been breeding from such a small gene pool that they magnify any problems they have. We will be able to tell, for instance, whether two chicks conceived from the same parent in two different years end up mating. We will never know without banding."

By the end of summer, the six whooper chicks had learned to fly, and in October they accompanied their foster parents on the first leg of the sandhill cranes' annual southward migration to the San Luis Valley and then Monte Vista National Wildlife Refuge in southern Colorado. They rested there for several weeks before proceeding on to New Mexico.

Rod Drewien, as he had in the past, followed the cranes south. By early December he had located four families. Two, as planned, had landed in the Bosque del Apache Refuge, while two apparently found ample feed some miles up the Rio Grande and stayed there.

During the winter of 1975-1976, one of the biggest hurdles was passed. No one was certain how the sandhill diet would suit the more aquatic whooper. In fact, the young whoopers appeared to thrive on the largely grain diet of their foster parents (whooping cranes normally eat shellfish and aquatic insects). Other answers remain, but Drewien has high expectations.

Eventually, he hopes, whenever there are sufficient adolescent whoopers at Grays Lake—and for this, of course, Patuxent must start producing eggs in greater numbers than the Aransas flock could ever provide—they will pair and stake out a territory of their own in the middle of the lake, where sandhills find it too wet to nest. As for the possibility of the whoopers having imprinted on their foster parents to the degree that they will want to mate only with sandhills, most experts agree that is remote. The highly stylized mating dance of the two species is so different that such a cross—though biologically possible—is considered unlikely.

Mating, of course, lies several years hence, but the grand experiment shows every sign of staying on course. Another crucial test was passed in mid-February of 1976 when the sandhill parents and their charges left New Mexico for their Colorado stopover and ultimately Idaho. Pat Edeal, a big, open-faced dairy farmer from Las Lunes and his wife, Mary, saw one group go. The mixed-crane family had spent the winter on Edeal's 550-acre farm, roosting in the river at night and flying into his fields to feed by day. As the winter wore on and the whooper's plumage grew increasingly whiter, it stood out within the flock as though spotlighted. They named it Pancho, and they were proud they had been singled out for this very special gift.

Pancho spent more time in Edeal's drainage ditch than the other birds, but otherwise he behaved just like the rest. On the morning of February 15, several flocks of cranes had passed over, flying north at high altitude. Their bugle call drifted down. The birds in Edeal's field lifted their heads. Five took flight, including Pancho and his foster parents. "It was early in the season, we knew," Edeal said later. "But we guessed it was all right. Pancho had real careful parents. They were never the first to fly anywhere and they always kept in the middle of the flock." It stood to reason. Rod Drewien had planned it that way.

Biologists tend caged peregrine fledglings at a former natural eyrie in New York's Shawangunk Mountains, one of five release points for Cornell-bred falcons. The three birds were caged until they could fly, and received daily feedings for six weeks, until they could hunt for themselves.

The Bid for Sun Power

GOVERNMENT APPLIES THE SPUR

by C. P. Gilmore

In Acton, Massachusetts, an ordinary-looking house possesses an extraordinary garage, with a steep-slanting southern roof surface sheathed in 324 square feet of shimmering glass. In a wooded area of the University of Minnesota campus in Minneapolis, a sharp-angled house sits half-buried in a hillside; part of its sloping roof is covered by sod, and the south front of its second story is encased in glass. Outside Santa Fe, New Mexico, a number of small squat adobe dwellings bear huge expanses of glass on their southern sides but otherwise seem much like the shelters built by the Pueblo Indians.

These diverse houses are examples of a new architectural phenomenon that may eventually transform the American landscape. Their gleaming glass surfaces are by no means merely esthetic in intent; along with other, less prominent structural features, they enable the houses to derive much of their heat—and in some cases their summertime coolness as well—from the energy of the sun.

Solar energy has enjoyed the close and eager attention of architects and builders ever since the oil embargo of 1974 and the skyward climb in oil and natural gas prices. Evidence of their interest is ubiquitous. By the end of 1976, as has been reported by the U.S. Energy Research and Development Administration (ERDA), solar heating systems will be installed or under construction in 1,300 United States buildings—hospitals, schools, factories, offices and hotels as

In a research project near Denver, a bank of four-foot-square mirrors concentrates light from a winter sun on the heat-measuring device reflected at lower left. The project's engineers envision a solar energy station of the future in which sunlight captured by acres of such mirrors could generate enough electricity to power 10,000 homes.

In an early attempt to exploit solar energy, 18th Century French chemist Antoine Lavoisier devised this lens system to study the effect of extreme heat on substances such as diamonds. The main lens—four feet in diameter and six inches wide at its center—was made from two sections of curved glass that were joined and filled with alcohol. A backup lens further concentrated solar rays and the whole apparatus could be turned on wheels to face the sun.

well as a number of smaller private residences.

A great deal of this activity has been spurred by various levels of government—and with good reason: home heating and hot water needs alone account for fully a third of all the energy consumed in the United States. Trying to encourage conservation of fossil fuels, 13 states have enacted laws giving tax breaks to those who install solar heating in their homes. The Department of Housing and Urban Development (HUD) has distributed more than $1 million to 143 experimenters around the country to construct solar homes and apartments. However, the principal backing for developing solar heating for private homes has come from ERDA's Division of Solar Energy, whose budget for research in trapping the radiation from the sun may very well double to $220 million in fiscal 1977.

The sun's appeal as an energy source is enormous. From a distance of 93 million miles away, our star bombards the earth with a constant flow of electromagnetic energy deriving from fusion reactions akin to those that take place in hydrogen bombs. Although the earth is hit by only an infinitesimal fraction of the sun's total radiation, its share is equivalent to about 160 quadrillion kilowatts of electricity—far more than mankind's foreseeable power needs; in only 15 minutes enough sunshine falls on the earth's illuminated side to satisfy our energy-hungry society for a full year. Sunlight is not only abundant, it is ecologically "clean," leaving none of the damaging pollutants that are linked with almost all of the other energy sources.

Impressive as its advantages may be, so are solar energy's problems. Even on the brightest days, sunlight comes in relatively small doses. At midday on cloudless days at central latitudes in the United States, about 200 British thermal units (BTUs) of solar heat strike each square foot of the earth's surface per hour. Since a typical house has hourly heating needs of 30,000 BTUs, any apparatus designed to collect solar heat must be very large.

Secondly, solar energy is fickle. On cloudy days it is sharply reduced, and at night it is not available at all—yet it is at these times that the need for heat is often greatest. The temporal mismatch between supply and demand means that a solar heating system ideally must be able to store energy for lean periods. Unfortunately, storage facilities that could hold enough heat for, say, an entire week of rainy weather would be too massive for ordinary buildings. Solar-heated buildings therefore require backup fossil-fuel or electrical systems to provide the heat that will be needed during prolonged periods of little or no strong sunlight.

Despite these handicaps, scientists and engineers are rapidly developing technologies that could soon make solar energy an important supplemental energy source. They are pursuing two distinct lines of attack. The first is thermal collection: the heat of the sun's rays is trapped and used however needed—to maintain a building's temperature or to heat water for baths or dishwashers. The second approach involves conversion of solar energy into electricity: sunlight falling on photovoltaic, or solar, cells like those in spacecraft can provide electric current for lights, appliances—or for space-heating systems that run on electricity. A great deal of work has been done in both fields, but the technology of thermal collection has been found to be far closer to bearing fruit.

Typically, the starting point for the design of a thermal collector is a flat metal plate painted black to absorb as much heat as possible when it is exposed to the sun's rays. The heat must, of course, be conveyed from the collector to the various living areas throughout the house. Some systems achieve this by making use of a network of thin pipes attached to the metal plate; a pump moves water through the pipes, steadily tapping the collector's heat supply and distributing it throughout the house or to storage as needed. Alternative schemes use air rather than water as the medium for the transfer of heat. The air is circulated over the black plate naturally or by means of a blower, picking up heat and then traveling from the roof to a conventional forced-air space heating system.

There are complications, however. A simple black plate might lose as much solar energy as it captures because of re-radiation or convection (heating of the air that touches its surface). As a result, one or two sheets of glass are usually installed over the metal plate to reduce those losses. In addition, heavy insulation is placed under the plate to prevent the escape of heat in that direction.

And finally, the heat-collecting apparatus is linked to a heat-storage unit. If the heating system uses water, the hot fluid can be stored in a large insulated tank; up to 5,000 gallons can be kept hot for days in such containers. If air is the medium, heat may be stored by passing the air through a bin of rocks. The rocks readily get hot, and the heat can later be extracted from them by blowing cool air through the bin and directing it to the living areas.

NEW WAYS TO STORE HEAT

Solar energy specialists have devised many variations on the basic principles of solar heaters. Several years ago, for example, physicist Karl Böer and Maria Telkes at the University of Delaware completed an air-heated house with a storage system that uses chemicals called eutectic salts instead of rocks. Since these substances can store far more heat than rock or water for a given volume, the size of the storage area can be significantly reduced.

Building a storage system big enough to take care of a home's heating needs during prolonged spells of cold or cloudy weather would be prohibitively expensive. Thus homes are usually equipped with enough solar equipment to take care of all of the hot water needs—but no more than 50 to 80 per cent of the heat needed to maintain a comfortable indoor temperature. A conventional furnace supplies the difference. Engineer George Löf of Colorado State University, a noted expert on solar energy, calculates that the installation of a solar heating system in his part of the country would raise the cost of a typical house by about $5,000. At current interest rates this additional expense would add about $500 a

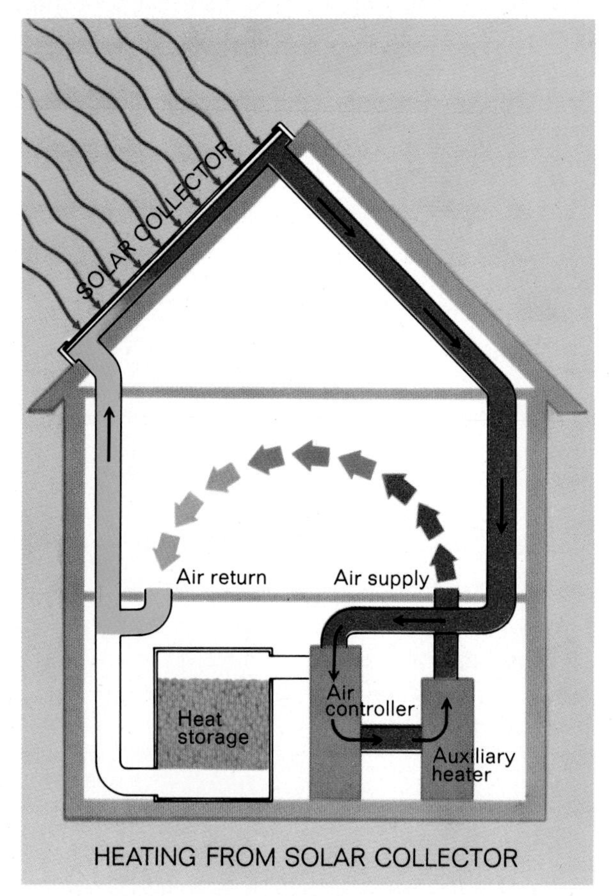

In a typical solar-heating system for a house, fans draw warmed air (red) from a rooftop energy collector down to an air controller that directs it into the living spaces. There the air gives up its heat and is recycled (blue) to the collector. A conventionally fueled auxiliary heater boosts the heat on cloudy days. By means of dampers, the air controller can divert hot air to a bin of rocks that will store the heat (the storage unit is shown cold in this diagram).

year to the buyer's mortgage payments—whereas he would probably only save $300 to $400 in annual oil bills. Sighs Löf: "There has been no incentive for using solar heat."

To be economical, solar houses must conform to a rule of thumb worked out by Hoyt Hottel, an M.I.T. energy expert and the designer of several such houses in and around Cambridge, Massachusetts. Hottel's rule states that a flat-plate solar system—collector, storage tanks, control equipment and so on—cannot cost more per square foot of the collector than I0 times the value of the fuel that the system will save every year. In such high-cost fuel areas as New England, the system cannot exceed about $5 to $I0 per square foot of the collector.

Most collectors alone, without any of the additional plumbing or installation costs, run that much or more; but as fuel prices continue their rise, the imbalance may be remedied. Already solar heating is creeping toward the break-even point in some regions. For example, Acorn Structures, Inc., a New England firm, recently built a solar home in Acton, Massachusetts, that boasts some promising economics. During a typical New England winter about 800 gallons of oil—worth $330 at current oil prices—would be needed to heat a house of that size; and if such a house were electrically heated, the bill would run to about $800 a year. The solar energy system of Acorn Structures, costing a total of $7,200, provides 65 per cent of the house's heating needs. Assuming a six per cent annual rise in the price of oil and taking into account additional taxes, maintenance and interest for the solar heating system, it should begin to break even in the 10th or 11th year. After that, the house owner should start to save money from his initial investment.

The house's builders are optimistic about its appeal. By the end of 1976 they hope to sell 20 such dwellings to people intrigued with the idea of paying higher initial costs for the heating system against the day when they will be saving money on fuel. Says Acorn's general sales manager, Art Milliken: "Up until now, the buyers have been inventor types who like to fuss around. Now we're ready for normal people."

Perhaps. But before solar heating systems can attract a truly substantial market, they must become much cheaper—by at least 40 per cent according to ERDA officials. Mass production of solar components will help whittle away at the price. PPG Industries, Inc., for example, estimates that the expensive, low-radiating black coating ($2 per square foot) on collectors it manufactures could be halved in cost if demand picked up sufficiently. But mass production alone cannot achieve price reductions sufficient to make solar heating systems competitive. The heyday of solar energy will not arrive until more efficient components are on hand.

Many large companies have research teams

A house built by a Boston architect near Ludlow, Vermont, is warmed in midwinter with the help of solar collectors that cover the first floor of the south wall. The aluminum overhang at the top of the house reflects the sun's low-angled rays onto the collectors and raises their heat output.

looking into the problem. Owens-Illinois, Inc. has developed a sophisticated new four-by-eight-foot collector containing 24 glass tubes mounted two inches apart over a reflective background. In each of the 24 tubes are two more concentric tubes. A fluid, usually water, flows the length of the assembly in one direction through the center tube, then back in the other direction through the space between the inner and middle tubes. The space between the middle and outer tubes is pumped free of air to minimize convection and conduction losses.

The big advantage of this arrangement is that the device collects heat from the sun both as it falls directly on the front of each tube and as it is reflected onto the rear. Owens-Illinois claims that the collector is at least twice as effective as existing flat-plate collectors, depending on operating temperature and other conditions. Its cost is impressive, too: $25 per square foot. But the figure could drop to $10 after large-scale production goes into effect within a few years.

Another approach is being explored by Northrup of Hutchins, Texas. The company has developed a collector in which a ridged Fresnel lens (named after the 19th Century French physicist Augustin Jean Fresnel, who first designed such lenses for lighthouses) focuses sunlight on a single tube running through the bottom of a trough. Northrup says that the system can produce more BTUs per dollar invested than most solar collectors. Eventually it should be able to achieve temperatures of up to 500° F. for industrial purposes.

In Northrup's light-concentrating system, the lens must track the sun as it moves across the sky to keep light on the tube. A tiny electric motor, controlled by two small solar cells, does the job. Although the lens-moving machinery adds to the price of the system, it allows summertime operation from shortly after sunrise to just before sunset, when the rays of the sun are much too slanted to operate more conventional solar heating systems.

Devised at the Argonne National Laboratory near Chicago, another light-concentrating method entirely eliminates the tracking problem by taking a cue from nature. As in the Northrup collector, the tube lies at the bottom of a trough. The trough is highly polished and so shaped that, even as the sun moves across the sky, its light is always reflected onto the tube. Where did the designers of the system get the idea for this unusual geometry? From the eye of the horseshoe crab, which has the property of focusing light in the same direction regardless of its incoming angle.

Collectors and concentrators are not the only tools in the solar-energy workshop. Recently solar energy enthusiasts have been experimenting with a device known as a heat pump, which is similar to an ordinary air conditioner. A heat pump can move heat against the normal thermal current, taking it from a cold place—the outdoors—to the warmer indoors, or taking it from the warm indoors and discharging it to the hotter outdoors. Moreover, it can do this fairly efficiently at temperatures down to about 20° F. Even though the outside air seems cold, it actually contains a great deal of heat since it is far above absolute zero—minus 459.69° F.

Heat pumps used in conjunction with solar collectors can provide exceedingly efficient heating systems—as demonstrated by a sophisticated solar house recently built in Aachen, Germany, by N. V. Philips, a giant manufacturer of electrical equipment. The ultramodern building is so well insulated that heat losses via walls, ceilings, windows and floors have been reduced to only a sixth of the losses in a typical German house. Nothing is squandered, thermally speaking. Before any waste water is discarded, its heat is recovered by a heat pump. On hazy days, water-type solar collectors on the roof make a major contribution to the heating needs of the house because the heat pump extracts heat even from the relatively cool water. In addition, the heat pump draws warmth from the earth directly beneath the house during the winter months and makes use of the ground for cooling the house during the summer.

A YEARNING FOR SIMPLICITY

While most work in the solar energy field has produced ever more elaborate systems, some researchers are heading in the opposite direction. In part they are motivated toward simplicity by a desire to live in harmony with nature without overwhelming it with extravagant technology. One such solar energy proponent is Harold Hay, a tall, white-haired chemist and inventor who initially began thinking seriously about the heating and cooling of dwellings when he spent some time in India two decades ago. Observing the miserable, rusty, sheet-metal shacks in which many Indian people lived, he realized that the dwelling must be excruciatingly cold at night and sweltering during the day—a situation that he believed could be easily reversed with the right sort of roofing material.

Back in the United States, Hay began a long collaboration with fellow experimenter John Yellott of Arizona State University. Together, they constructed a 10-by-12-foot building in Phoenix with a sun-heated water tank on the roof. At nighttime during the summer months, they opened the tank, letting the water radiate its heat to the sky until it eventually became chilled. During the heat of the day, they covered the water tank with a lightweight foam insulator. Sitting directly on top of a metal ceiling, the cold water kept the room so thoroughly chilled that it practically made the inventors' teeth chatter. "When it was 95° outside," Hay remembers, "I had to wear a sweater and coat inside to stay warm."

Hay's "Skytherm" house, as he calls it, has limitations. It will not function well in those parts of the country where temperatures fall below freezing. The house also needs clear night skies in order to work properly since water will not radiate its heat readily if there is a thick cloud cover. On the plus side, such a rooftop apparatus is relatively simple to construct and would not add significantly to the cost of a house.

One innovative house that operates in close harmony with nature—and in a cool climate to boot—was planned and built by an environmental design class at the University of Minnesota in 1974. The house is partially buried in a hillside so that its north side is completely underground. In addition, the south-facing roof is covered with a thick layer of sod. The grass covering acts as insulation year round, but it is doubly effective during the winter when it is covered with snow. In summer, vents in the roof can be opened up, creating a chimney-like draft that draws cool air into the building. Even on the hottest days of the summer, the indoor temperature remains 15° cooler than the outside temperature.

Some solar houses are actually made out of earth. In and around Santa Fe, New Mexico, an architectural firm called Sun Mountain Designs has built approximately 100 houses that have thick walls of adobe—baked mud—which can store heat for days. Huge expanses of glass line the south side of each house, letting sun pour in throughout the day and warm the mud walls from within. At night, panels of Styrofoam, in accordion folds, are lowered from the ceiling to close off the windows and trap the collected heat. The only backup heat comes from either a single fireplace or a wood-burning stove.

SOLAR POWER: AN ENERGY LONGSHOT

Although most of the work in solar housing has been aimed at collecting the sun's energy directly in the form of heat, some experts are convinced that solar houses can eventually utilize solar cells to convert sunlight directly into electricity. This would give the homeowner a unique advantage: by drawing current from his own rooftop, he could be virtually freed from the threat of rising electricity rates. (An additional benefit of rooftop electricity would be the elimination of unsightly power lines.)

Solar cells, invented by scientists at Bell Telephone Laboratories two decades ago, have proved themselves in dozens of spacecraft, but they are still too expensive for almost everyone except NASA. Similar to the transistor, solar cells must be fabricated from ultra-pure crystals of silicon (which must be "doped" with an impurity to make them generate an electric current). Moreover they convert only about 12 per cent of the sunlight that strikes them into electricity. To produce enough electricity to light up a 100-watt bulb would require as much as $60,000 worth of rooftop cells. In addition, the building would have to be bathed in the full glare of the noonday sun.

While solar cells are still an energy longshot, scientists are hopeful that in time their efficiency and price can be sufficiently improved to make them practical for ordinary homes. Already, a

With the four hinged window lids of the Baer house lowered, oil drums stacked in the south windows sop up the sun's heat —including rays that are reflected off the polished aluminum lid surfaces. The outside ends of the water-filled drums are painted black to increase heat absorption. Sloping solar heaters located at the corners of the building provide 130° F. hot water to the kitchen and baths. All water is pumped from a well by the windmill behind the house.

Because of their lightweight construction, the window lids can be easily raised or lowered by hand-cranked pulleys. Their insulating cores, sandwiched between thin aluminum skins, consist of cardboard honeycomb filled with a plastic foam.

Designed for Sun

"I got into the solar energy thing purely for esthetic reasons," says inventor-designer Steve Baer, whose sun-heated home outside Albuquerque, New Mexico, ranks as a masterpiece in the field. Baer's heating system is at once decorative, highly effective and extremely simple. Each of the four south-facing walls of the rambling house is an enormous steel-framed glass window backed by 55-gallon, water-filled oil drums stacked on their sides. During winter days, sunlight heats the water; at sunset, the windows are sealed by massive, hinged lids filled with insulation, and the drums radiate their stored heat into the rooms. On summer nights, the window lids are left open, allowing the cool, dry desert air to chill the water. After the lids are cranked up at sunrise, the temperature inside the house rarely reaches more than 80° F., although the outside temperature may be over 100° F.

The white-painted ends of heat-storage drums form an elegant wall in Baer's house—known as a passive solar home since it lacks complex mechanical equipment.

Massachusetts firm, Mobil Tyco Solar Energy Corporation, has devised a new fabrication scheme. In recent trials, the company produced thin ribbons of silicon crystals at the astounding rate of six feet an hour; they expect to improve on that soon.

The Solarex Corporation of Rockville, Maryland, is trying a different tack. It is developing a technique for making solar cells out of cheaper, less pure silicon, which would cost only a fraction of the highly refined stuff but work almost as well. If such experiments are successful, scientists predict, the cost of producing electricity by solar cells could be cut from its present price of as much as $600 a watt to only 50 cents or less by the late 1980s.

Solar cells are just one way to generate electricity from the sun's energy. ERDA recently awarded contracts worth $8 million to four industrial teams for the design of a system to produce electricity by large-scale thermal collection. An array of thousands of motor-driven mirrors, spread out across the sun-drenched southwestern desert, would catch the sun's rays and focus them onto a slim 30-story-high tower in their midst. Inside the tower the concentrated sunshine would produce superheated steam at a temperature of 1,000°, and the steam, in turn, would drive conventional generators. ERDA hopes for an acceptable design by 1977 and expects to build a 10-megawatt pilot plant by 1980. Later ERDA hopes to construct a 50-megawatt plant. And finally it will set its sights on a 1,000-to-3,000-megawatt facility, comparable to today's fossil-fuel and nuclear-power plants. By the year 2000, according to one forecast, a solar power plant could be producing 40,000 megawatts.

No one can say for sure whether such visionary solar energy schemes will ever be realized. Solar energy pioneer Hoyt Hottel warns colleagues that their unreserved enthusiasm may one day be remembered as a "period of midsummer madness brought on by the sun." But others are more optimistic.

"Late in the 21st Century," says Piet B. Bos, manager of the solar energy program of the Electric Power Research Institute, "our civilization may be powered directly and totally by the energy of the sun. And because nothing would be mined and no fuels burned, there would be relatively little impact on the environment."

Bos's vision is admittedly a solar-powered utopia. Still, even something short of a total solar society would also be a goal worth seeking. The solar house pioneers have already shown that the sun's power can make an important contribution to daily energy needs. In the future as precious fossil fuels become more scarce, solar energy's contribution should steadily grow. As Bradley University engineer Y. B. Safdari puts it: "There are no ifs involved with solar energy anymore. It's merely a question of when."

Mounted on a mechanism that keeps them facing toward the sun, parabolic mirrors at an experimental solar station near Genoa, Italy, concentrate the radiation of the sun on an elevated boiler, turning its water into steam that could someday drive an electricity-producing turbine.

The Big Koala Comeback

In February 1976, an unusual television celebrity died of natural causes at the San Diego Zoo. His name was Teddy, and he had starred in the advertising campaign for the Australian airline Qantas. He was also the last surviving male koala outside Australia, which maintains a strict ban on the animals' export—initiated five decades ago to preserve them from extinction. The conservation effort has been aided by worldwide affection for the appealing creature and by a growing scientific interest in its mode of living. In fact, experts in koala habits and habitat gathered this year in Sydney for the world's first scientific symposium devoted solely to this animal.

The koala's first published portrait was this hand-colored etching from an 1810 nature book. The author uncharitably described the animals as "torpid, senseless creatures."

Named *Phascolarctos,* or pouched bear, the gentle koala is no relative to the true bear. It is a marsupial, a type of mammal whose young develop after birth in a pouch, or marsupium, on the mother's abdomen. The vast majority of marsupials are found in Australia where, cut off from the rest of the world, they have never had to face a challenge from the more highly developed placental mammals in the evolutionary struggle.

For the koala, survival meant adapting to a single source of sustenance—the leathery leaves of a few species of the eucalyptus, or gum, tree. The trees provide food, shelter and even water from the dew and moisture in the leaves *(koala* means "no drink" in an aboriginal dialect). High in their 40- to 100-foot eucalyptus abodes, the koalas feed actively at night and spend most of the day dozing.

This extreme specialization was nearly the animals' undoing. The widespread loss of their habitat to fire, loggers and land developers, coupled with disease and mindless slaughter by hunters, nearly destroyed the species. Yet, as a heartening sign that koalas are on the increase in their native land, the symposium scientists unanimously recommended that San Diego be allowed to import replacements for Teddy.

Model for a million cuddly toys, koalas maintain their adult weight of 20 to 30 pounds by feeding every day on about two and a half pounds of pungent eucalyptus leaves.

A mustachioed hunter stands with his foot on a dead koala. Another corpse hangs limply in the tree and one sprawls on the ground nearby. The animals were easy targets, since they do not have the instinct to flee from danger.

Grasping an uprooted male koala by the scruff of the neck to avoid the slashing claws and teeth, a Victoria wildlife officer frees it in the wild. Such programs have helped reestablish koalas throughout much of their original range.

The Fight for Survival

When the first Europeans settled in Australia in 1788, millions of koalas roamed the thick eucalyptus forests that covered the eastern coast of the continent. By the late 1920s, koalas were fast approaching extinction—mostly because of the relentless efforts of hunters like the jaunty individual at upper left. The hunters' motives were purely mercenary: koala pelts, used for coats, hats, bags and belts, were worth $13.90 a dozen. In 1924, no fewer than two million skins, shot both by licensed hunters and by poachers, were exported from Australia.

At the time, the only remaining koala colonies of any size were in the forests of Queensland. Yet in August of 1927, in a bid for the hunting vote, officials of the Queensland state government ignored the warnings of conservationists and declared a one-month open season on the defenseless animal. The resultant killing spree yielded nearly 600,000 pelts, not counting 20,000 young koalas thrown to the dogs or left to die. The mass slaughter horrified most of the Australian public. One scientist commented bitterly that "anyone who would shoot a koala would feel at home with a gun amongst a flock of sheep." As a result, the killing of koalas was prohibited throughout the nation.

In some quarters, the fight to save koalas was already underway before the Queensland carnage. Five years earlier, the state of Victoria had set aside protected areas for koalas, and soon afterward several private sanctuaries were set up in the eastern states. By mid-century, one estimate put the total koala population at 50,000.

Today, koalas have reproduced to the point where they are defoliating the eucalyptus in some areas, giving game managers a gratifying new job of capturing surplus animals and releasing them in the wild.

A Solicitous Upbringing

Much of the current scientific scrutiny of koalas is understandably concerned with their breeding and nurturing capabilities. Koalas, it has been found, generally produce young at the rate of one every other year, and the mother is inseparable from her offspring for as long as a year and a half. However, as with all marsupials, the infant's survival hinges on its ability to cling and climb by itself when it is only minutes old.

After a gestation period of about 35 days, the newborn koala is scarcely three quarters of an inch long, and the only well-developed features of its semitransparent body are a mouth, a nose and disproportionately large forelimbs tipped with claws. Immediately after birth, the embryonic infant makes a critical arm-over-arm journey through its mother's fur into the pouch where it fastens tightly to a teat *(below left)* for the next three to four months.

Between the age of six and eight months, the infant leaves the pouch for increasingly long stretches of time; at the end of that period, the youngster has grown too large to reenter, although it continues to nurse for nearly another four months by sitting in the mother's lap and poking its head into the pouch. Even when fully weaned, it sticks close to its mother for another six months or so. Then it either moves to a nearby branch or breaks the bond entirely and sets off to claim a tree of its own.

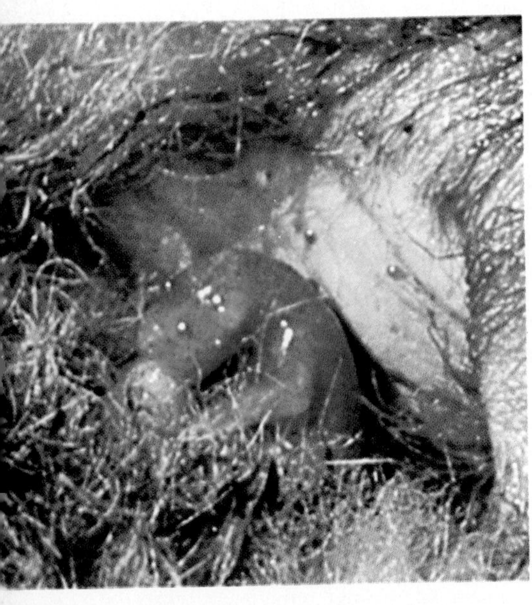

Hairless, blind and deaf at birth, the koala instinctively clings to the teat in its mother's pouch with contracted mouth muscles. Its hold is so firm that observers long thought the young koala grew as a kind of bud from the nipple.

Having almost outgrown its mother's pouch, a koala dangles out in the open. The elastic opening to the pouch —normally hidden by thick fur—is clearly visible as the parent reaches up with her hind foot to scratch vigorously.

Riding in its favored piggyback position, a koala watches its mother select a eucalyptus leaf. Its first taste of the staple diet is a semidigested mass of leaves that is processed in its mother's appendix and passed through her digestive system.

Wedged against a branch, the koala juvenile naps in its mother's embrace. Until it is almost half grown, the mother cuddles her offspring when it is tired, wet or cold.

With a youngster clinging to her side, a koala leaps from one tree to another. The powerful opposing digits on each paw are spread wide to ensure a perfect landing.

Life in the Treetops

A male koala stretched between two branches reveals a brown stain on his chest produced by scent-gland secretions used to mark trees and branches within his territory.

In its anatomy as well as its behavior, the koala is inextricably and uniquely linked to the eucalyptus tree. Eucalyptus leaves are indigestible to most other mammals, but the koala is endowed with a huge, convoluted appendix—up to eight feet long and capable of expanding to six inches in circumference—which contains microorganisms to convert the fibrous vegetation into a nutritious diet.

It has been calculated that a koala ranges over about 100 trees during its 15-year life span. The animal remains in one tree until it has finished all the leaves it can reach. It then changes trees by bending branches into a bridge, jumping across the gap, or by descending and walking on the ground. Koalas sometimes cover several miles on foot, although overland travel exposes them to the danger of automobiles, as well as dogs and other predators.

Adult koalas are not social creatures. While they live in clusters of one male and two to seven females, each animal prefers to keep to its own tree, except when mating or mothering.

A sleepy koala lolls in a tree with its tongue hanging out. Some experts believe koalas are addicted to cineol, a tranquilizing chemical that occurs in some eucalyptus.

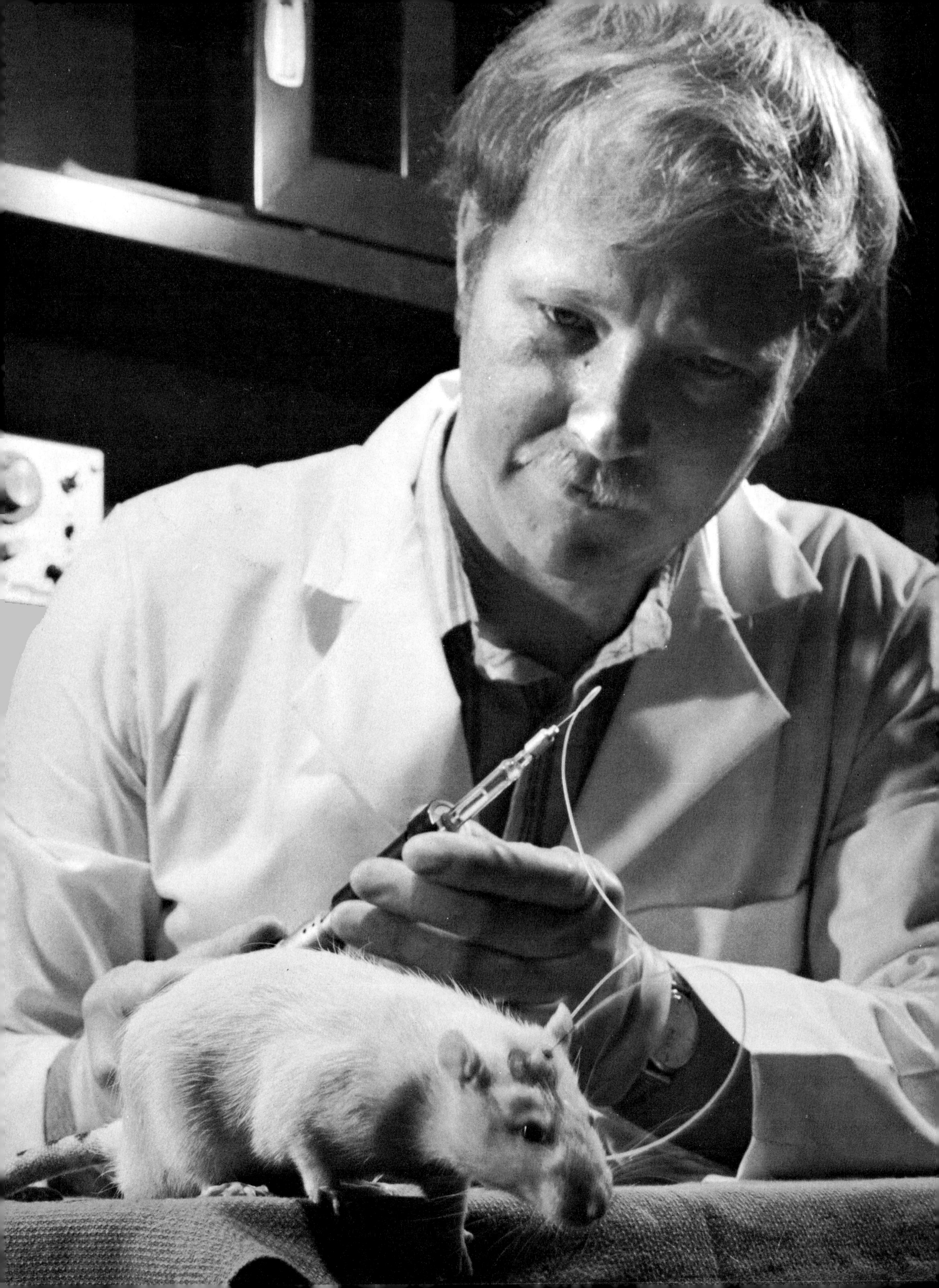

The Brain's Own Narcotic

A SELF-GROWN CHEMICAL HOLDS PAIN IN CHECK

by Gerald Jonas

During the Second World War, many doctors serving in frontline hospitals were astonished by the behavior of soldiers who were brought in directly from the battlefield with extensive wounds. Men with seared and broken flesh, shattered bones and massive internal injuries often denied that they were in any pain and insisted that they did not need injections of morphine, the standard pain-killing drug. Their apparent immunity to pain might have been understandable if the wounded men had been delirious or in shock. Yet when the medics jabbed them with hypodermic needles, they complained just as loudly as any of the other patients. According to one first-hand observer, it was as if the soldiers' great relief at being alive had somehow taken the pain out of the sensations arising from their terrible wounds. How this could happen was a total mystery to the doctors who observed it. But a recent discovery about the brain's machinery for sensing and suppressing pain may help explain the strange behavior of the soldiers.

The stage for this discovery was set in the early 1970s, when scientists learned that morphine and morphine-like drugs (known as opiates) suppress pain by acting on specific sites in the nervous system. These sites were dubbed "opiate receptors." Follow-up research showed that they were located on nerve cells, and that the cells were linked to neural pathways that transmitted pain sensations from various parts of the body to the higher brain centers. The flow of pain sensations was apparently cut off when morphine activated the receptors on the pathways.

The existence of specialized nerve cells with a high sensitivity to opiates made it easy to un-

Seeking one of medicine's top priority drugs—a nonaddictive pain killer—psychobiologist Agu Pert injects a new nerve-cell extract into a rat's brain in his laboratory at the National Institute of Mental Health. Pert will then measure the rat's reaction to mild electric shocks.

derstand why morphine was such an effective painkiller. But it raised an entirely new question: Why should the brain have cells that are selectively sensitive to chemical compounds not normally found in the body? Opiates, as their name implies, are derived from a substance manufactured by the opium poppy. It strained the imagination to assume that the cells in our brain and the cells in a small red-petaled flower native to Asia Minor had somehow evolved in tandem over millions of years. A more plausible hypothesis was that the brain's opiate receptors normally interacted with some substance made *inside* the body, and that morphine just happened to be similar enough to this substance to mimic its effects on the nervous system.

Although no trace of such a substance had ever been found in brain tissue, the reasoning sounded so logical that, in recent years, researchers all over the world have been vying for the distinction of being the first to isolate and identify it. The race was won in 1975 by a research team in Scotland. John Hughes and Hans W. Kosterlitz of the University of Aberdeen, making inspired use of biochemical techniques pioneered elsewhere and adding some new features of their own, found what amounts to the brain's own morphine. They named the substance enkephalin—a Greek-derived term that simply means "something found in the brain."

Why does the body need a pain-suppressing mechanism? One evolutionary reason seems obvious: The ability to block out pain selectively would have been an important survival trait whenever a sick or injured animal—or human being—had to flee from danger. Over-stimulation of such a mechanism might even account for the prolonged pain-free state of the severely wounded soldiers during World War II. In any case, the discovery may have profound consequences. By studying the interaction between enkephalin and its network of opiate receptors, scientists hope to gain a better understanding of the basic nature of pain, while opening the way to that long-sought panacea—a non-addictive pain-killing drug with all the strength but none of the harmful side effects of morphine.

Pain closely resembles the sense of touch, with one important difference. While touch brings us useful news about the world we live in—differences in texture, pressure and temperature—pain keeps us informed about the damage that the world is doing to our body. In other words, pain is touch that brings us nothing but bad news. Under normal circumstances, we are never indifferent to pain, as we sometimes are to the other senses. Aside from a few pathological exceptions, to feel pain is to want it to end, and the more painful the sensation, the more motivated we are to seek relief. Everyone knows from his own life that the perception of pain is qualitatively different from other sensory experiences. But only in the early 1900s, when scientists began tracing the pain pathways through the nervous system, did they realize just how different the pain sense is.

SLOW AND FAST PATHWAYS FOR PAIN

Anatomical studies, carried out with laboratory animals, human cadavers and cooperating patients undergoing neurosurgery, indicated that what we call pain is actually two kinds of sensation, each transmitted from body to brain via specialized nerve fibers. These fibers travel up through the spinal cord in roughly parallel tracks, before diverging in two functionally distinct pathways. One pathway runs through the center of the brainstem and the midbrain, where the body's general arousal mechanisms are located; then it fans out to contact those higher brain structures known to be involved in emotional reactions (the so-called limbic system). Because the fibers that feed into this pathway conduct nerve impulses at relatively low speeds—as slow as three-and-a-half feet per second—the pathway is usually referred to as the slow pain pathway. The other pathway has fibers that conduct nerve impulses a hundred times faster; messages carried by these fibers go directly to those parts of the brain that monitor where things happen in the body.

The anatomy indicates a sharp division of labor between the two pathways: The slow pathway is responsible for the suffering associated with persistent pain, while the fast pathway carries the sharp but fleeting twinges of acute pain. If subjective experience is any guide, both pathways are involved in the pain we feel after an injury to the surface of the body, either to the skin itself or to muscles lying just below the skin. For example, when we step on a tack, we are immediately aware of a sharp pain that we can localize to within a fraction of an inch on the skin surface; however, this sensation soon gives way to an unpleasant throb over a more widespread and less clearly defined area. By contrast, pain that involves visceral organs, glands or internal muscles may not go through an acute phase; this kind of pain from deep within the body seems to be carried exclusively on the slow pathway. One example is the chronic burning sensation in the abdomen that may signal an ulcer, an inflamed liver or some other visceral ailment. This sensation can rarely be localized with any precision; a patient who tells a doctor, "My stomach hurts," usually finds it hard to be any more specific.

Knowledge about the two types of pain pathways is by no means complete. Neuroanatomists cannot say for sure what nerve endings in the skin, muscles and internal organs initiate specific pain sensations, and they have not yet succeeded in tracing the two pathways to their destinations in the cerebral cortex—the wrinkled layer of gray matter at the top of the brain that is considered to be the seat of conscious thought. But even an incomplete neurological map has proved useful in explaining why opiate drugs suppress some kinds of pain and not others—a fact that has puzzled clinicians for years.

Opiate receptors are not found exclusively in the pain pathways; in fact, their widespread distribution in the nervous system indicates that they may have other functions besides the control of pain. But it is true that the receptors are densely clustered along the slow pain pathway, in the vicinity of the arousal and emotional centers, and this is also where the highest concentrations of enkephalin are found. Furthermore, most parts of the brain that transmit only fast pain contain neither opiate receptors nor enkephalin. On the basis of this anatomical evidence, it is not surprising that opiates are most effective in blocking the suffering associated with persistent pain, while they have little or no effect on acute sensations. For example, when post-operative patients get a shot of morphine, they often report that they can still feel stimulation of the tender area, but that it "doesn't hurt."

The extent to which pain is regulated in the brain—and so can presumably be suppressed there—is most vividly demonstrated by certain pathological conditions in which something has gone drastically wrong with the ordinary regulatory mechanisms. One of the most painful conditions known to medicine is a bizarre malady named causalgia, which appears in about one out of 30 cases of damage to peripheral nerves. A Civil War soldier whose causalgia developed when he was recovering from a gunshot wound in the arm, described the sensations in these words: "It is as if a rough bar of iron were thrust to and fro through the knuckles, a red-hot iron were placed at the junction of the palm and thumb with a heavy weight on it, and the skin were being rasped off my finger ends." The slightest movement of the sensitive area, or even adjacent areas, can intensify the torture of causalgia. These symptoms may continue unabated long after the damaged area is healed. Although the exact cause is unknown, apparently the slow pain pathway is activated by stimuli that normally fail to arouse any reaction at all.

Even more tragic (although fortunately more rare) are the cases of people who are born with no pain sense at all. One famous case, reported in Canada in 1950 and known in medical literature as Miss C, appeared normal in every way except one: She experienced no pain, or even momentary discomfort, when scalded with hot water, shocked with electricity, poked with sharp sticks or plunged into an ice bath. Her skin was not numb; she recognized the stick and the shock and the hot and cold for what they were; it was just that none of these sensations ever became unpleasant for her. As a child, she bit off the tip of her tongue without realizing anything was wrong until she saw the blood. As she grew older, her health inexorably deteriorated. Her knees, hips and spine became inflamed because, unlike a normal person, she had no way of knowing when to shift her weight to relieve pressure on a particular limb or joint. Despite almost constant medical attention, Miss C died at

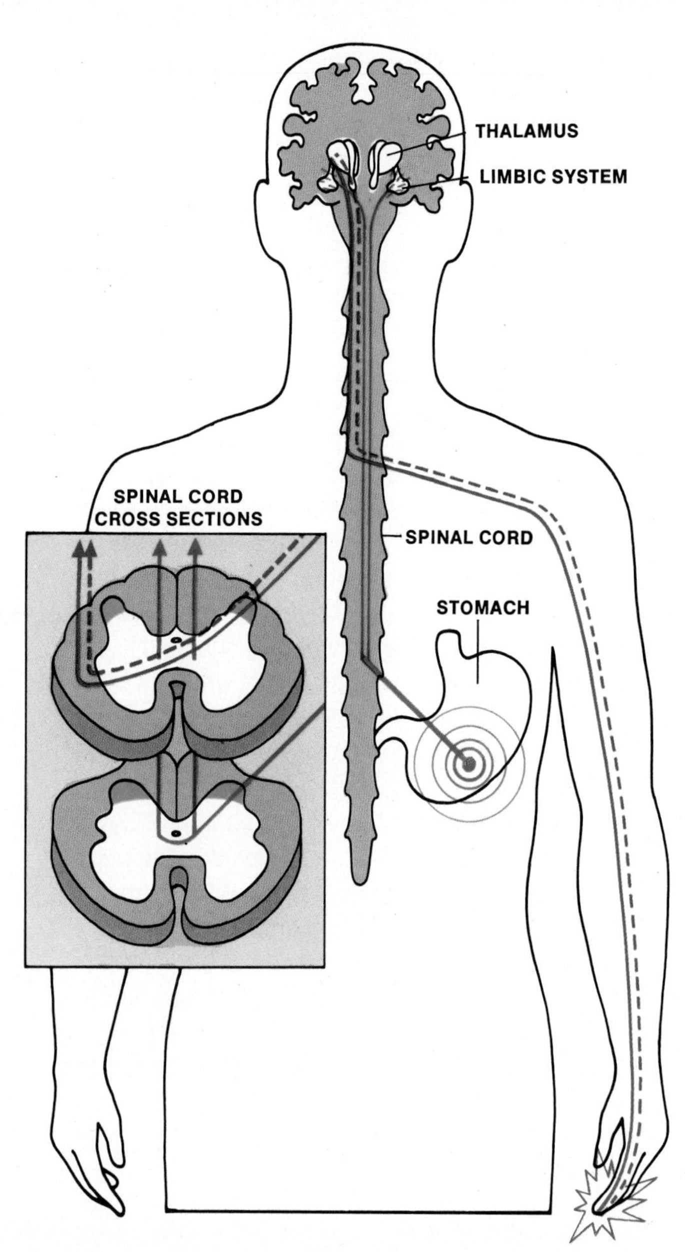

A simplified drawing of the body's pain-transmitting system shows that two distinct neural networks lead to the brain—one for external pain (red), the other for internal aches (blue). As indicated by the inset diagram, both networks enter the spinal cord through an area (green) that is rich in opiate receptors—nerve-cell sites that are activated by morphine and other painkillers. Internal pain is transmitted slowly via a pair of parallel pathways running through the middle of the butterfly-shaped center of the cord, while external pain impulses cross to the cord's outer rim. Within the external network, the immediate sensation of pain is transmitted along a fast-pain pathway (dotted red line); if the pain persists, it reverts to the slow pathway (solid red).

the age of 29 from "massive infections" brought on by "extensive skin and bone trauma." It might be said that the real cause of her death was a lifetime of feeling no pain.

Normal pain perception, of course, must fluctuate between these two extremes. If every move we made brought us agony, life would not be worth living; but without the constant warning signals of pain—what Shakespeare called "the thousand natural shocks that flesh is heir to"—we could not survive very long in a hostile environment. No matter how unpleasant in the short run, the sensations of acute pain are never entirely unwelcome, since they cry out for attention while there is time to avert impending danger or at least to repair damage recently done.

Slow pain, too, can have survival value. In the days before plaster casts, pain alone kept broken limbs immobilized, giving the bones an opportunity to knit. The trouble with slow pain is that it tends to go on long after we get the message. Beyond a certain point—as in the chronic suffering of the arthritis victim or the terminal cancer patient—it ceases to be a signal at all, and must be treated as a symptom of pathology in its own right.

Without denying that some pain may, in effect, be good for their patients, doctors have always recognized that part of their job—often the major part—is to alleviate unnecessary suffering. One of the earliest known medications was a brown powder prepared from the squeezings of the unripe fruit of the opium poppy. The pain-killing properties of opium have been appreciated in Europe and the Middle East for thousands of years. Long before opium dens were a social problem in China, restless children in ancient Mesopotamia were given poppy fruits to chew in order to keep them quiet. Laudanum, a kind of opium cocktail, was the mainstay of Western medicine from the 16th Century until the beginning of the 19th. In 1803, the principal active ingredient in opium was isolated. Under the name morphine, it soon became the standard treatment for the relief of severe pain, and even today it remains one of the most widely used of all medications.

Any drug that suppresses pain without deadening all sensation is called an analgesic; an anesthetic, by contrast, completely eliminates feeling. Aspirin is a mildly effective analgesic. Morphine is one so potent that even a small dose brings immediate relief from otherwise debilitating pain. Unfortunately, if morphine is given repeatedly to suppress pain, patients soon develop a tolerance for the drug: They need higher and higher doses to get the same relief. And the more they take, the more dependent they become on the drug, both physically and psychologically, so that they feel sick when it is withheld from them. Tolerance and dependence are the classic symptoms of drug addiction—a high price to pay for pain relief.

Once the dangers of chronic morphine use were recognized in the latter half of the 19th Century, an extensive search was launched for a substitute to suppress pain without causing addiction. Chemically, morphine is classified as an alkaloid, one of a vast number of biologically active (and often toxic) substances manufactured by green plants. A molecule of morphine contains 40 atoms—nitrogen, oxygen, hydrogen and carbon—arranged in a very complicated three-dimensional configuration. Like all complex molecules, its properties can be altered by modifying its structure—adding or removing an atom or a group of atoms here and there, but the effect of such changes is hard to predict.

The result of more than a century of tinkering with the morphine molecule is a mixed bag of so-called morphine "analogues" that produce a wide range of effects when injected into the human body. One of the first of these new drugs was heroin, which was introduced into clinical medicine as an allegedly safe analgesic in 1898. Its highly addictive nature remained unclear for a decade—too late to forestall its adoption by drug abusers, who found that it gave them an even stronger sense of euphoria than morphine.

The disastrous experience with heroin prompted the development of more reliable procedures for testing the new compounds on animals and on humans. In the United States, literally hundreds of morphine analogues were systematically evaluated in the 1930s under the auspices of the Committee on Drug Addiction of the National Research Council. Although the investigators failed to find the safe analgesic they were looking for, they learned a great deal about the way that morphine-like drugs act on the nervous system—knowledge that eventually led to the discovery of the brain's opiate receptors.

One thing that the work with morphine analogues showed was the extraordinary sensitivity of the nervous system to even minor modifications in the morphine molecule. For example, one slight change of the molecule yielded a substance with hardly any analgesic effect. A slightly different change produced another drug called etorphine that has 5,000 to 10,000 times the pain-killing ability of morphine; it is used today in narcotic darts that can knock out large animals like elephants almost on contact.

Still another molecular change caused an even more astonishing transformation: a drug that

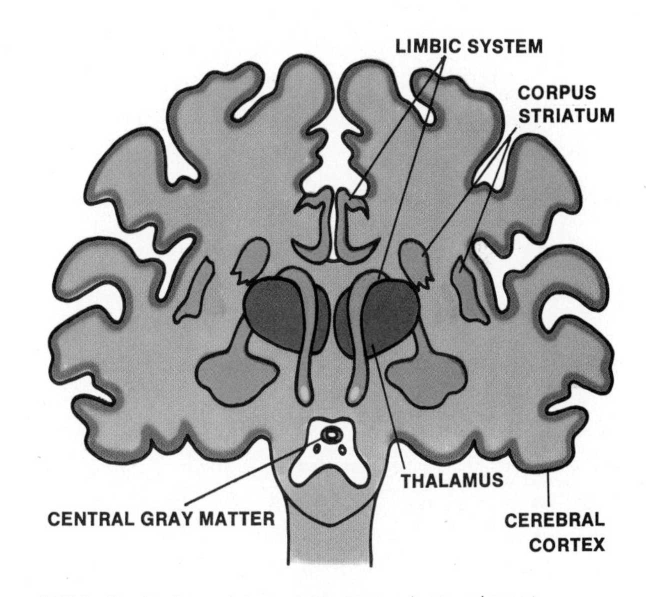

Within the brain, opiate receptors are clustered most densely in the areas colored green, less so in the orange areas and least in the brown. Among many other functions, these parts of the brain probably perceive, interpret and react to pain. Although scientists are still unsure about the exact division of labor, they theorize that both the central gray matter of the midbrain and the more complex thalamus may act as relay stations, sifting information passing to and from the decision-making cortex. The corpus striatum, believed to coordinate some body movements, may be involved in voluntary physical reactions to pain, while psychological reactions to pain are probably controlled by the limbic system, seat of the emotions.

counteracts the effects of morphine. Drugs with this curious veto power are known as morphine antagonists. Some antagonists have dual properties; when given in conjunction with morphine, they block its analgesic effect, but when given alone, they relieve pain, just as morphine does. Other antagonists, however, appear to be entirely inert except when combined with morphine; for example, a drug called naloxone does not relieve pain, slow down breathing, make people euphoric or do any of the things that morphine does. Yet naloxone prevents morphine from working. If a person in pain is injected with morphine and naloxone simultaneously, he will get no pain relief whatsoever. If an opiate addict is given naloxone, classic withdrawal symptoms appear almost immediately. This is remarkable because such symptoms (which include muscle aches and twitches, vomiting, diarrhea, acute anxiety and an overpowering craving for a restorative shot of opiate) usually do not show up in full strength until an addict's body has been free of drugs for a day or two.

The importance of molecular structure in determining opiate effects became even clearer when scientists tested subtly differing pairs of drugs known as stereoisomers. This term applies to two molecules that have identical chemical formulas but whose atoms are arranged in configurations that are mirror-images. With opiates, scientists found that one stereoisomer killed pain while its mirror-image was inert.

On the basis of all these findings, researchers in the United States and England began to suspect in the early 1950s that the brain possessed a kind of switch that could turn pain on or off. Before the switch could be operated, it had to be unlocked, and this required a molecular "key" with the proper three-dimensional configuration. The better the fit between lock and key, the more potent the analgesic effect.

In suggesting that morphine analgesia could be explained in terms of a molecular lock-and-key mechanism, the opiate researchers were simply borrowing and extending a concept that had already proved useful in other areas of biology. This was the concept of the "receptor." A receptor is any chemically active molecule in the body that appears to have been designed to interact with a specific "messenger" molecule manufactured elsewhere in the body. Most receptors are found on the outer membranes of cells. Because of their molecular configuration, they can only be activated by a molecule of one particular shape—hence the lock-and-key analogy. Once a receptor and a messenger are properly united, the result is usually a change in some metabolic process within the host cell. For example, there are insulin receptors on fat cells, and in the presence of insulin, they help speed the cell's conversion of sugar to usable energy.

Another kind of receptor, found on nerve and muscle cells, makes possible the cell-to-cell communication that lies behind our most complicated behavior. Wherever a nerve cell establishes contact with one of its neighbors, the membranes of the two cells remain separated by a tiny gap called a synapse. The electrical signal that constitutes a nerve impulse is not strong enough to leap across the synapse; in order to reach the target cell at all, it must first be converted into a type of chemical messenger called a neurotransmitter. Such messengers are released by the transmitting cell and travel across the gap to join receptor molecules on the target cell, lock-and-key fashion. Neurotransmitters either excite the target cell, causing it to generate a new impulse, or they inhibit the target cell, inducing it to stop firing.

A NEW NEUROTRANSMITTER?

The theory that opiates worked on receptors built into the brain carried the clear implication that morphine suppressed pain by mimicking the action of some natural inhibitory neurotransmitter. But speculation about the nature of the neurotransmitter that activated the opiate receptors was a futile pastime until someone could prove that such receptors actually existed. And this turned out to be a formidable task.

The general method for identifying receptor molecules on a piece of living tissue was developed in the early 1960s. Basically, the experimenter takes a tissue sample and gives it a chance to combine with messenger molecules that have been "labeled" with radioactive atoms.

Radioactive labeling does not change the chemical behavior of a molecule; it simply lets that behavior be monitored with a radiation counter, a device that counts particles emitted by a radiation source.

In the search for opiate receptors, samples of ground-up brain tissue were soaked in a bath containing a radioactive opiate. The experimenters knew that any opiate receptors in the tissue would bind the labeled molecules into lock-and-key combinations which would be radioactive —and therefore detectable. They also knew that this radiation would be mingled with background radiation from other labeled molecules that just clung to the cell membranes indiscriminately, like burrs on a sweater. To reduce background radiation, the experimenters routinely washed their tissue samples before taking a reading, the thought being that loosely attached molecules would wash out more readily than molecules that were tightly bound to receptors. But the technical problems were greater than anticipated. Plant alkaloids are notorious for their tendency to stick to tissue, and the only way to lower the background radiation to an acceptable level was to treat the tissue so harshly that the lock-and-key combinations would be broken up—defeating the purpose of the experiment.

There seemed to be no way out of this impasse until 1971 when Avram Goldstein, a professor of pharmacology at Stanford University, came up with a new experimental wrinkle. Goldstein was a well-respected research scientist with a penchant for tackling difficult problems. A few years earlier, he had become embroiled in a controversy over whether individual memories are recorded in special molecules in the brain *(Nature/Science Annual 1974 edition, pages 18-27).* Another scientist had claimed to have proof that such memory molecules existed. While many of Goldstein's colleagues expressed doubts about this claim, Goldstein put his reputation on the line by trying to duplicate the critical experiment; the publication of his negative results, in 1971, was a major blow to proponents of the memory molecule theory.

Now Goldstein thought he saw a way to determine whether or not the brain contained opiate receptors. His plan was to modify the radioactive labeling experiments to take advantage of the difference between "left-handed" and "right-handed" stereoisomer opiate molecules. Scientists usually distinguish between the molecules in a mirror-image pair by labeling one isomer with an l and the other with a d (from the Latin for left, *laevus* and right, *dexter*). Since only the l isomers are biologically active, Goldstein figured that only molecules with l configuration would be able to enter an opiate receptor.

His strategy for exploiting this bias was ingenious. First, he soaked two samples of brain tissue in preliminary baths of non-radioactive opiates—one bath consisted entirely of l molecules, the other of d molecules. He reasoned that the two kinds of molecules would cling to brain tissue in exactly the same proportions—except where opiate receptors were present. In the first sample, the l isomer molecules would quickly form non-radioactive lock-and-key combinations with all available receptors, while the receptors exposed to mirror-image molecules in the second sample would remain empty, like so many locks waiting to be filled by proper keys. Then Goldstein would provide the proper keys—by flooding both samples with a radioactive opiate of the l configuration. The background radiation would be the same in both samples, but the second sample should have a higher radiation count, since its opiate receptors would be filled with radioactive drug while the receptors in the first sample would be occupied by molecules that were not radioactive. Any significant difference in radiation between the samples would flag the presence of opiate receptors.

To eliminate chance variations that might mask the difference, Goldstein performed the same sequence of operations with many sets of samples and averaged the results—a standard procedure in biochemical research. The experiment turned out to be both a success and a disappointment. There was a difference in the average level of radiation between the differently treated samples, but the difference was only two per cent. This was not enough to prove to the skeptics that opiate receptors existed. But it was enough to prompt Goldstein and other researchers to try to do better.

Within two years, three other research groups had reported much more convincing results. The three groups were headed by Solomon H. Snyder of the Johns Hopkins University School of Medicine, Eric J. Simon of New York University, and Lars Terenius of Uppsala University in Sweden. Working independently, all had come up with essentially the same improvements on Goldstein's technique. They all began, as he had, with a non-radioactive mirror-image drug that could not enter the opiate receptors. But for the second step they used a labeled opiate concentrate that was much more radioactive than the material Goldstein had had available. This meant that the experimenters could use less of the drug in the bath and still be sure of getting lots of labeled molecules in lock-and-key combinations. With less radioactive drug to begin with, there was less background radiation to worry about; and to reduce that still further, the experimenters devised ways of washing their samples just vigorously enough to remove the loosely bound molecules, but not so vigorously as to dislodge the "keys" from the "locks."

With this careful treatment, the extra radioactivity of the opiate receptors stood out dramatically. Now, instead of a two per cent difference between samples, the radiation count in one sample might be 20, 30, even 90 per cent higher. Furthermore, when a wide variety of opiates was tested under the same conditions, the drugs that were known to be the most potent pain-killers produced the most impressive differences between tissue samples. Only the presence of highly selective opiate receptors could account for such results.

Once the existence of opiate receptors was conclusively established, the pace of research quickened. In the forefront of the developments was Solomon Snyder, a thin, intense man of 37, whose laboratory at Johns Hopkins University mounted an ambitious effort to characterize the receptor in complete detail. By injecting radioactively labeled tracers into the nervous systems of laboratory rats, Snyder and his associates found dense clusters of opiate receptors along the nerve pathway that the neuroanatomists had implicated in the sensations of slow pain.

But a final assessment of the role that these receptors play was impossible until their precise location on individual nerve cells was known. To determine their whereabouts, Snyder and his colleagues broke up the brain tissue of the rats into different fractions, and tested each fraction separately. The receptors turned up in the fraction that contained nothing but synaptic membranes—those located at the gap between neighboring nerve cells. This was just where one would expect to find a receptor for a neurotransmitter.

Since, as Snyder put it, "We can assume that nature did not put receptors in the brain solely to interact with the juice of the opium poppy," the obvious next step was to find the substance that the opiate receptors had been designed for. That breakthrough was made in 1974 at the Unit for Research on Addictive Drugs at the University of Aberdeen. John Hughes, working with the Unit's director, Hans W. Kosterlitz, found the substance he later called enkephalin in an extract of pig's brain. The key to the discovery was a laboratory preparation that he and Kosterlitz had devised in order to study the properties of opiate receptors under carefully controlled conditions. In essence, they stuck a little piece of tissue containing opiate receptors in a dish, kept it alive in a nutrient solution, and showed that morphine had certain unmistakable effects on it. To make sure that these effects were actually being mediated by opiate receptors, they added naloxone to the dish. Naloxone does nothing but block opiate receptors; when naloxone reversed the effects of morphine on the piece of tissue, Hughes and Kosterlitz knew that they were dealing with properly functioning opiate receptors.

Once this was established, they simply added pig-brain extract to the dish; it produced the same effects as morphine, and these effects were also speedily reversed by naloxone. By testing various fractions of the brain extract and discarding the inactive fractions, Hughes and Kosterlitz were able to purify the morphine-like ingredient until they had it down to an amorphous white powder. This was enkephalin. Chemically, it appeared to be a simple protein—or peptide—consisting of a small chain of amino acids, the basic building blocks of all living tissue.

Almost simultaneously with Hughes, both Snyder and the Swedish scientist Lars Terenius reported that they too had extracted from animal brains a peptide that behaved like morphine. Although their laboratory preparations differed, their results were remarkably similar. Apparently all three had discovered the same peptide—a coincidence that could not fail to impress any remaining skeptics.

As yet, there was no proof that enkephalin had significant pain-killing powers. The only way to find out if enkephalin was a potent analgesic was to inject it into some live animal and compare the animal's response to painful stimuli before and after the injection. But in order to perform properly controlled tests, large amounts of enkephalin were needed; and extracting it from ground-up brains was a tedious process.

The only answer was to synthesize enkephalin. Piecing together a specific peptide from commercially available amino acids is a relatively simple task for protein chemists. But first they have to know the exact sequence of amino acids in the peptide chain. In December 1975, Hughes and his associates published the formula for enkephalin in the British journal *Nature.* Actually, there were two nearly identical formulas, because enkephalin turned out to be a mixture of two peptides whose amino acid sequences differed only slightly. Within days after this issue of *Nature* appeared, a number of other laboratories had begun to synthesize their own enkephalin. And in tests conducted soon afterwards on live animals, enkephalin was shown to be a powerful analgesic—when injected directly into the brain.

This development has launched a new phase of the research race—led by some giant drug companies that see an enormous market for a non-addictive analgesic. But many problems remain. For one thing, pure enkephalin has no analgesic effect whatsoever unless it is placed directly on the opiate-sensitive cells of the brain. Indeed, investigators have reason to believe that normal intravenous injections of enkephalin—via hypodermic needle into the bloodstream—do not even reach the brain. The body is filled with enzymes that have the ability to break apart any small peptides they come across, and enkephalin molecules circulating in the blood would be prime targets.

Morphine, of course, gets through to the brain with no trouble. This is because the body's enzymes cannot break apart plant alkaloids so easily. Although morphine and enkephalin molecules are similar enough in shape to fit into the same receptor, they are made of quite different materials—just as two keys to fit one lock can be made out of blanks of different metals.

MAKING IT SAFE AND EFFECTIVE

If enkephalin is ever to be utilized as an analgesic drug, chemists will have to modify the molecule to increase its resistance to enzymatic destruction. But there is a possible catch: A hardier enkephalin molecule may turn out to have the same addictive side-effects as morphine. Although the biochemical events responsible for opiate addiction are still unknown, some researchers believe that both tolerance and physical dependence stem from the fact that morphine molecules remain attached to the receptor much longer than a natural neurotransmitter would. This upsets the normal equilibrium between the slow pain pathway and the pain-suppression mechanism. Because an unawareness of pain can be fatal, one would expect the nervous system to try to restore the equilibrium. According to this view, a morphine addict is a person whose nervous system has adjusted to the presence of morphine so that his pain perception is normal despite the persistent inhibitory effect of the drug. A non-addictive analgesic would somehow have to fool the pain cells into accepting long-term inhibition without triggering the compensatory response.

No one knows whether this can be done. To find out, several laboratories are now exploring the most fundamental aspects of the problem, from the synaptic processes that regulate all cell-to-cell communication to the internal adjustments that cells make when their receptors are occupied. Out of this basic research may emerge not only a better pain-killer but also new insights into the neural mechanisms that let us feel pain and help us overcome it at the same time.

Filming Insect Acrobats

Some of the most astonishing photographs ever made were published last year in a book titled *Borne on the Wind,* by the English naturalist-photographer Stephen Dalton. Nearly a decade ago, Dalton determined to do what no other photographer had ever done: obtain sharp pictures of insects in their natural airborne state. He succeeded magnificently, and in the process he learned some things about the flight of insects that had been suspected but were hitherto unproved—and some others not even suspected.

Until Dalton made this multiple exposure, no one knew precisely how a fly landed on a ceiling. Some scientists believed that as the insect approached the overhead surface with legs hanging down, it did a barrel roll at the last instant; other experts felt the landing maneuver must be a loop. But Dalton's stop-action pictures proved both theories wrong. The fly goes straight at the ceiling, reaches up to catch hold with its front legs (center), then cartwheels its body (left) so the other four legs make contact.

Focusing on something as small, swift and unpredictable as an insect on the wing is fiendishly difficult. Dalton decided the only way he could do it was to put the elusive creatures in a large box opening on a light source. He reasoned that an insect would fly toward the light, and that he would need an electric-eye beam to trigger both a prefocused camera and an electronic flash unit when the insect flew through the beam. Unfortunately, when he conceived this method, there was no camera shutter fast enough to open during the instant the subject was in focus, and no electronic flash quick enough to freeze the movement of an insect's wings—which, in the case of some gnats, move a thousand times a second. Also, there was the large probability the insect would miss the pencil-thin beam altogether.

With some expert engineering help, Dalton eventually developed an electronic shutter that could open and shut within 1/450 second and a strobe light whose powerful flash lasted just 1/25,000 second. He heightened the likelihood of the insect flying through the beam by arranging mirrors that reflected the beam in a network of crisscross patterns in the box. Even so, there were many failures, and Dalton made 15,000 exposures during his experiments. He tried photographing the green lacewing on page 145 more than 900 times before he got what he wanted.

Heading for the camera, a June bug displays brown appendages of armor—possessed by all beetles—that must be raised out of the way before the true wings (rear) can work. The fringes on the head are part of the antennae.

A large fly backs off from a water-mint flower. Flies are among the most versatile acrobats of the insect world. This one, in order to reverse direction, has turned its wings around so the leading edges are to the rear. Flies have only two wings, most other insects four.

A hawk moth simultaneously curves its wings and rotates them in order to hover. The heavy-bodied, fast-flying moths use this flight technique in order to hang in the air in front of blossoms while their long tongues probe deep into flowers to obtain nectar.

One of Dalton's most extraordinary pictures is this three-exposure sequence of a green lacewing, showing the floppy, seemingly haphazard movements of its delicate wings as it rises vertically in the air and then executes a deliberate backward half loop from a Cotoneaster leaf.

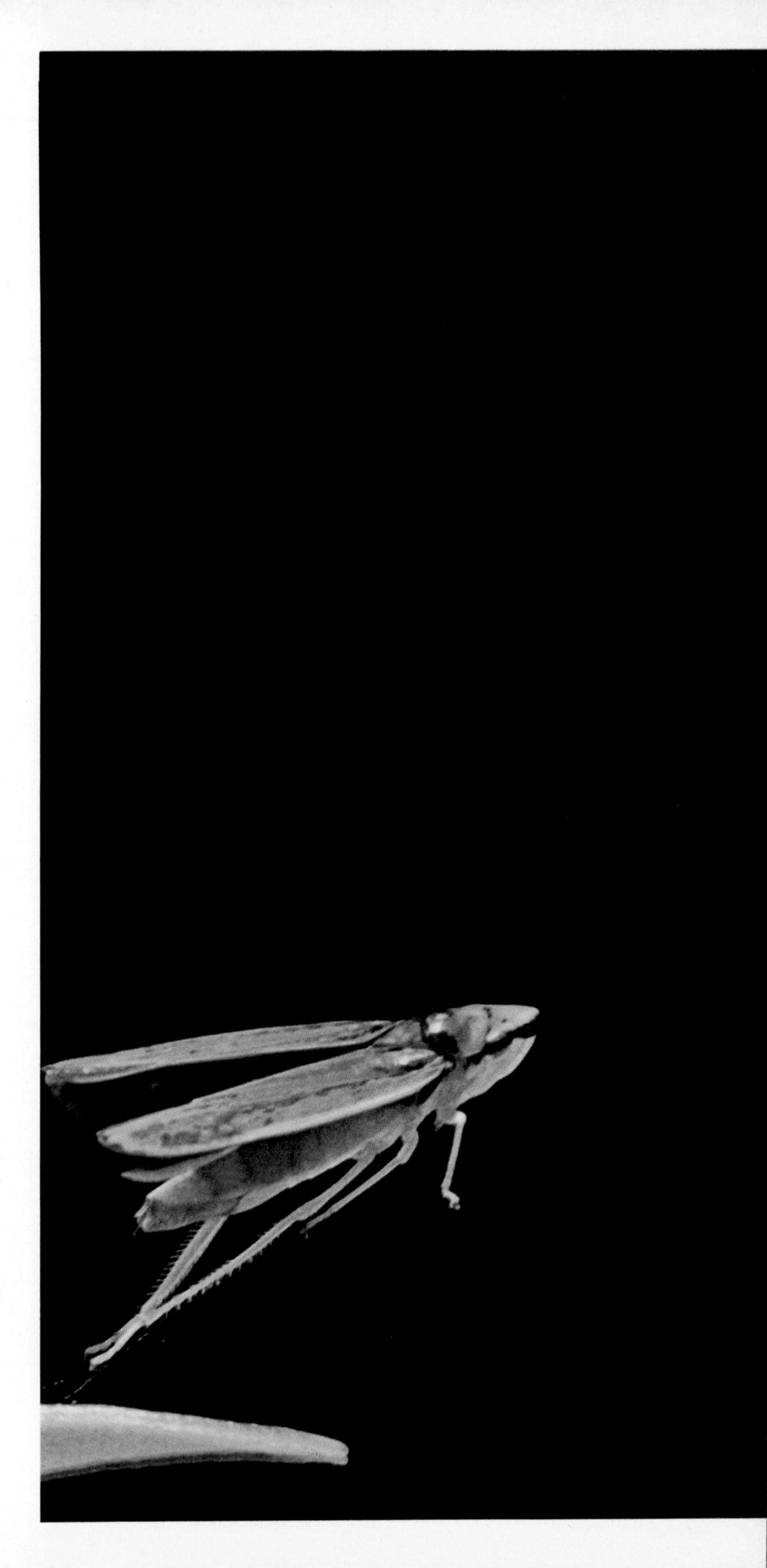

A leaf hopper demonstrates a combination of propulsive methods in its high-speed take-off. In the first image, it has just pushed off and its powerful rear legs are fully extended, while its wings are not yet opened. The second image shows the wings open and the jumping legs beginning to retract. In the third, the hind legs are entirely retracted and the insect is in full flight. Over short distances, these insects usually propel themselves by leg power alone.

Two shots of a paper wasp illustrate how the insect carries its legs and antennae extended in flight. Its wings are brought crisply to the vertical on the upstroke and to the horizontal during the downstroke, with none of the droopy movement exhibited by the lacewing (page 145).

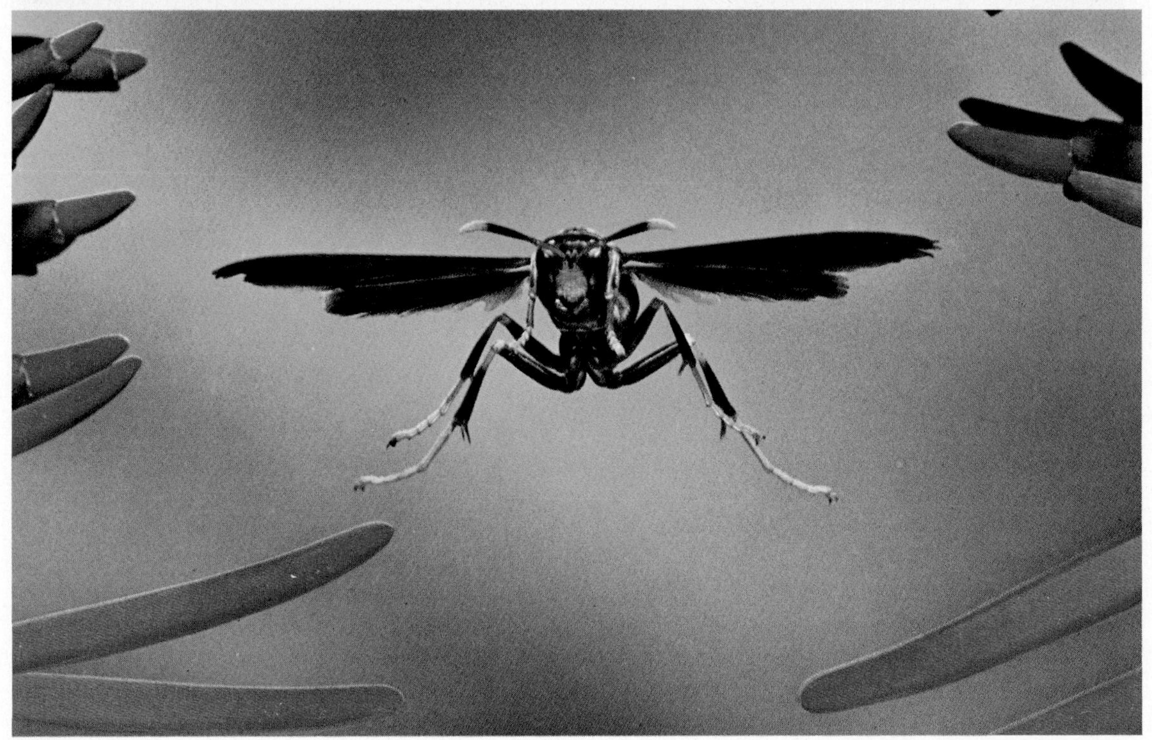

An owlet moth nonchalantly performs what seems to be a barrel roll above an algae-covered twig. While mammals and birds have internal gravity-sensing mechanisms to maintain their balance, the far lighter insects appear oblivious to gravity and sometimes even fly upside down.

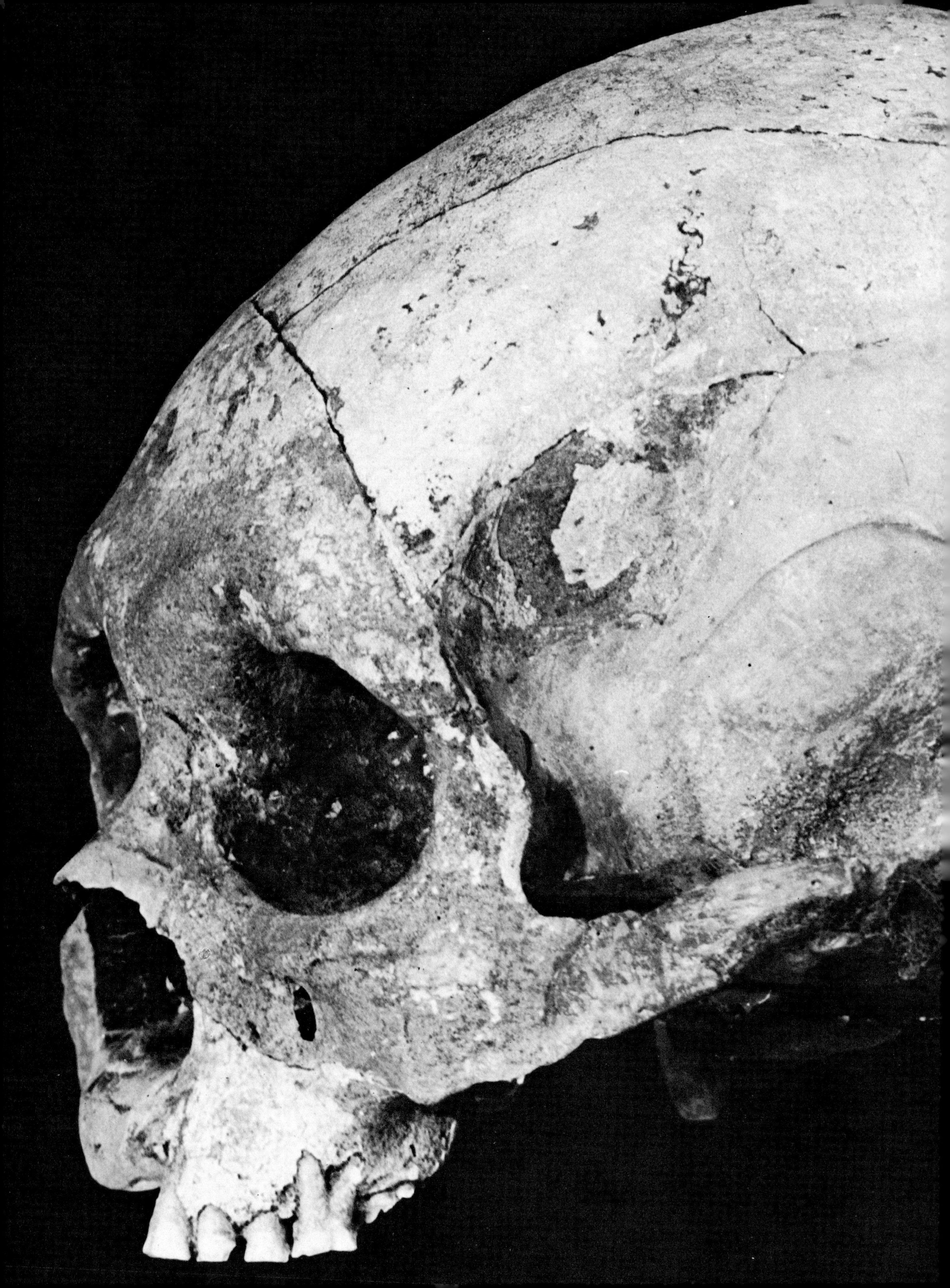

New-World Man Redated

PROTEIN MAY HOLD THE KEY

by Thomas Froncek

Virtually all experts on early man agree that humans first arrived in the New World sometime during the most recent ice age, which lasted from approximately 10,000 to 70,000 years ago. Great sheets of ice then covered much of North America, extending as far south as Puget Sound on the west coast and present-day New York City on the east. During this frigid period, so much of the earth's moisture supply became locked up in glaciers that ocean levels dropped several hundred feet, exposing vast areas of former sea bottom. One such exposed region lay between Siberia and Alaska, now separated by the 53-mile-wide waters of the Bering Strait.

According to the generally accepted scenario for man's discovery of the Americas, Siberian hunters, ancestors of today's Indians, crossed this exposed land bridge to Alaska in pursuit of migrating herds of woolly mammoths, caribou and other animals that fed on the region's tundra vegetation. Eventually they veered south, probably along an unglaciated corridor east of the Rocky Mountains, until they penetrated to the very heart of the continent. From there, some fanned eastward to the Atlantic, others went to the Pacific and still others ventured south, slowly making their way into Mexico and beyond.

When did the entry into this pristine wilderness take place? Lacking any direct archeological evidence of the event, many scientists are

This fossilized skull, unearthed at a site near Del Mar, California, in 1929 and recently subjected to a new dating technique based on bone protein, may be 48,000 years old—an age that is well outside the traditional timetable for the arrival of ancient Indians in the Americas.

content to estimate the earliest date when it could have occurred, while they admit that it might have occurred later. The crossing, they say, must have been made sometime after 30,000 B.P. (archeologists generally designate dates as "B.P."—before the present—rather than "B.C.") The reason for their belief is simple: according to all evidence currently available, humankind did not develop the sort of clothing, shelter and survival skills required to approach the land bridge until about that time. Northeastern Siberia is one of the most inhospitable environments in the world: the average January temperature along the coast is minus 4° F. today, and winters must have been even worse during the ice age.

The case against a crossing prior to 30,000 B.P. would thus appear to be open-and-shut. However, the study of early man is notorious for the frequency with which rude shocks are administered to what seem to be ironclad theories—and just such a shock now threatens the commonly accepted chronology of man's conquest of the Americas.

NEW DATES FOR NEW WORLD MAN

The challenge comes not from a professional archeologist in the field, but from a scientist who pursues an entirely different discipline: Jeffrey Bada, a young organic chemist at Scripps Institution of Oceanography in San Diego. There, Bada has been pioneering a new fossil-dating technique based on a phenomenon called amino-acid racemization. Last year he dated more than half a dozen human fossils that have turned up in California over a period of several decades. All of them, according to his racemization findings, are between 40,000 and 50,000 years old.

Bada's controversial dates are only the latest in a long series of revisions in the length of man's tenure in the New World. As late as the 1920s, many scholars refused to accept any suggestion that the Americas might have been inhabited before 4,000 years ago.

Such scientific caution was not entirely unwarranted: In the 19th Century, an Argentine professor had boldly asserted—without bothering to offer any real proof—that *Homo sapiens* originated in his country at least a million years ago. In reaction to such wild guesswork, scientists after the turn of the century established rigorous rules of evidence. As far as they were concerned, the only indubitable archeological signs of a human presence in America prior to the arrival of Columbus were such ruins as the mud-packed pueblos of the U.S. Southwest, or the more elaborate structures and artifacts left by the Incas in Peru and by the Aztecs, Maya or their ancestors in Central America. The experts admitted that the engineering and artistic skills displayed by these people must have taken many centuries to develop, but until solid proof of earlier and more primitive settlers turned up, they preferred to avoid speculation.

In 1926, a sharp-eyed black cowboy named George McJunkin helped push the ancestry of the Indians far back in time. While riding along a dried-out river bed near Folsom, New Mexico, he spotted odd-looking bones sticking out of the sun-baked clay. Word of his find reached an expert on the natural history of the region, and this scientist identified the bones as the fossilized remains of an extinct species of bison known to have died out at least 10,000 years ago. Along with the bones, excavators uncovered remnants of a flint spear—apparently chipped by some ancient inhabitant of the area—that may well have been used to slay the beast. Apparently hunters roamed the Americas as long ago as the tail end of the ice age a hundred centuries ago.

Recent finds have indicated that there were humans in the Americas well before the glacial epoch concluded. In 1971, for example, a U.S. expedition to the Andean highlands of Peru found man-made stone tools of unexpectedly ancient vintage: radioactive dating of animal bones from the same layer of earth (and presumably of the same age as the artifacts) suggested that the crude stones were at least 14,000 years old.

In the same year, scientists were surprised by some more direct evidence of a human presence in the Americas during the last glacial period. After gathering dust for years on a museum shelf, a human skull dug up in the 1930s during a public works project near Los Angeles was finally subjected to radioactive dating. Playfully dubbed Los Angeles man, it was determined to be about

24,000 years old. Other human bones and artifacts that may be nearly as ancient have been found in such widely dispersed sites as Lewisville, Texas; Santa Rosa, California; and Tlapacoya, Mexico.

Even before Bada made his astonishing announcements, a few scientists argued that Los Angeles man and his contemporaries were by no means the earliest Americans. They cited chipped stones found in layers of sediment that may have been deposited 50,000 to 80,000 years ago near Calico Hills, California, outside Los Angeles. No less experienced an archeologist than the late Louis Leakey—an expert on the earliest forms of humankind—insisted that the stones were shaped by human hands. But most experts countered that the stones could have been hammered into their tantalizing tool-like shapes by natural geological wear and tear.

Such squabbling, in any case, could not be settled by existing fossil-dating techniques. In attempting to trace the spread of humanity around the world, anthropologists had been relying on the so-called carbon-14 clock, discovered in the late 1940s by the American chemist Willard Libby. All living things absorb from plants, or directly from the air, two forms of carbon: ordinary carbon 12 and minute quantities of radioactive carbon 14 (the numerical designations

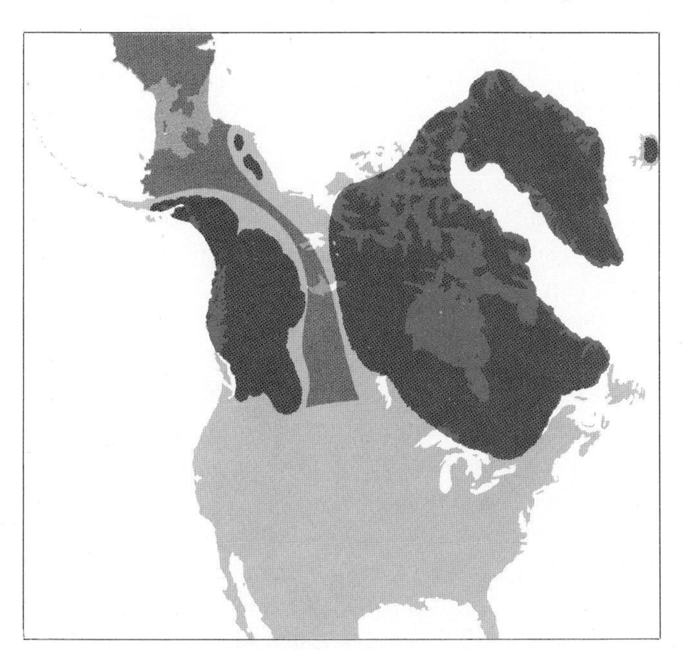

The nomadic hunters who invaded the Americas during the latter half of the last ice age first crossed a land bridge existing between Siberia and Alaska, then moved south via a corridor between two ice sheets (beige). The expanding glaciers probably closed the corridor some 20,000 years ago, thwarting any further migration from the polar regions until rapid melting set in about 7,000 years later.

of the element refer to the total number of protons and neutrons in the atoms' nuclei).

After an organism dies, it ceases to absorb carbon 14, and the fossil's store of the radioactive isotope dwindles at a fixed rate as it decays into simpler atoms. By contrast, the amount of nonradioactive carbon 12 remains constant. Thus, if scientists measure the ratio of carbon 14 to carbon 12 in a fossil, they can determine its age —up to a point. In spite of recent efforts to make the carbon-14 clock more accurate, fossil dates greater than 20,000 years are considered somewhat unreliable, and any dates beyond 40,000 years are extremely suspect. Beyond the latter age, the amount of radioactive carbon that still remains in the material becomes so small as to be virtually undetectable.

There are alternative radioactive clocks—involving, for example, the decay of uranium, potassium 40 or rubidium—but they cover an entirely different time span. Uranium and rubidium have such a long half life (the interval it takes half of the atoms in a given sample to decay) that they cannot date objects less than half a million years old. The potassium-40 technique can date volcanic rock only a few hundred thousand years old, but it cannot date bones directly.

The lack of an accurate atomic clock for estimating the age of bones in the period between 500,000 B.P. and roughly 40,000 B.P. has been a grievous handicap to the study of early man, but Bada's new technique could fill that anthropological gap. In contrast to the other kinds of atomic clocks, it does not depend on the gradual decay of radioactive atoms. Instead, it involves the chemical activity of molecules called amino acids. When these extremely important organic molecules are linked together, they form still larger molecules called proteins, which are, in turn, the building blocks of all living things, from microbes to man.

Living tissue contains 20 different amino acids, but all of them—with the sole exception of glycine—have a common characteristic. If a beam of polarized light (whose waves vibrate in a single plane, like a rope wiggling only up and down) is directed through them, the direction of the emerging waves will be slightly rotated to the left, or counterclockwise. But after an organism dies, the ability of its amino acids to rotate polarized light will gradually diminish and eventually disappear altogether.

Chemists have long been aware of the underlying reason for this optical quirk. Like the models that children make out of Tinkertoys, a molecule can be built in two different ways: the same number and type of atoms can be arranged to create mirror-image versions of the molecular structure. For reasons yet unknown, all amino acids in living organisms have a left-handed configuration. By contrast, amino acids found in nonliving things—for example, meteorites—contain some molecules that are right-handed; that is, they can rotate polarized light in a clockwise direction. In such cases, the number of left- and right-handed amino acids is usually about equal, so that the light-rotating effects of the material cancel each other out and a polarized beam shows no change.

THE LAWS OF CHANCE—CHEMICAL STYLE

There is an important footnote to these chemical rules. Amino acids are structurally unstable. After an organism dies, its left-handed amino acids undergo changes, losing loosely linked hydrogen atoms, among others. The losses are only temporary, for the amino acids pick up replacement hydrogen atoms, usually from neighboring water molecules. However, since the amino acids are no longer part of a living system, there is no particular preference for the reacquisition; the replacement atoms can link up on either the left or right side of the molecule. Furthermore, as the game of chemical roulette continues—operating strictly under the laws of chance—the quantity of right-handed molecules will slowly increase. In fact, their population will eventually become so large that the number of left- and right-handed amino acid molecules should precisely balance out.

Among chemists, the tendency of molecules to reach such a state of equilibrium is known as racemization, from the Latin word for "mix." Virtually all amino acids originally formed in living organisms undergo racemization. In any given temperature range, the pace of the process varies widely, depending on the acid. At 0° C., isoleucine, for example, takes approximately 10 million years before the number of left- and right-handed molecules balances; aspartic acid at the same temperature takes only three or four million years. But in every case, the rate of racemization is predictable. Thus, it would seem obvious that the process could be used to calculate the age of a once-living organism. One would simply measure the ratio of right- to left-handed amino acids to tell a fossil's age.

The possibility of such a dating technique was, in fact, anything but obvious. Until about 25 years ago, no one even realized that fragile amino acids were present in fossils. Before then, scientists assumed that amino acids decomposed so rapidly after the death of a plant or animal that they soon vanished altogether. This view was corrected by Philip H. Abelson, a physical chemist at Carnegie Institution in Washington, D.C., who performed a series of meticulous experiments that revealed traces of the acids in some fossilized bones, shells and teeth millions of years old. The surprising longevity of amino acids fascinated one of Abelson's colleagues, P. Edgar Hare. He began studying the molecules in the fossilized shells of cherrystone clams and found that the proportion of left- to right-handed amino acids did indeed change with time. In 1966 Hare and an associate, Richard Mitterer, suggested that racemization be used to date fossil shells.

At about that time, the same idea occurred to Bada. Then at Harvard University on a one-year fellowship, Bada was also studying racemization in marine fossils. As Hare and his colleagues had done, Bada found that fossils recovered from deeper (or older) layers of sediment on the ocean floor displayed a greater degree of racemization than fossils in higher layers. But a crucial question remained unanswered. Could racemization be used to provide clues to the age of fossils other than shells, whose amino acids were protected from chemical interference by multiple layers of calcium carbonate?

Hare had his doubts. In his early experiments, he had found that since bones were more porous than sea shells, they could be contaminated by amino acids from younger organisms, including bacteria in the soil. According to Hare, these amino acids invaded the buried fossils along with the groundwater that seeped through the earth —and thus seriously distorted any calculations of the fossil's age. Discouraged by dating experiments with fossil bones, Hare and his colleagues decided to concentrate on sea shells, using their ages to date marine and glacial sediments as clues to the earth's geological history.

Bada, also, had reservations about dating bones. As he saw it, the main problem was not contamination of the fossils, but variations in the temperature to which they may have been subjected during their long history of interment in geological deposits. Unlike radioactive decay, racemization is highly sensitive to temperature: if an amino acid's environment heats up, the rate of racemization will speed up. Only if he had a fairly good idea of a fossil bed's past climate, Bada realized, could he make a reasonably good calculation of the age of any bones from it.

TESTING FOR ACCURACY IN BURIED CAVES

By then, scientists had already developed several subtle techniques for determining climates far back in the past. These included analyzing ancient pollen found at a site, studying the content of various isotopes of oxygen in layers of ancient shells or glacial ice, and analyzing soil for symptoms of low temperature. But Bada felt that none of these methods would give him the accuracy he hoped to achieve. He was stumped —until a colleague, geochemist Karl Turekian of Yale, suggested a way of avoiding the temperature difficulty altogether. He urged Bada to use bones buried in a subterranean cave on an island, where—because of the moderating influence of the surrounding water—the temperature was likely to have remained relatively close to the present level for thousands of years, even during the most intense ice-age cold snaps.

In 1971 Bada joined the Yale researcher on a trip to Majorca, off the coast of Spain, where Turekian knew of a cave full of fossils of an extinct species of goat. This cave seemed especially promising for a tryout of the racemization dating technique, since the island lay far from any ice sheet of the past.

Bada carted several goat fossils back with him to Scripps, where he now worked, and used the racemization of their amino acids to calculate their ages. At the same time, he sent fragments of the specimens to a laboratory at the University of California in Los Angeles to be dated by the carbon-14 clock. The two methods produced almost identical results. Carbon-14 tests indicated that the goat bones were 28,000 to 29,000 years old, while the amino-acid technique produced a range of 25,000 to 30,000 years.

Bada was elated. "Everything worked so well I couldn't really believe it," he recalls. "It seemed almost too good to be true." Yet even though he was now persuaded of the validity of his approach, he knew that other scientists would not accept racemization as a reliable dating tool until he was able to adjust his results for the effects of temperatures that differed markedly from those at present. The carbon-14 cross-check suggested a means for doing just that.

Since the extent of racemization of a fossil bone is dependent upon both time and temperature, either one of these variables can theoretically be calculated if the other is known. Bada figured that if he took a fossil specimen less than 40,000 years old and obtained a reliable carbon-14 age, he could then use racemization to deduce the average temperature the bone had been exposed to since it was deposited. After this temperature had been determined for a particular site or locale, it would, in turn, permit calculation of the ages of other bones in the vicinity by racemization, including those beyond the range of the carbon-14 clock.

Bada concedes that this ingenious technique is not absolutely foolproof. Warm spells that may have occurred in the period beyond the range of carbon 14 could affect his dates. But at worst, he argues, any errors would be very small, because the rate of racemization is determined not so much by temperatures over a few years or even over hundreds of years but by the average temperature throughout the fossil's history. As it happens, in spite of occasional fluctuation, the global temperature remains remarkably steady over the long haul.

Almost as soon as Bada began publishing his

At the start of the racemization-dating process, the fossil sample is dissolved in a beakerful of powerful hydrochloric acid. The resulting solution will be boiled for 24 hours; then the hydrochloric acid will be evaporated off to gain a bone residue whose amino acids can be easily extracted.

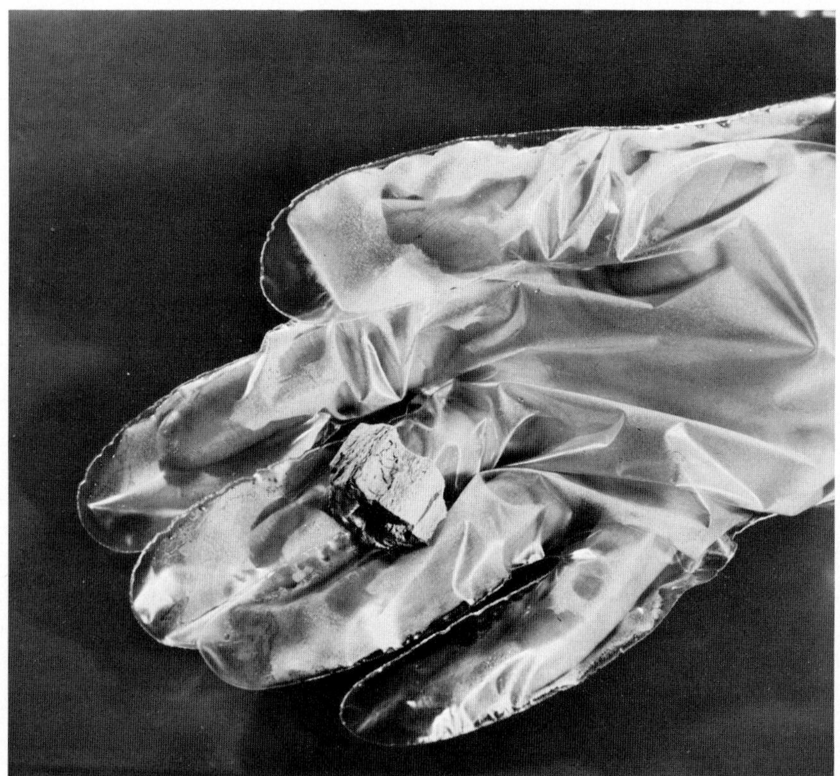

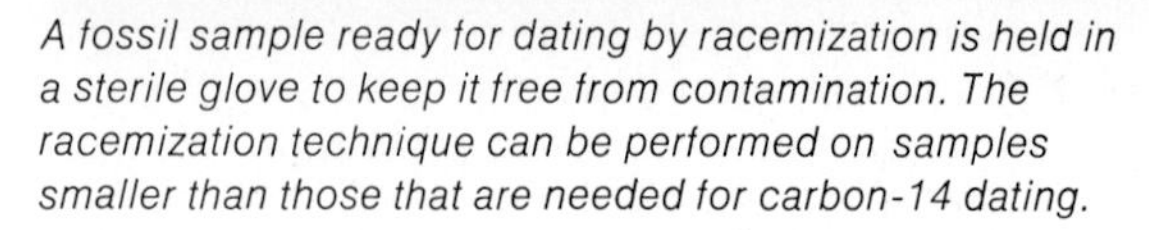

A fossil sample ready for dating by racemization is held in a sterile glove to keep it free from contamination. The racemization technique can be performed on samples smaller than those that are needed for carbon-14 dating.

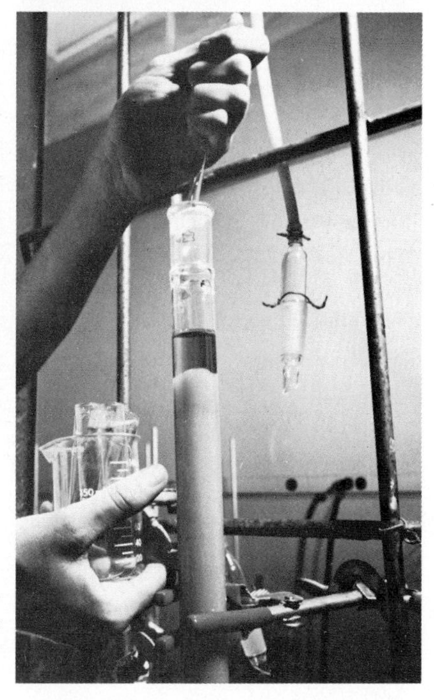

Bone residue is passed through a glass column containing a resin that traps all of the amino acids. The blended acids will later be placed in a second resin-filled column that segregates them by exploiting their different rates of flow.

results, anthropologists everywhere began sending him fossils for dating. One scientist whose interest was especially aroused was George F. Carter of Texas A&M University. Somewhat of a maverick in his field, Carter had long been convinced that humans were in the Americas as far back as 100,000 years ago. He failed to persuade most of his colleagues because of some all-too-obvious shortcomings in his case. His belief was based not on human remains but on what appeared to be man-made implements, and he could estimate the age of these implements only by rough geological means—for example, by the number of layers of sediment above them.

On a scientific hunch, Carter urged Bada to try racemization dating on some fossils that had been virtually ignored in a San Diego museum. Among them was part of a human skull unearthed in 1926 during construction at the La Jolla Beach and Tennis Club, barely three quarters of a mile down the road from Bada's laboratory. Other fossil candidates suggested by Carter were a skull, a jawbone and ribs found three years later poking out of an eroding sea cliff between the nearby towns of Del Mar and Solana Beach. Though the geological setting in which the bones were discovered indicated an age of many thousands of years, the fossils created only a brief flurry of in-

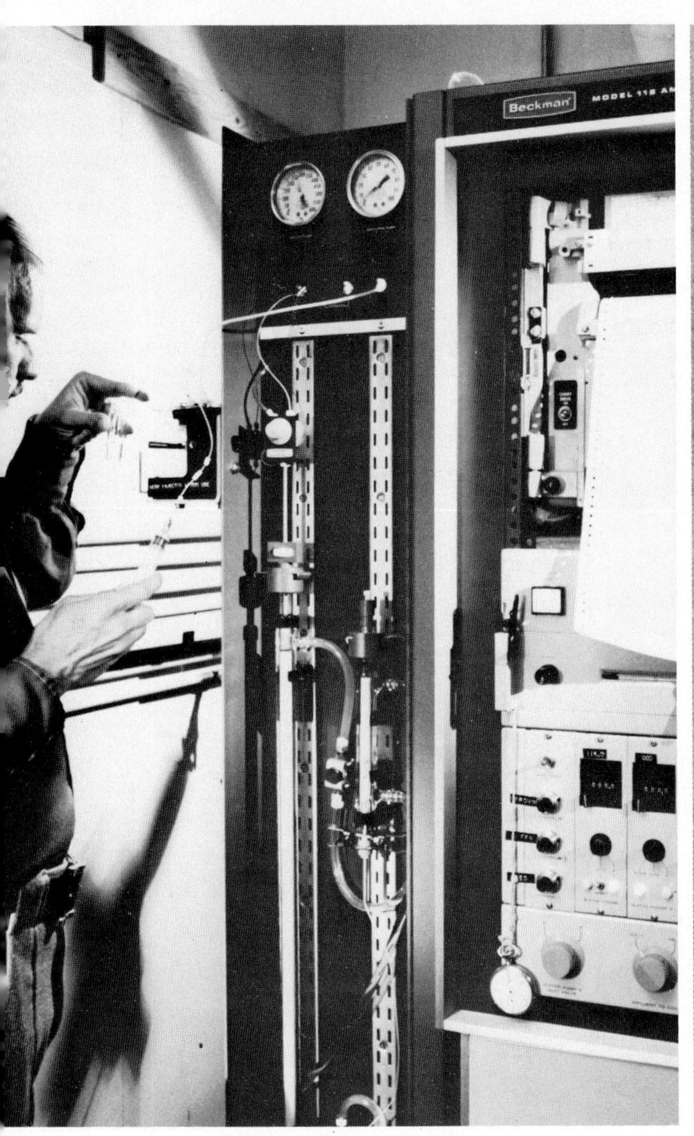

Jeffrey Bada prepares an amino acid derivative to be injected in the instrument at right, which separates left- and right-handed molecules and graphs their relative amounts.

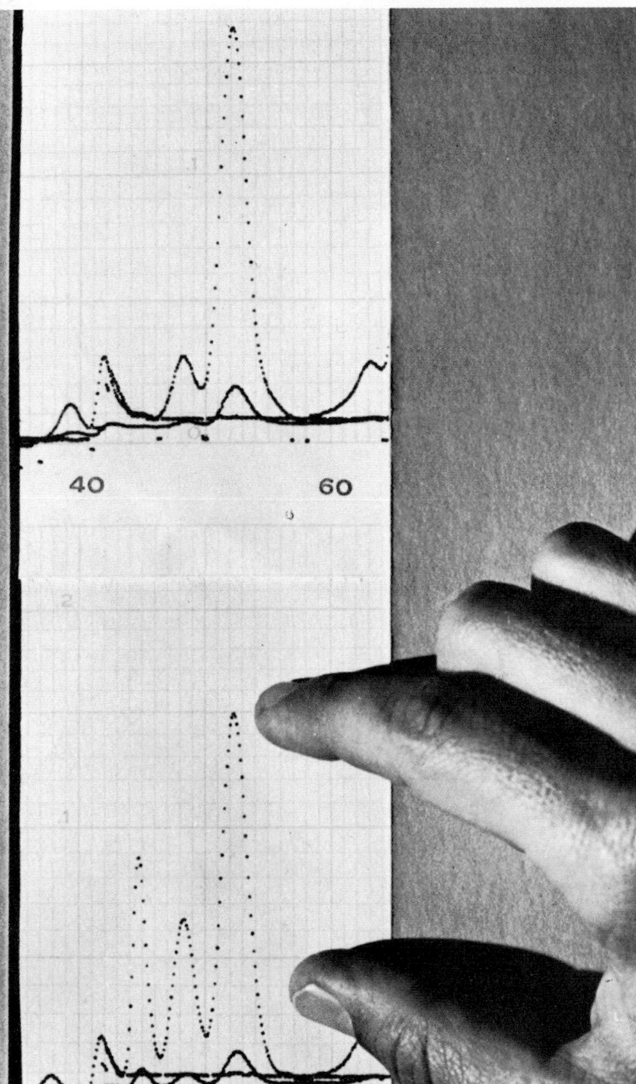

The graph peak pointed out by Bada measures left-handed molecules. A comparison of this peak to the adjacent one for right-handed molecules indicates the sample's age.

terest at the time of their discovery and soon were put in storage.

Excited by Carter's suggestions, Bada and a graduate student, Roy Schroeder, retrieved the bones from oblivion and subjected them to the lengthy series of steps involved in racemization dating. First, they cut off a chip from each specimen and, following standard procedure, washed the fossil material thoroughly in distilled water and a weak solution of hydrochloric acid. To dislodge any foreign material that might contain extraneous amino acids, they exposed the bone fragments to the vibrations of ultrasonic waves. These high frequencies, beyond the range of normal human hearing, are often used by scientists to knock off tiny bits of matter that might have loosely attached themselves to a bone or artifact during its long burial.

After additional treatment with hydrochloric acid and water, the bone material was subjected to a laboratory technique called ion exchange chromatography, which segregated the various acids. For his tests, Bada sought aspartic acid. Its rapid racemization rate makes it especially suitable, since significant racemization takes place in the time span datable by carbon 14, facilitating the procedure for evaluating the effects of temperature.

Ice-Age Pennsylvanians

Until recently, the oldest known evidence of man's presence in the eastern United States dated back only 11,000 years. It has now become clear that nomadic hunters reached the easterly portions of the continent at least 5,000 years earlier—still a far cry from Bada's racemization findings for California fossils, but a substantial increase nonetheless.

The discovery that revised the timetable for transcontinental migration grew out of a routine training exercise in 1973 for a group of University of Pittsburgh archeology students. To teach them excavation techniques, their professor, James Adovasio, decided to conduct a summer dig at a large rock shelter about 25 miles southwest of Pittsburgh. Located on a hillside above a stream, the shelter consists of a broad sandstone ledge partly protected by a rocky overhang. For years the place had been a favorite lovers' nook and hunting camp for local folk, who marked their visits by strewing the area with bottles.

Adovasio decided to investigate it at the urging of Albert Miller, an amateur archeologist on whose farm the shelter stands. Miller suspected that a site with such natural advantages must have attracted hunters long before the days of guns and beer bottles; in fact, he had already turned up a few stone tools, animal bones and shells. Adovasio and his students expected to find much the same sort of thing.

The results of the dig bore out their expectations. After bushels of beer bottles were cleared from the shelter, a trench that cut down through the soil produced numerous artifacts and—at the lowest level of occupation, 16 feet deep—several fire pits containing charcoal. As a matter of course, charcoal samples were sent to the radio-carbon laboratory of the Smithsonian Institution for dating.

In mid-1974, Adovasio heard some startling news from Robert Stuckenrath, director of the laboratory: Tests indicated that the charcoal was 13,000 to 15,000 years old. At first, Adovasio thought that the Smithsonian scientists might have made an error in their calculations. But further excavation at the shelter the following summer uncovered fire pits whose charcoal dated back some 16,000 years.

The site's antiquity is not the only factor that makes it, in Adovasio's words, "an excavator's dream." Since the shelter was occupied continuously until the coming of white settlers, it has turned out to be a layer cake of important clues to cultural advances made by early Americans. Among the most significant discoveries were:

- Some very early ceramic pieces, dating from 900 to 800 B.C.
- Evidence of carbonized squash that may date to 800 B.C. Its presence suggests that scientists will have to push back their estimates of when agriculture first appeared among the eastern Indians.
- Tools made from at least six different types of stone. Because only about 10 per cent of this stone comes from the immediate area, Adovasio believes that people living at the site may have engaged in trade with other bands.

Just how the earliest occupants reached the shelter can only be conjectured. For primitive nomads, the path of least resistance from the west probably lay near the edge of the great North American ice sheet, where tundra-like grazing lands offered ample game. When the first small party—perhaps only eight or 10 people—stumbled upon the rock shelter, it would have seemed a natural stopping place. Indeed, during the ice age, the great blue wall of ice lay about 80 miles to the north, and the shelter may have been the only place within miles where these trailblazing hunters could find adequate protection from the snow and bitter winds that came roaring down off the glacier. Here they dug their fire pits, huddled awhile against the cold, then moved on, leaving behind dying embers that would one day testify to their ancient conquest of a far corner of the continent.

Laboring in a trench that slices through deposits at an ancient Indian site near Pittsburgh, archeology students collect dirt samples. The markers on the trench wall, labeled according to the different levels of stratification, pinpoint discoveries of artifacts—including some of ice-age vintage.

Testing Claims of Extreme Old Age

The racemization dating technique pioneered by Jeffrey Bada may turn out to be a highly versatile tool: in addition to its promise for investigations of early man, it seems capable of serving as an accurate chemical clock for studying the actual ages of contemporary people who are not sure how old they are.

Scientists have long been aware that the same sort of racemization of amino acids that takes place in ancient bones also occurs in living organisms. Suspecting that these chemical changes play a part in the aging process, Bada decided to see if they occur at a steady, predictable rate in living tissue. Because the rate can be detected only in tissue that does not regenerate itself, he chose to work with aspartic acid isolated from tooth enamel, which is synthesized early in life and is not renewed. The results of his tests, made on teeth from individuals of different ages, indicate that as a person grows older, racemization in his dental enamel does indeed show a corresponding and predictable increase.

This discovery may well resolve a controversy over the limits of a human lifetime. A number of people living high in the Andes of Ecuador and in the Caucasus range of the U.S.S.R. are said to enjoy extraordinary longevity—upwards of 120 years—but have no birth certificates to confirm it. Many experts feel that such claims of hoary age are false, but until now there was no way to be sure. Bada's racemization technique may soon be applied to teeth from these elders shortly after their death, to determine whether their owners were true supercentenarians or mere youngsters of 70 or 80.

The penultimate step was accomplished with the help of a sophisticated laboratory apparatus called an amino-acid analyzer. This device, used in conjunction with a special chemical compound, separated all the left-handed molecules from the right-handed ones and measured the extent of racemization on a graph. Finally, Bada and his colleague made the necessary calculation to account for temperature, using a human skull that was excavated at nearby Laguna Beach and carbon 14 dated to about 17,150 B.P. After the temperature adjustment was made, the La Jolla bones turned out to be approximately 44,000 years old. The reading for the Del Mar bones was 48,000 years.

These findings touched off a furor when they were published in *Science* magazine. One highly unfavorable reaction came from Paul S. Martin, a professor of geoscience at the University of Arizona. "All this early, early man game is just that —a big, fat game," said Martin, who wants to know why, if man has lived in the New World for 50,000 years, there are not many more bones and artifacts. Bada's answer was disarmingly simple: "There probably are," he said, "only no one has really bothered until now to look for them."

Some scientists were decidedly enthusiastic. Richard S. MacNeish, director of the Peabody Foundation for Archeology in Andover, Massachusetts, said flatly, "I believe the early dates." Field work he had done in Peru suggested that some living sites in the Andes date back at least 20,000 years, and he thinks that humans probably would have had to enter the New World tens of thousands of years earlier in order to reach the Andes by that time.

Most authorities felt that, at the very least, judgment should be withheld until Bada's methods were more closely scrutinized. Among other doubts, they noted that the 17,150 B.P. carbon-14 date for the Laguna Beach skull—used for adjustment of temperature—was not universally accepted as correct. But perhaps the most troubling objection was entered by a pioneer of the process, Edgar Hare. Reopening his investigation of the applicability of racemization dating to old bones, he reported that the presence of water at a fossil site may be even more disturbing than he had originally supposed. The water, he says, not only contaminates a fossil but also leaches out protein and other organic compounds, including amino acids. Unless these effects were taken into account, Bada's findings were "premature."

But again Bada was not deterred by the criticism. If leaching were indeed a significant factor in the racemization rate, he pointed out, there would not be such a strong correlation in the ages of fossils, such as the goat bones, that had been dated by both carbon 14 and amino-acid techniques. At present, he has done such comparative dating for bones from more than 20 different sites around the world, and the average difference between the carbon-14 and racemization readings is only 6 per cent.

NEW MYSTERIES TO PONDER

Pending final resolution of the various questions that have been raised about his technique, Bada's findings pose some formidable riddles for students of early man. One obvious difficulty is the current lack of evidence that might justify the existence of cold-weather survival techniques that would have enabled Indian ancestors to approach the land bridge to Alaska some 50,000 years ago.

Richard Klein of the University of Chicago, who is an expert on archeological developments in the Soviet Union, believes that humans were utterly incapable of dealing with the climate in Siberia at that time. Klein points out that the oldest known signs of human habitation in northeastern Siberia have an age of only 20,000 years. However, he does note that "over the most relevant parts of Siberia, early man archeology is only now really getting underway, and it would be premature to argue that the oldest sites there have already been found."

Archeologists are not alone in looking upon Bada's dates with furrowed brows. If the California fossils are indeed nearly 50,000 years old, the standard picture of human evolution will have to be modified. Most physical anthropologists —specialists in human evolution—believe that man did not attain his final form until about 35,000 or 40,000 years ago. Before then, it has been presumed that the earth could have been inhabited only by less-developed humans: the thick-skulled, heavy-jawed Neanderthal-type man whose remains have been found in widely scattered areas of Europe, Africa and Asia. But the bones dated by Bada are distinctly modern in appearance—"robust, tall and totally lacking any Neanderthal features," says Gail Kennedy, an anthropologist at California State University in Northridge who has carefully examined the fossils.

How could modern-type humans have lived in North America at least 10,000 years before their counterparts appeared elsewhere? Did primitive Asian men—perhaps kin of Peking man or Java man, half-million-year-old members of the early human species known as *Homo erectus*—somehow make their way across the Bering land bridge far back in the past and gradually evolve into higher forms of man in the New World? This seems highly unlikely. Kennedy thinks that there is only one other plausible answer: modern man might have evolved earlier in eastern Asia than he did in Europe, Africa or other parts of Asia. Richard MacNeish agrees, and he adds that some members of this evolutionary vanguard in Asia may already have been spotted: in the upper level of the cave in China where Peking man was discovered, a team of excavators turned up seven skeletons that are reminiscent of early American Indians and that may be anywhere from 30,000 to 50,000 years old.

And there, for the moment, the matter stands —still in scientific limbo. While most scientists admit that Bada could be right, his racemization technique continues to run a gauntlet of tough questioning. Bada not only is optimistic about full acceptance, but also suspects that his dates are somewhat conservative and that humans actually reached the New World well before 50,000 B.P. Perhaps so. Yet if future archeological discoveries merely bear out his 48,000 B.P. date for the earliest Americans, he will have revolutionized our view of prehistory.

Venus' Face Unveiled

Centuries of speculation about what sort of landscape might be found on Venus ended last year when two unmanned Russian spacecraft landed there and sent back to Earth the first pictures ever taken on another planet *(pages 166-167)*. The tranquil-looking rocky terrain revealed in the photographs seemed at odds with what scientists had already learned about Venus. Sensors aboard earlier, cameraless probes had registered a scorching surface temperature of some 900°F.—twice the melting point of tin—and a crushing atmospheric pressure as great as that 2,400 to 3,000 feet below earthly seas.

The face of Venus had remained an enigma because the planet's ever-present veil of clouds extends some 40 miles above the surface. Even the close-up seen opposite discloses no features under the clouds.

While Venus has now been stripped of some secrets, there are still plenty to tantalize astronomers. For example, the planet lacks a magnetic field like the one that surrounds Earth's atmosphere and that deflects much of the solar wind—low energy particles streaming from the sun. The particles therefore bombard Venus' atmosphere directly, perhaps compressing it or affecting it in other ways not yet understood.

Such puzzles are all the more vexing because Venus is Earth's nearest neighbor and has about the same size and mass. But there the similarity ends. Venus rotates only once in 243 Earth days, making it by far the slowest spinner in the solar system. And it turns from east to west while the other planets spin in the opposite direction.

Other questions posed by this mysterious planet may be answered in 1978, when the United States will launch two unmanned Venus-bound craft. One will orbit the planet and the other will loose probes to further explore the ferocious environment under the blanketing clouds.

As photographed by the U.S. craft Mariner 10 in 1974, the loftiest clouds on Venus appear thin, white and broken as they swirl around the planet at 200 mph. The dark, streaky areas are merely lower, denser cloud layers.

A Dank or Arid World?

Until the Russians pierced the clouds enveloping Venus, scientists could picture the surface only by fleshing out a few facts with generous doses of imagination. Late-19th Century astronomers, using the then new technique of spectroscopy—identifying elements in a planet's atmosphere by studying wavelengths of its reflected light—thought they detected plentiful water in the omnipresent clouds. Thus they inferred a Venus with swampy jungles like Earth's Carboniferous era of some 280 million years ago.

By the 1920s, more sophisticated spectroscopy showed that the signs of water resulted from reflected light of Venus passing through Earth's own moisture-laden atmosphere; the planet was now seen as a vast desert. Like Earth, Venus might have once been eroded by wind or water, but any water had long ago boiled away in its intense heat. The Russian probes proved Venus to be a dry wasteland; and the forces that shaped it were probably nothing like Earth's.

This drawing, based on surface photographs taken last year, suggests the true appearance of the Venusian landscape—a rubble of small boulders and a mixture of weirdly sculpted rocks firmly imbedded in sand.

Illustrations from a French astronomy text of the 1930s contrast the contemporary picture of Venus as a barren desert (left) with the turn-of-the-century concept of a fecund swampland (top). The unmanned landings on Venus found not the slightest trace of water near the planet's surface.

Unexpected Views from a Short-Lived Camera

Climaxing a journey of four and a half months and 186 million miles, the Russian spacecraft Venera 9 parachuted down through the dense Venusian atmosphere in October 1975 and landed upright on the planet's torrid surface. For 53 minutes, until its equipment was overcome by the heat, it transmitted a stream of pictures and other data back to Earth. To scientists examining the pictures transmitted by the Venera 9 camera, the rugged terrain *(below)* looked startlingly familiar: a scattering of small, sharp-edged boulders that would not seem out of place in the Rockies. Three days later a sister spacecraft, Venera 10, set down 1,370 miles away and sent back photographs of a very different landscape composed of rounded and pitted rocks nested in a bed of sandlike soil.

Confronted by pictures of rocks of such contrasting forms, astronomers immediately began to speculate about the forces that may have shaped them. Rounding by water or by sandblasting wind had to be discounted, since the space probes' instruments indicated no hint of surface water, and the wind at both landing sites averaged about two miles per hour.

Cornell University astronomer Carl Sagan suggested two other processes that might account for the rocks. The rounded ones may have been weathered chemically by a powerful mixture of sulfuric, hydrofluoric and hydrochloric acids known to be present in the atmosphere of Venus. Or all of the rocks may have started out as angular boulders like those photographed by Venera 9; the planet's crust may overlie molten rock that oozes to the surface and breaks into those shapes as it cools. If they retain fairly low melting points, over a period of time the forgelike surface temperature of Venus may remelt them enough to produce rounded forms similar to those of the rocks pictured by Venera 10.

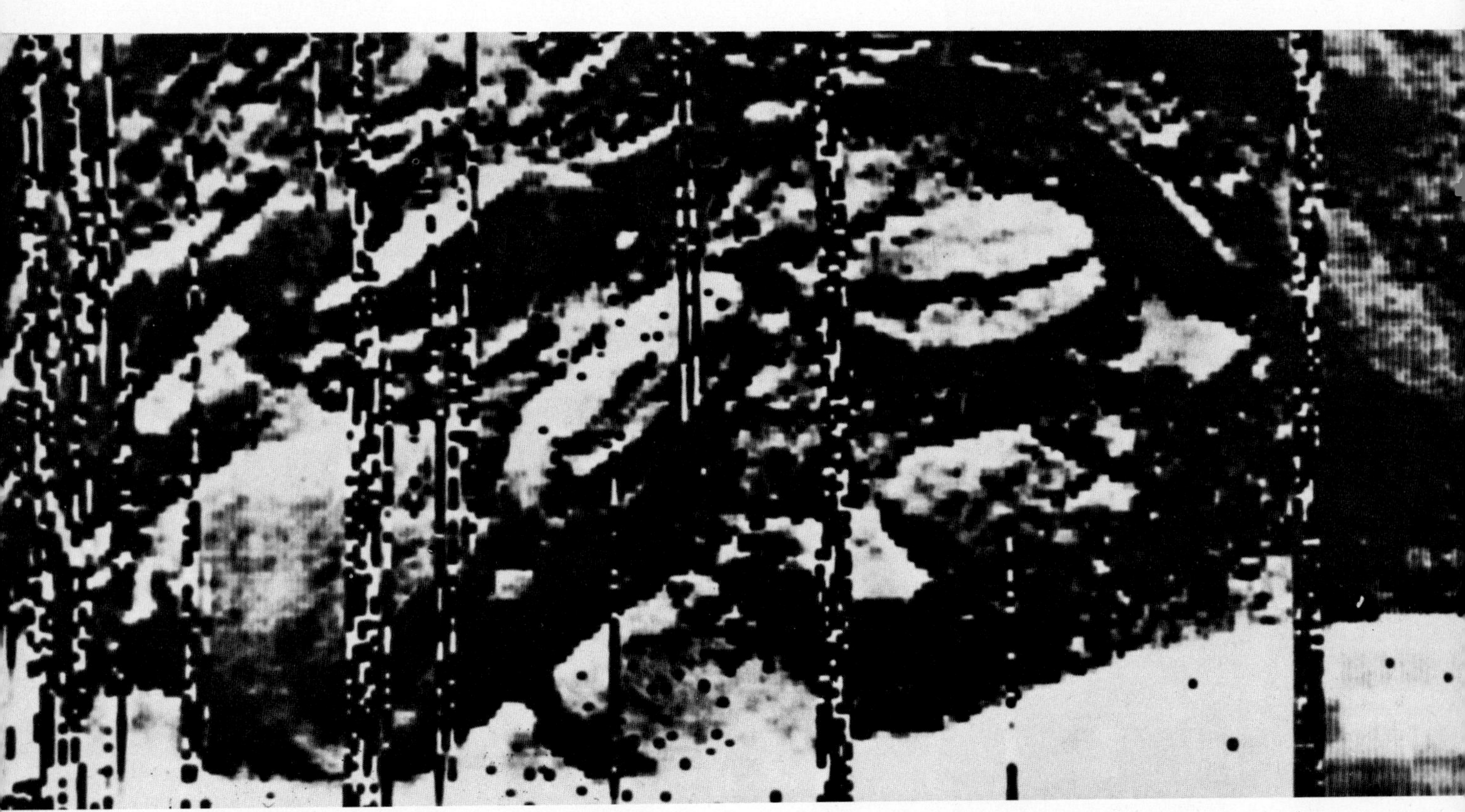

The photographs snapped by Venera 9 were received on Earth as a series of numbers, which a computer then translated into dots to create the image above. Picture-taking was interrupted on a regular basis in order to relay data on temperature, atmospheric pressure and wind velocity; these transmissions show up on the photographs as vertical speckled lines. The cameras remained stationary, but mirror attachments that reflected the surrounding terrain enabled the cameras to scan an area reaching from Venera's base (the curved object in the foreground and about four feet from the lenses) to the horizon some 600 to 900 feet away at right.

A technician checks out a Venera spacecraft at the Soviet launching site. Photographs on Venus were made by cameras near the top of the craft, just below a saucer-like disc that helped brake the craft during its descent.

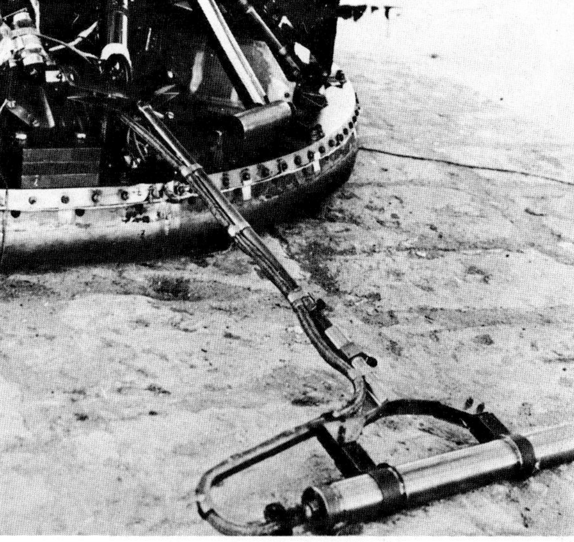

A radiation densitometer, protruding from the base of a Venera craft awaiting launch, measured the density of Venusian rocks and gathered data on their composition.

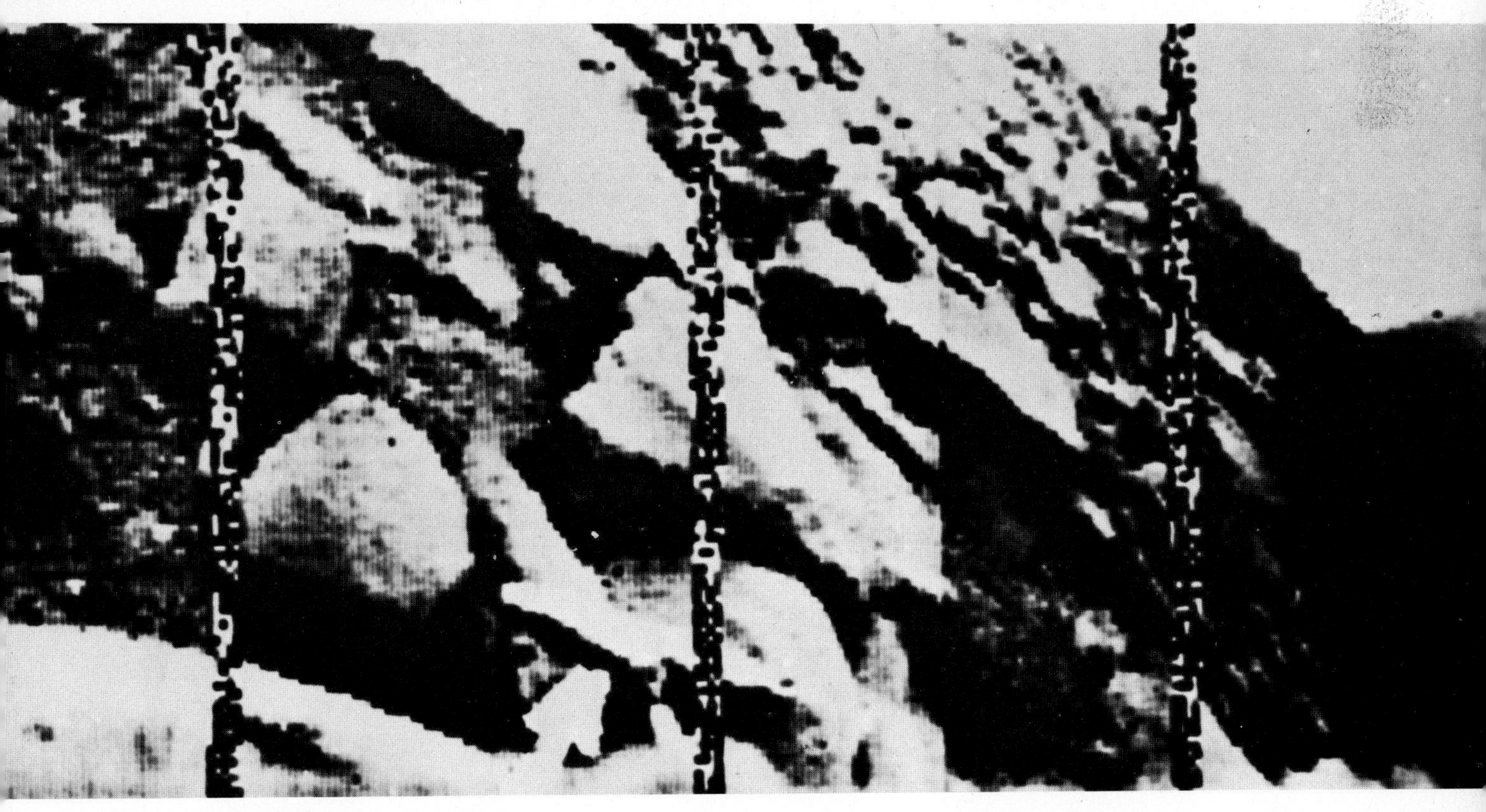

Next Mission to the Hidden Planet

Venus' leisurely rate of rotation makes it a meteorologist's dream: an Earth-sized, slow-motion subject on which to study the circulation of an atmosphere—and perhaps gain a better understanding of our own terrestrial climate. To that end, the U.S. space program, starting with the first fly-by of Venus in 1962, has focused on discovering what elements make up the planet's massive atmosphere and what forces generate the violent winds in its upper layers while stirring mere zephyrs near the surface.

These and other puzzles may finally be resolved by the two-part Pioneer mission that the United States will launch toward Venus in 1978. An orbiting craft *(right, top)* will use radar to map the surface, and infrared and ultraviolet sensoring equipment to monitor the planet's cloud cover through at least one full eight-month rotation. A second, independently launched vehicle *(right, below)* is a "bus" loaded with three small probes and one large one; they will separate to descend through the lower atmosphere.

One of the chief aims of the small probes will be to find out how solar energy, the force that drives atmospheric circulation, is absorbed by the Venusian atmosphere and how it stirs things up. The large probe will measure the chemical composition of the atmosphere and perhaps solve a basic puzzle of Venus: is its veil of clouds made up of gas, liquids or solids?

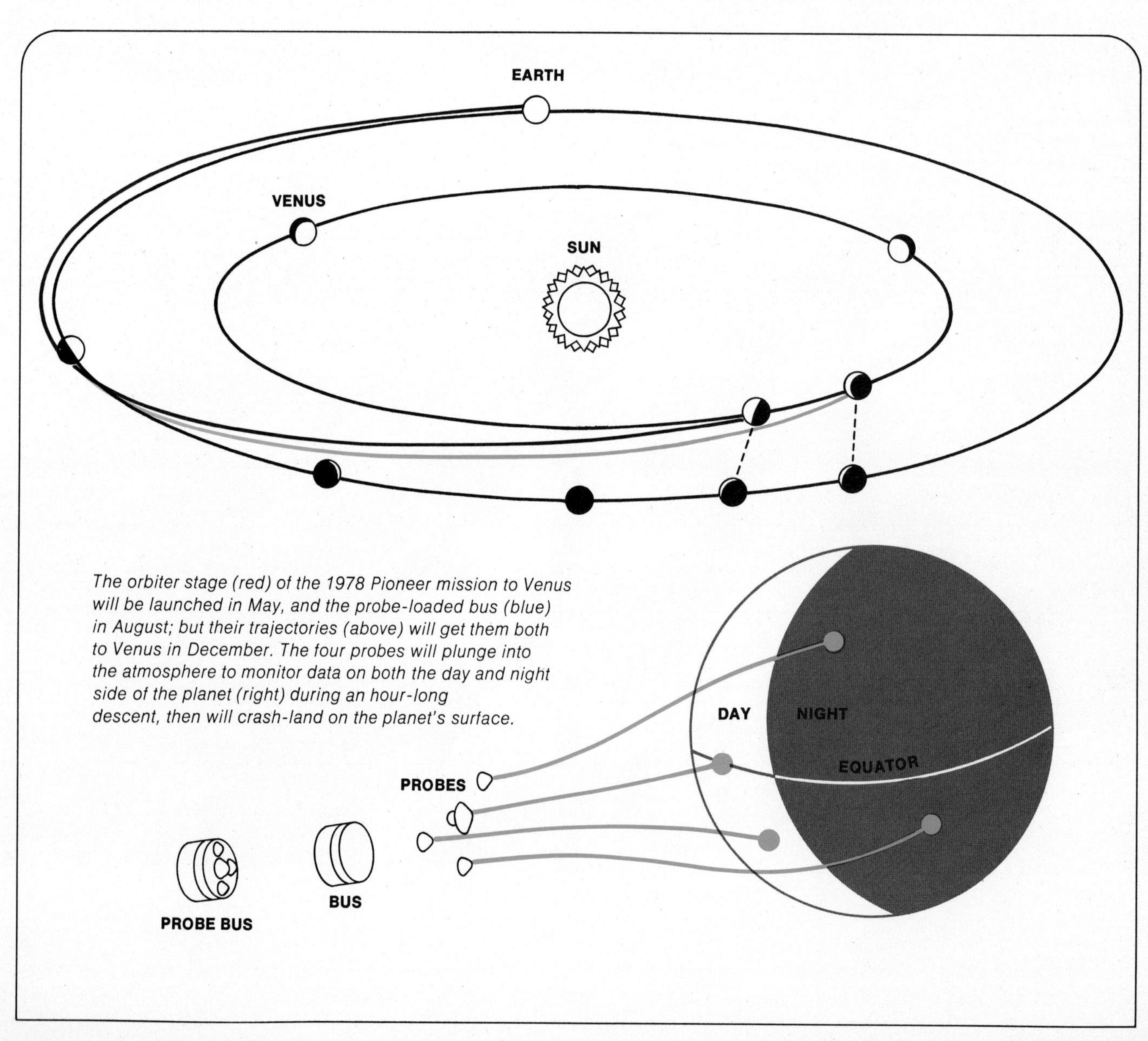

The orbiter stage (red) of the 1978 Pioneer mission to Venus will be launched in May, and the probe-loaded bus (blue) in August; but their trajectories (above) will get them both to Venus in December. The four probes will plunge into the atmosphere to monitor data on both the day and night side of the planet (right) during an hour-long descent, then will crash-land on the planet's surface.

Summing Up the Year

A BRIEF REVIEW OF EVENTS, DISCOVERIES AND DEVELOPMENTS

ANIMAL BEHAVIOR

Probing the odd corners of the insect world, researchers discovered tool use among ants, complex defensive sprays among termites and a victim-locating system among mosquitoes. And while paleontologists were speculating on how one species of dinosaur kept cool, other scientists were untaming zoo animals and solving the mystery of why woodpeckers do not peck themselves dizzy.

HOW MOSQUITOES FIND PREY

How does a mosquito find its human or animal prey? Not by the scent or sight of the target, according to chemist R. H. Wright of the British Columbia Research Council, but by the warmth, moisture and carbon dioxide given off by the victim.

In the July 1975 issue of *Scientific American,* Wright described the mosquito "attack program" that he and a colleague, physicist Philip Daykin, had determined: the mosquito is alerted by a rise in the level of carbon dioxide produced by the exhalations of an approaching animal. Taking off, the insect flies until it finds warm, moist air—a convection current created by the warmth of the skin and transpiration of moisture through it. The mosquito follows this current to the source and lands on its prey.

The Canadian researchers' basic experimental apparatus consisted of three small cylinders set side by side in a wind tunnel. One cylinder was warm, one was wet and the third was both warm and wet. After carbon dioxide was added to the air entering the wind tunnel to alert the mosquitoes, the scientists counted the number that landed on each cylinder. In a typical experiment, the warm target drew seven mosquitoes, the wet one 22, and the warm and wet one 358.

In another experiment to learn how chemical repellents worked, a third British Columbia scientist, F. E. Kellogg, attached microelectrodes to the sensory hairs of mosquito antennae and found that repellents prevent the moisture sensors from detecting increased humidity. Thus, as a mosquito approaches its target, it suddenly loses track of it and flies off in another direction.

SOLDIER TERMITES

A Cornell team studying insect behavior and led by biologist Thomas Eisner has found that the Australian termite *Nasutitermes exitiosus* possesses an astonishingly sophisticated system of community defense. When ants, centipedes or spiders approach one of the huge mounds in which the termites live, cadres of soldier termites with nozzle-shaped heads attack the intruders. They spray a sticky, odorous compound that restricts the movement of their enemies and partially suffocates them.

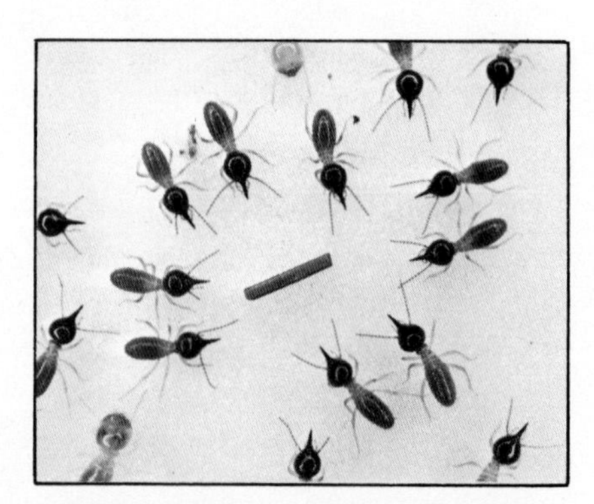

TERMITES APPROACH "ENEMY" FOR ATTACK.

Aware that similar defensive sprays are used by some species of bees and ants as chemical alarms to summon more defenders to the site, the scientists set up a novel experiment to determine if the termite spray has this additional function. The researchers placed a small rotating magnet under a Petri dish full of Australian soldier termites. Then they put a small bar of metal in the dish; the piece of metal, twirled by the field of the rotating magnet, simulated an ant invader. Using movie cameras with closeup lenses, they filmed the termites' reactions. As soon as the first soldier sprayed the pseudo-ant, soldiers from across the dish converged on it. This indicated that the spray contained a pheromone, an odor message, that acted as a call to arms.

Writing in the January-February 1976 issue of the *Journal of Behavioral Ecology and Sociobiology,* the Cornell scientists reported that, in addition to a pheromone, the compound sprayed by the soldier termites contained unidentified chemicals that also may help to repel attackers. Concluded Eisner: "By studying their chemical defense systems, we're hoping to discover what termites have learned during millions and millions of years . . . and perhaps help ourselves fight insects . . . more effectively."

TOOL-USING ANTS

University of Maryland zoologists Joan and Gary Fellers first observed the phenomenon in a wood lot in College Park, Maryland. As part of a study on ant behavior, they had placed several index cards smeared with jelly on the ground. The bait soon drew ants of the *Aphaenogaster rudis* species, which briefly surveyed the area, departed and returned with pieces of leaves, putting them on the jelly. Then, after 30 to 60 minutes, the ants began to remove the leaves—which were visibly covered with jelly—and carried them back to their colony some five feet away. This process, as the husband-and-wife team reported in an April 1976 issue of *Science,* was the first observation of "tool use in a social insect."

Further investigation by the Fellers established that three other *Aphaenogaster* species use dry mud and small clumps of sand, in addition to leaves, to transport soft food from a comparatively distant source to the colony. By using tools, the researchers found, each ant can carry back an amount of food about equal to its body weight—a far bigger load than it could carry in its crop (an internal pouch). Because leaf fragments or other tools enable the ants to forage more efficiently and to spend far less time at the food source, *Aphaenogaster* can compete successfully with more aggressive ant species that, in most cases, quickly seize control of a food site.

WHY WOODPECKERS AREN'T DIZZY

When woodpeckers tap their beaks on wood, they deliver as many as 44 powerful blows in less than three seconds. The staccato rapping serves many purposes: to bore into trees and posts for insects, to tunnel out nesting holes, to attract a mate—or simply to relieve tension. But why doesn't this continuous percussion cause the woodpeckers to suffer brain damage, or at least headaches? In February 1976, that question was addressed in the British medical journal *The Lancet* by a group of researchers under the direction of UCLA psychiatry professor Philip May.

To determine "why the countryside is not littered with dazed and dying woodpeckers," the researchers had compared the heads and beaks of woodpeckers with the skull of a toucan, a related bird with a long bill that neither taps nor drums. They found that, compared with the toucan, the woodpecker has a very narrow space between the brain and its tough outer membrane; because this gap holds less fluid than in a toucan, transmission of shock waves from the skull inward may well be reduced. The investigators also discovered that the woodpecker's brain is tightly packed with relatively dense yet spongy bone, and that the bird has a large and powerful muscle system in its head that may absorb shocks and prevent any sudden rotational movement that could damage brain tissue.

Taking a cue from the woodpecker, May suggested that improvements might be made in traditional sport and crash helmets worn by humans. Instead of a hard outer shell with an interior harness that provides an air space between helmet and skull, he said, a firm but spongy form-fitting helmet with a hard outer shell might give better protection. For additional safety, humans could wear the equivalent of the woodpecker's head-muscle system—a protective neck collar to act as a brake against rotary motion.

UNTAMING ZOO ANIMALS

Lulled into a languorous state by regular feeding, many zoo animals abandon their normal patterns of behavior and seem to lose their hunting instinct. In December 1975, Chicago's Brookfield Zoo began an experiment to restore "wildness" to some of its animals. Animal behaviorists Gil Boese and Ron Snyder installed a plastic, mechanized, but realistic marmot in an enclosure occupied by a pair of seven-year-old pumas. The marmot remained hidden until one of the pumas climbed onto a "stalking" branch about seven feet above the ground. This activated a control device that, at an unpredictable time in the next 20 minutes, caused the marmot to scoot out of a hole, race across an open area on a track and disappear into another hole.

If the puma leaped from the branch and began pawing the marmot's exit hole within one and a half seconds, a conveyor belt delivered the cat's reward: a portion of raw meat. But if the cat was not fast enough, it went hungry and had to start the process all over again.

The game worked so well with pumas that the Brookfield Zoo extended the concept to two Siberian tigers. These cats were conditioned to grab a concrete deer and shake it vigorously so raw meat automatically dropped into a bin representing the "body cavity" of their prey.

THERMOSTAT FOR A DINOSAUR

One of the strangest looking of all dinosaurs was the stegosaurus, an ungainly two-ton creature with bony plates standing upright along either side of the midline of its back. In contrast to the bilateral—or paired—symmetry of features in most other vertebrates, these plates were arranged in an alternating pattern. Paleontologists generally have believed that they served as protective armor and

CAPTIVE PUMA PREPARES TO LEAP DURING A MECHANIZED HUNT.

perhaps, like peacock feathers, as a kind of ostentatious sexual display. In June 1976, a group of Yale scientists suggested that the plates may have had a more important function: as heat dissipaters that controlled body temperature.

In a report to *Science,* paleontologist James Farlow and engineers Daniel Rosner and Carl Thompson compared the bony plates to cooling fins used in such devices as refrigerator cooling elements. To test the theory, they built three simple aluminum models roughly shaped like the dinosaurs: one with continuous paired fins; one with interrupted paired fins; and one with stegosaurus-type staggered fins. Each model was tested for heat transfer effectiveness in a wind tunnel—first, in a position facing directly into the wind and then in a transverse position, against the wind. The results: the stegosaurus-like arrangement was more efficient in dissipating heat, particularly in the transverse position, which caused a sharp drop in efficiency in the other two models, but practically no change in stegosaurus.

In examinations of fossilized stegosaurus plates, the scientists also discovered that the bony structures had many branching grooves. These were probably vascular channels through which blood flowed in quantity, further helping the dinosaur to get rid of excess body heat.

BONY PLATES ALONG ITS SPINE MAY HAVE KEPT THE STEGOSAURUS COOL.

ANTIHORMONES FOR PEST CONTROL

A promising weapon was added to the arsenal of biological insecticides in April 1976, when chemist-entomologist William Bowers reported that he had isolated two plant substances that prevent insects from reproducing. Working at the New York State Agricultural Experiment Station, Bowers found that the substances—extracted from ageratum, a common garden plant—function as antihormones, deactivating juvenile hormones; normally, these hormones regulate the development of ovaries, the production of sex attractants and the timetable for growth.

After Bowers applied the substances to immature forms of two pests—the cotton stainer and the Mexican bean beetle—the bugs quickly matured into sterile adults. Tested on the Colorado potato beetle, the compounds caused the insect to stop feeding, climb off the plant into the soil and go into hibernation, from which it never emerged.

Bowers' findings represented a radical departure from another promising biological insect-control technique that involves the use of an insect's own juvenile hormones. Sprayed on a field infested by a particular kind of insect, a synthesized version of that pest's juvenile hormone can prevent it from ever reaching sexual maturity—if the attack is correctly timed. As Bowers noted in his report, the synthetic juvenile hormone has this effect only if it is applied during the relatively brief period when the insect is not producing juvenile hormone itself and is passing into the adult stage. Because natural juvenile hormone is present during most stages of development, the odds are much better that an application of Bowers' antihormone compounds will disrupt the insect's life cycle.

ARCHEOLOGY

Fossil bones that extend the lineage of man back toward the four-million-year mark turned up in Africa, where traces of an ancient canal were also found. Other discoveries challenged the role of Mesopotamia as the cradle of civilization, revealed the tomb of one emperor and the bronze head of another, and located two long-ago losses to the sea—the oldest-known shipwreck and a sunken Spanish treasure.

NEW LIGHT ON HUMAN EVOLUTION

Some 25 miles south of Tanzania's Olduvai Gorge, where she and her late husband, Louis Leakey, discovered so much about man's origins, anthropologist Mary Leakey made still another momentous find. Digging through ancient layers of volcanic rock in a remote region called Laetolil during the winter of 1974-1975, she unearthed jawbones and teeth that clearly belonged to members of *Homo,* the genus of modern man. It was not until the following September—when the age of the rock was determined by potassium-argon tests—that Leakey realized just how important her fossils were.

The bones and teeth were 3.6 million years old. That made them the most ancient fossils of hominids (human ancestors and their relatives) ever found, pushing back man's lineage at least several hundred thousand years.

Since Mary Leakey's find, other major discoveries in East Africa have shed additional light on human evolution. In Kenya, Mary Leakey's son Richard unearthed a complete skull of beetle-browed *Homo erectus,* acknowledged as a direct ancestor of *Homo sapiens,* or modern man. Reliably dated at around 1.5 million years, this skull indicates that *Homo erectus* evolved much earlier than was previously believed; hitherto his best-known representative was China's Peking Man, estimated to be a mere 500,000 years old.

The new skull is also important because it turned up in deposits that, according to Leakey, have provided incontrovertible evidence of *Australopithecus*—a more primitive hominid regarded as the ancestor of *Homo erectus.* The coexistence of the two seems to show that at least part of the *Australopithecus* stock came to a genetic dead end, although earlier australopithecines may have been ancestral to *Homo erectus.*

When Richard Leakey described his findings at a press conference in March 1976, fellow anthropologist Donald C. Johanson reported equally remarkable discoveries in Ethiopia's Afar region. There, Johanson had come upon a concentration of bones belonging to hominids who apparently were killed together in a flash flood between three and three and a half million years ago. Johanson views the bone trove as "evidence for the idea of cooperative behavior which I feel formed the basis for early human survival." From the bones, a composite three-million-year-old hand has been pieced together that is about the size of modern man's and seems fully capable of using tools.

BALLOON OVER NAZCA PLAINS

A new and startling explanation of how the ancient Peruvians may have created the giant figures of animals, geometric designs and straight lines etched onto the bleak Nazca plains has been suggested by members of the International Explorers Society, a Florida-based organization of world travelers. Laid out as early as 400 B.C., the patterns are so large (some of the lines extend five miles) that they can be discerned only from the air and thus were not discovered until man flew over them in planes.

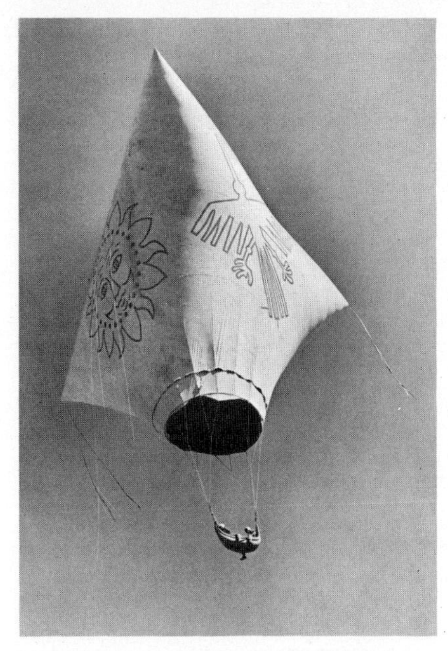

BALLOON TESTS THEORY OF INDIAN FLIGHT.

One recent theory states that the Indian artists of southern Peru first sketched the drawings on small plots of land and then used their knowledge of geometry and a complex system of strings and central piles of rocks to enlarge the figures. Others have insisted that even though there are no nearby mountains, the Nazcas must have had an elevated vantage point. According to a few freewheeling thinkers, such a perspective may have been supplied by extraterrestrial visitors hovering above in spacecraft and relaying instructions to the workers below. But members of the I.E.S. have a less fanciful theory. Basing their belief in part on a picture on an ancient Nazca ceramic pot that seems to represent a hot-air bag, they think that, many centuries before the age of flight, Nazca observers in balloons directed the gigantic projects. In November 1976, I.E.S. members attempted to prove their point by flying a crude balloon over the Nazca plains.

The I.E.S. balloon, called *Condor I,* had an 88-foot-high envelope made from a fabric similar to the amazingly close-woven cotton textiles recovered from Nazca gravesites. The balloon's lines and fastenings were made from native plant fibers, and the boat-shaped gondola was woven from totora reeds that grow in Lake Titicaca.

On its maiden flight, the *Condor* quickly rose to 600 feet, but ran into brisk winds that drove it back to earth. It hit with a thud that bounced both pilots out of the gondola, then rose again without passengers to about 1,200 feet, flew unmanned for about two miles over the plain and gently landed. That clinched it for I.E.S. director Michael DeBakey (son of the heart surgeon): "We set out to prove that the Nazcas had the skill, the materials and the need for flight," he said. "I think we have succeeded."

FIRST SUEZ CANAL

When it was opened for traffic in 1869, the Suez Canal was hailed as one of the outstanding engineering triumphs of modern man. Yet the Suez apparently had an ancient predecessor that was equally remarkable. That is the conclusion of three Israeli scientists who first spotted traces of a far older canal in aerial photographs taken during their country's 1967 conquest of Sinai.

In later visits to the area, geologists Amihai Sneh, Tuvia Weissbrod and Itamar Perath determined that, about 4,000 years before the construction of the Suez waterway, the Egyptians built a canal that headed southwest some 30 miles from the Mediterranean to a point near the modern city of Ismailia. At that point, it divided into two branches, one connecting it—through the Gulf of Suez—to the Red Sea, the other turning west to join the Nile.

After making soil studies, the geologists concluded that the waterway, which they call the Eastern Canal, was nearly 230 feet wide at the surface and from seven to 10 feet deep—compared to the modern Suez Canal's width of 179 feet and depth of 40 feet. Summing up their discoveries in the September-October 1975 issue of *American Scientist,* the Israelis noted that the canal was more than adequate to handle the barge traffic of the day; moreover, the branch linked to the fresh-water Nile probably provided water for irrigating fields along its banks. But its most important function, they suggested, was as a barrier to protect Egypt against the forays of tribesmen from the Sinai Desert and would-be invaders from western Asia.

HADRIAN'S HEAD

In July 1975, as he neared the end of a visit with his married sister's family at the kibbutz Tirat Tzvi, south of the Sea of Galilee in Israel, Morton Leventhal, an American stockbroker who is also an amateur archeologist and numismatist, decided to try one last dig. Bicycling to a nearby wheat field that was lying fallow, he began sweeping back and forth with his electronic metal detector. Suddenly the beep-beep in his earphones changed

BRONZE HEAD OF HADRIAN DUG UP IN ISRAEL.

to a wail. Unsheathing his Boy Scout knife, Leventhal dug into the dry soil and unearthed a cylindrical object that he thought was "just another sewer pipe." Close by, the metal detector located a second buried object—and this time Leventhal knew that he had struck pay dirt. It was an intricately carved bronze head, which he wrapped in T-shirts and a towel and carried back to the kibbutz, where he proudly displayed it in the dining hall.

It did not stay there long. Alerted to the discovery, an archeologist from the Israeli Department of Antiquities rushed to the kibbutz, claimed the find for Israel under national law and identified it as part of a statue of Roman Emperor Hadrian, who ruled from 117 to 138 A.D. and was the scourge of the Jews in Palestine. Leventhal's "pipe" turned out to be Hadrian's arm, and further digging produced other parts of the statue, including the breastplate, magnificently decorated with warriors in hand-to-hand combat. All of the parts were promptly sent to the Israel Museum in Jerusalem for cleaning and assembling. "This is the equivalent of digging up a Rembrandt," said Cornelius Vermeule, curator of classical art at Boston's Museum of Fine Arts. Leventhal's reward: at his own request, some ancient Jewish coins to fill out his collection.

CHINESE ARMY STATUES

While sinking wells in China's north-central province of Shensi, farmers from a commune near the city of Sian dug into some underground chambers and stumbled upon one of the most important archeological finds in recent history. In July 1975, after government archeologists had worked at the site for nearly a year, Peking finally released news about the discovery.

In the chambers, the scientists found an army of life-sized warriors and horses made of pottery and arranged in rows and ancient battle formations. The ceramic army, estimated to consist of 6,000 figures, was arrayed near the tomb of Ch'in Shih Huang Ti, the first emperor of a unified China and the founder of the Ch'in dynasty in 221 B.C. It was a thoroughly formidable force to impress the emperor's power upon the afterworld: the warriors, standing nearly six feet tall, carried real spears, crossbows and bows and arrows. Officers bore swords that reportedly were still shiny and unstained when unearthed.

The army chambers are just one part of the emperor's huge (1,560 by 1,440 feet) tomb mound. Archeologists suspect that another series of chambers may exist, perhaps containing pottery replicas of ministers and other members of government. The burial vault itself has yet to be excavated. There, experts believe that they will find the actual remains of Ch'in Shih Huang Ti and some manifestation of his concubines. If the emperor was consistent in his beliefs—he was the first to take statues instead of live people to the next world with him—the concubines will be ceramic.

OLDEST-KNOWN SHIP

To the untrained eye, the large lumps lying at a depth of some 70 feet on the seabed near the Greek island of Dhokós would not have been worth a second glance. But New York archeologist Peter Throckmorton, skin diving off the shore, recognized an ancient shipwreck when he saw one. "It's as though you took the ship and her cargo, mixed them all up in a cement mixer, then laid them out on the seabed and poured a couple of feet of concrete over everything." The "concrete" was actually sediment and marine encrustation that had accumulated on the shattered ship, its cargo and its ballast stones since it sank.

That maritime disaster, according to an announcement in September 1975 by the Hellenic Institute of Marine Archeology, took place sometime between 2700 and 2200 B.C., which makes the Throckmorton discovery the oldest shipwreck on record.

Estimates of the date of the shipwreck were based on 24 shards of pottery recovered by Throckmorton and other divers—cooking pots, jugs, cups and sauceboats typical of those produced by Cyclades islanders of the Aegean during the early Bronze Age.

Very little of the ship itself remained at the bottom; Throckmorton estimated that only about 1/20 of the original wood of the vessel was still there. But, based on designs that he had seen on other Cycladic pottery, he assumed that the ship had probably looked "like a centipede," with 20 to 30 oars on each side, a ram at one end and a stern curving outward to a height of eight or 10 feet.

Until the discovery of the Cycladic ship, the oldest-known shipwreck had been one that dated from 1300 B.C. and was found in 1960 off the Turkish coast. Its discoverer: Peter Throckmorton.

SPANISH GALLEON FOUND

Loaded with treasure plundered from Indians in Central and South America, a 28-ship Spanish fleet left Havana on September 4, 1622. The next day, west of the Florida Keys, a hurricane struck, sinking nine of the ships and taking the lives of 550 passengers and crew. Treasure hunters have been searching ever since for the wreckage of the ships, especially the galleon *Nuestra Señora de Atocha,* which Spanish records show was carrying 47 tons of silver and gold.

In July 1975, after years of searching the ocean floor some 40 miles west of Key West, Treasure Salvors, Inc. announced that it had found nine bronze cannons, each weighing about two tons. The cannons undoubtedly marked the site of the *Atocha's* demise, a company spokesman said, because that ship was the only one in the fleet to carry that many large guns.

A discovery made two years earlier had convinced Treasure Salvors divers that they were on the right track. Using metal detectors to probe the bottom, they had found several silver and gold bars at the site, three of them identified by their markings as having been listed on the *Atocha's* manifest. The recovery of the cannons removed any lingering doubts about the *Atocha's* location, but it will probably take many months or even years for the divers to recover the remainder of the *Atocha's* treasure; the wreckage lies in 50 feet of water in an area of the seabottom covered by constantly moving quicksand.

A NEW CRADLE OF CIVILIZATION

It is conventional wisdom among historians and archeologists that the Bronze Age began sometime between 3500 and 3000 B.C. in Mesopotamia—the valley between the Tigris and Euphrates rivers where man is believed to have built the first true cities, developed advanced writing techniques and established central governments. But in May 1976, an expedition headed by scientists from the University of Pennsylvania and the National Museum in Bangkok provided evidence that a civilization perhaps more advanced than Mesopotamia's was thriving even earlier on the Khorat Plateau in northeastern Thailand—and had already mastered the art of making bronze.

The archeologists based their conclusion on 18 tons of sophisticated clay pottery and stone and metal objects excavated over a two-year period from ancient burial grounds and habitations near the contemporary town of Ban Chiang. Both radiocarbon and thermoluminescent dating indicated that some of the artifacts, including a bronze spearhead and bronze anklets and bracelets, were produced around 3600 B.C. The excavations also turned up evidence that these people cultivated rice and raised chickens and pigs.

"This was a very sophisticated society," stated Pennsylvania archeologist Chester Gorman. "In terms of metallurgical skill, it seems to have been unparalleled anywhere in the world." Because the level of civilization displayed by the inhabitants of the Khorat Plateau led to urbanization in other cultures, the archeologists decided to continue digging in the area, looking for buried Bronze Age cities where no one had ever suspected that they might exist.

BEHAVIOR

Surveys shed light on topics as diverse as the sex habits of American women, the public attitude toward scientists and which United States cities offer the most satisfying living. Other behavioral studies linked diet and aggressiveness, presented a new hypothesis for the strange behavior of Salem's "bewitched," and explained why Israelis and Arabs often give confusing directions.

HOW READING AFFECTS THE BRAIN

As many American tourists have noticed, it is not uncommon for an Israeli to give confusing travel directions—pointing to the left for example, while saying: "You must turn right." Neurologist Martin Albert of Boston University's Medical School Hospital thinks that he knows why this occurs. In a report to *Nature* in July 1975, he suggested that native-born Israelis and Arabs may have difficulty with left-right orientation because of the effect that their reading habits have on the functioning of their brains.

Albert bases this conclusion on two sets of tests. First, he examined 400 right-handed students—half native-born Israelis, the remainder recent immigrants from Europe and North or South America. Each volunteer was asked to respond to one of two commands: "Look to the right" or "Look to the left." Among the immigrants, 97 per cent reacted correctly—compared with only 64 per cent of the native Israelis. In similar tests of right-handed Arabs, only 57.7 per cent made the correct response.

Albert believes the trouble stems from the fact that Arabs and Israelis learn to read from right to left, rather than left to right like Americans and Europeans. When Europeans and Americans start to read, both hemispheres of their brains become immediately activated: the right hemisphere by the initial movement of the eyes toward the left-hand side of the page; the left in preparation for verbal comprehension, which is always handled in that portion of the brain. When Israelis and Arabs begin to read, the movement of their eyes to the right-hand side of the page activates the left hemisphere, which is also put to work in its role as verbal decoder; the right hemisphere, which handles the sensing of direction, remains temporarily inactive.

Among the Americans and Europeans, years of reading from left to right may well foster the quick, simultaneous activation of both sides of the brain and lay the groundwork for the speedy initiation of tasks that requires the use of both hemispheres—such as talking and pointing at the same time. But because the reading habits of Israelis and Arabs inhibit the immediate activation of the right side of the brain, tasks that require integrated use of the hemispheres are more likely to be performed slowly or incorrectly at first by these groups.

ZINC AND AGGRESSION

Scientists have long been aware that too low a level of zinc in the diet during pregnancy can affect the development of the brain and central nervous system in animal fetuses. There may be another significant effect of zinc deficiency. In September 1975, a study published in *Nature* indicated that laboratory rats deprived of zinc during pregnancy produced abnormally aggressive offspring.

In the study, conducted at the University of North Dakota, 10 pregnant rats were placed on a zinc-deficient diet. Ten other pregnant rats were given the same quantity of food supplemented by normal amounts of zinc. Later, the offspring of the test animals were tested for aggressive behavior by placing a pair at a time in a cage with a floor that could deliver an electric shock; when shocked, rats will sometimes attack their cage mates. After a series of tests, the researchers concluded that female rats that had been zinc-deficient before birth were more likely to bite, spar or assume an attack posture following a series of shocks than were females that had been fed sufficient zinc. This tendency was noted in male rats, but the differences in behavior between zinc-deficient animals and the others were not as clear-cut.

While there is no existing evidence that the test results could apply to humans who had prenatal zinc deficiency, the North Dakota scientists recommended that researchers look into the possibility. If zinc deficiency does cause developmental problems in humans, poor people are most likely to suffer, since their diets tend to be low in the animal products—meat, fish, milk and eggs—that are a primary source of zinc.

BOY STUDENTS BETTER

Despite textbook revisions and attitude changes spurred by the women's liberation movement, males continue to outrank females in academic achievement. That was the gist of a report released in October 1975 by a federally financed group of researchers working on a project entitled National Assessment of Educational Progress.

According to the report, tests given in the previous six years to some 900,000 students and young adults indicated that the sexes at age nine are roughly equal in science, social studies, citizenship and mathematics (although boys are slightly better at geometry and measurement). But by age 13, boys have pulled ahead of girls in all four of these categories—and their lead increases into young adulthood. In reading ability and knowledge of literature, girls are ahead of boys until about age 17, when they begin to fall behind in a decline that continues as they grow older. Only in writing ability and music do females continue to outperform males into adulthood.

The article gave no explanation for the superior educational achievement of males. "As a strictly census-like, data-gathering organization, National Assessment doesn't have the answers," said Roy Forbes, its director. But there was obviously ammunition in the findings for both male chauvinists and feminist militants. Concluded William Greenbaum, a Harvard researcher commissioned by the Carnegie Corporation to review the report: "You can just as easily conclude that women are naturally intellectually inferior to men or that they don't do as well because of social and family influence."

REDBOOK'S SEX POLL

Do you achieve orgasm: A. All the time? B. Most of the time? C. Sometimes? D. Once in a while? E. Never? F. Don't know. That was one of the 60 questions asked by *Redbook* in what it called "the most important survey of female sexuality since Kinsey." Responses were received from more than 100,000 American women—nine out of 10 of them married, 74 per cent of them between the ages of 20 and 34 and most of them middle class. In September 1975, *Redbook* printed the results. Among the more remarkable:

- "Strongly religious" women reported more sexual satisfaction, more orgasms and better communication with their husbands than "fairly religious" women. "Nonreligious" women were least satisfied with the frequency and quality of intercourse.
- Women under 25 had intercourse an average of 12 times a month, while those between 25 and 34 averaged nine or 10 times per month.
- Although less than four per cent had participated in wife swapping, 24 per cent of those who had not said that they might like to try it.
- Nearly half (47 per cent) of the married working women had had extramarital sex.
- Seven out of 10 women occasionally had sex while under the influence of alcohol, and 63 per cent of those under 25 sometimes smoked marijuana before sexual intercourse.
- Nearly 60 per cent of the women usually had orgasms within 10 minutes after beginning sexual intercourse, but 3.2 per cent required 26 minutes or more.
- Nine out of 10 women had experienced oral sex.
- While only 12 per cent objected to a son's having premarital sex, 24 per cent opposed it for a daughter.

RANKING THE CITIES

Which cities in the United States are the best places to live? Armed with a grant from the Environmental Protection Agency, the Midwest Research Institute—a Kansas City, Missouri, think tank—decided that the best way to find out was to measure the "quality of life" in the 243 official United States metropolitan areas. In September 1975, M.R.I. published the results of its research. Among the 65 metropolitan areas with populations of 500,000 or more, Portland, Oregon, was ranked first while Jersey City, New Jersey, came in last.

To reach their conclusions—which inspired a rash of mostly angry editorials in local newspapers—the think tank's researchers took into account 123 variables that fell into five broad categories: environment, politics, economics, health and education, and "social components"—such as racial equality and cultural facilities. Altogether, the list of variables, M.R.I. declared, covered "both the concerns of the individual and the well-being of the community." After the researchers rated the metropolitan areas numerically on each variable, the numbers were fed into a computer, which printed out separate rankings for large, middle-sized and small cities.

Among the large metropolitan areas in the survey, Southern cities in general ranked low, making up seven of the nine characterized as "substandard" at the bottom of the list. Of the 13 "outstanding" large cities six (including the top four) were located on the West Coast. Among the surprises of the survey: dynamic Atlanta ranked only 45th (which placed it in the "adequate" class) because of poor ratings in all categories except economics. Washington, D.C., with large slum areas and a high percentage of low-income families, ranked 20th ("excellent") because of very high ratings in health and education.

M.R.I.'s hometown, Kansas City, Missouri, stood 35th: "good."

STILL TWO CULTURES

What does the public think of scientists, and does the public view differ from the scientists' self-image? Those were the questions posed by two British magazines in a joint survey of their readers. In August 1975, *New Scientist* and *New Society* reported the results, based on 1,559 replies. The conclusion: scientists see themselves quite differently from the way nonscientists view them.

In general, the survey found, scientists considered themselves approachable, sociable, open, unconventional and popular. But nonscientists thought scientists were withdrawn, secretive, conventional, unpopular and absent-minded. Scientists thought of themselves as humane and moral, nonscientists felt that they "think of people in terms of statistics" and doubted they "would stop their work if they thought it was harmful." The scientists and nonscientists agreed only that scientists were cautious, calm, realistic, intelligent, well educated in their fields—and atheistic.

CULTURE AND CORONARIES

Low incidence of heart-disease deaths among Japanese men—only 92 per year for every 100,000 males, compared with 378 per 100,000 in the United States—has long been attributed to the low-fat, fish-and-rice Japanese diet. Study results announced in August 1975 by University of California at Berkeley researchers seemed to show that stress, or lack of it, makes the difference.

In the 10-year study, 3,809 Japanese men living in the San Francisco Bay area were given a 24-page questionnaire dealing with their backgrounds and life styles. They were asked about the number of years they had spent in Japan, whether they had attended Japanese or American schools, and the religion they practiced. They also described their diet, exercise and smoking habits. Finally, they received physical examinations.

When the data were analyzed, it became clear that the men who maintained traditional Japanese cultural behavior—staying in a close-knit group, leading quiet lives and being noncompetitive—had by far the lowest number of coronaries. Even the traditionalists who had adopted high-fat diets seemed to fare well. But those who opted for the more aggressive and competitive American way of life paid the price. The study concluded that Japanese-Americans who made a moderate transition to Western ways suffered two and a half times as many heart attacks as the traditionalists. Among those who became fully Americanized, the rate was five times as high.

WERE SALEM "BEWITCHED" HIGH?

In an attempt to explain the strange occurrences in Salem, Massachusetts, that led to the famous witchcraft trials of 1692 and the execution of 20 innocent citizens, experts have looked for evidence of political opportunism, sensation seeking, mass hysteria and a variety of psychological aberrations. In April 1976, Linnda Caporael, a graduate student in psychology at the University of California suggested another cause: ergot, a fungus that grows on rye.

While studying records of the trials, Caporael was struck by the fact that the complaints of many of the "bewitched" girls—crawling sensations in the skin, tingling fingers, vertigo, headaches, hallucinations, convulsions, vomiting and diarrhea—also described symptoms of convulsive ergotism. That disorder is caused by eating ergot, which contains—among other powerful chemicals—lysergic acid amide, a compound similar to LSD. Further research showed that the 1691 growing season had been warm and unusually rainy—ideal conditions for the growth of ergot on rye, the principal grain raised around Salem. It was only after the 1691 rye crop had been used for baking that the Salem girls were afflicted with their mysterious symptoms.

Concluded Caporael in a report to *Science:* "Of course, there can never be hard proof for the presence of ergot in Salem, but a circumstantial case is demonstrable. . . . Without knowledge of ergotism and confronted by convulsions, mental disturbances and perceptual disturbances, the Puritans seized upon witchcraft as the best explanation."

A SALEM "WITCH" FACES HER ACCUSERS.

BIOCHEMISTRY

Advancing on the fronts of both pure and applied research, biologists created a microbe that may be able to gobble up oil spills, discovered a purple pigment that turns sunlight into energy, and gained new insights into the body's mechanism for initiating the formation of internal organs and other specialized parts of the anatomy.

CELLULAR MASTER SWITCH

For years, scientists have suspected the existence of a substance within the nucleus of an embryonic cell that acts as a "master switch," initiating the process of specialization. This process starts soon after the fertilized egg cell of a newly conceived organism begins its rapid subdivision. Although each of the dividing cells contains all the genetic information needed to produce a complete creature, only selected genes come into play—those necessary to form a cell that will be part of the organism's skin, heart, kidney or whatever.

Until recently, the identity of the substance that triggers specialization remained a total mystery. But now, according to two reports in *Nature* in March 1976 describing new research in Britain and the United States, identification of the master switch that governs this fundamental life process may not be far off.

In experiments at the Laboratory of Molecular Biology in Cambridge, England, a research group led by John Gurdon inserted the nuclei of human cells into the nuclei of frogs' eggs. The human-cell nuclei swelled as much as a hundredfold and began producing large quantities of ribonucleic acid (RNA), which plays a role in the cell's production of protein. The inference was clear that dormant genetic information in the human cell had been "switched on" by some substance in the frog's egg; this, in turn, seemed to suggest that the master-switch substance may be similar in widely differing species.

In parallel research at Indiana University, Ann Janice Brothers reported experiments with egg cells of the axolotl, a relative of the salamander. Some axolotls produce eggs that do not progress beyond the earliest stages of subdivision and show no tendency to differentiate. Brothers and her colleagues found that such mutant eggs lacked a substance that was present in normal eggs—a large and somewhat acidic protein molecule. The role of that substance became clear when the researchers injected it into mutant eggs: the eggs immediately began to develop normally. Further experimentation along these lines, Brothers believes, may provide clues to the origin of some birth defects in humans.

ENERGY FROM A PURPLE PIGMENT

Scientists have long believed that living organisms can convert sunlight directly into energy for their life processes only by means of the green pigment, chlorophyll. That dogma, however, was rudely upset in March 1976, when biologist Walther Stoeckenius, along with colleagues at the University of California and a team from NASA's Ames Research Center, announced that a purple pigment called bacteriorhodopsin performs the same function as chlorophyll.

The maverick pigment comes from the bacterium *Halobacterium halobium*, often found in the Dead Sea and in salt flats. After years of analysis, Stoeckenius determined that the substance functions as a kind of electrical pump. Light striking a molecule of the pigment causes it to eject a hydrogen ion, or proton, which passes out through the membrane of the bacterial cell. Because the proton has a positive charge, its departure leaves an excess of negative charge inside the membrane. This voltage differential causes an electric current to flow through the membrane, providing the energy that the bacterium needs to synthesize adenosine triphosphate (ATP), the energy-storing molecule common to all living cells.

Although the purple pigment converts only about 10 per cent of the absorbed sunlight directly into electrochemical energy (compared with chlorophyll's 30 per cent), it is more stable than chlorophyll and might be useful in man-made devices like photoelectric cells. Moreover, because it helps the bacteria to push salt through their membranes to the outside so that they can survive in salt water, it could also be used to desalinate water. But Stoeckenius was most interested in his discovery's meaning for cell biology. "All living cells need to pump ions across their cell membranes," he said. "It seems to me that we are close to discovering certain basic cellular functions."

OIL-EATING BUG

In their search for more effective ways of combating oil spills, scientists have discovered several strains of bacteria that "eat" petroleum, converting it into protein, carbon dioxide and water. Unfortunately, each of these strains attacks only a fraction of the many different hydrocarbons in oil, and each works much too slowly to be considered for cleaning up massive spills. But in September 1975, General Electric microbiologist Ananda Chakrabarty announced that he had combined the oil-eating capacities of the various strains into a superbug.

Five years earlier, Chakrabarty and colleagues at the University of Illinois had discovered that a microbe's ability to digest oil hydrocarbons is transmitted genetically on plasmids—tiny circular rings of DNA that exist outside the chromosomes ("Wonderful Sickly Microbe," *pages 92-97*). After joining GE's Research and Development Center, Chakrabarty began trying to crossbreed four different bacteria strains to produce one that would contain the plasmids of all. Although the bacteria freely conjugated, or exchanged genetic information, the different plasmids proved to be incompatible and would not stay together within the same cell.

Chakrabarty finally discovered that by irradiating his cells with ultraviolet light, he could fuse the genetic material together and thus fix the alien plasmids in place. The result was a hybrid with a catholic appetite for hydrocarbons and an ability to consume petroleum at a rate from five to 100 times as fast as any one of the four component strains. While GE cautioned that it might take as long as five years to convert the superbug into a practical weapon for fighting oil spills, the company called Chakrabarty's work "the first successful application of advanced genetic engineering techniques."

ENVIRONMENT

Energy needs and environmental concerns came into sharp conflict around the world. In the western United States, environmentalists blocked plans for a huge coal-burning power plant, while on the Eastern Seaboard, a newly approved floating nuclear plant met a barrage of criticism. In Africa and Asia, where wood is the main fuel, exploding populations threaten to destroy the remaining forests —and generate new ecological problems in the process.

A SHORTAGE OF FIREWOOD

The "most profound ecological challenge of the late 20th century" will likely stem not from air or water pollution but from the denuding of the earth's forests. That was the gloomy prognosis of environment expert Erik Eckholm in September 1975 after a tour of parts of Africa and Asia where most of the population is dependent on wood as a fuel for cooking and heating. In a paper published by the Worldwatch Institute, a Washington-based independent research organization, Eckholm reported that rapid population growth has hastened tree-cutting and is creating a firewood shortage in underdeveloped lands. The crisis has been further heightened by the sharp jump in oil prices, which has raised the price of kerosene beyond the reach of millions who once used it for cooking and now have turned to firewood.

Uncontrolled tree-cutting can have important environmental repercussions. In some areas of North Africa, the Sahara is expanding by about 250,000 acres per year as a result of deforestation. In Pakistan, India and Bangladesh, denuded hillsides are rapidly eroding, and rainfall that once soaked into the slopes is now running off, increasing the frequency and severity of floods. Also, as wood becomes increasingly scarce in the Indian subcontinent, peasants are turning more and more to cow dung for fuel, depriving farmland of badly needed nutrients and organic matter.

The current firewood crisis has an ominous historical parallel. According to Boston University historian William Te Brake, writing in the journal *Technology and Culture,* a population explosion in medieval England greatly increased the demand for firewood and set off a chain of disastrous events. As the number of Englishmen grew (from 1.1 million in 1086 A.D. to 3.7 million in the early 1300s), forests disappeared around cities and towns, and the price of firewood soared. In London, a low-grade coal was substituted for wood as early as the 13th Century, and by 1307 smoke from the fires had so fouled the air that a royal proclamation prohibited the use of coal kilns in the city—under punishment of "grievous ransoms." Even worse, the cleared, overfarmed land around the cities began to decline in productivity, contributing to a cycle of famines, followed by plagues, that by 1430 A.D. reduced the population by 40 per cent.

FLOATING NUCLEAR PLANT

In a landmark report made public in April, the Nuclear Regulatory Commission recommended that a construction permit be granted for the world's first floating nuclear power plant. Proposed by the Public Service Electric and Gas Company of Newark, the plant would be located in the Atlantic Ocean 2.8 miles off the New Jersey shore just north of Atlantic City. According to the NRC, the floating plant would pose a "very low" risk of radioactive contamination of either the air or the water.

The report was actually the first draft of an environmental impact statement, which could be modified by state, local and other federal agencies before Public Service is allowed to begin construction. Its reassuring tone brought little comfort to many residents of the most affected area, Atlantic County, which has a $4 billion per year tourist industry. Citizens' groups voiced fear that once the plant was in operation, the possibility of a nuclear accident—no matter how remote —might cause vacationers to shun the New Jersey shore, bringing economic ruin to the area.

Taking note of this concern, the NRC report cited the experience of resort communities near nuclear plants at Scriba, New York, and Pope County, Arkansas; neither suffered any loss in tourism. "In the absence of adverse publicity," the commission said, "it is unlikely that the tourist and summer resident economy will be adversely affected."

The NRC conceded that dredging for a protective breakwater would stir up 127 acres of seabottom, creating heavy silting, and that 43 acres of marsh and forest land would have to be torn up for cables to bring electricity ashore. But these disadvantages would be outweighed, the commission concluded, by the benefits the plant would bring: the reduction in purchases of expensive foreign oil by the Public Service Electric and Gas Company and the avoidance of the "environmental effects of fossil fuel combustion."

NIX ON COAL-BURNING

Environmentalists claimed one of their biggest victories of the year in April 1976, when two Western utilities, part of a consortium that had planned to build a huge coal-fired power plant on Utah's desolate Kaiparowits Plateau, decided to drop the project. The consortium, led by Southern California Edison, had already pumped some $22 million into plans for the $3.5 billion installation, which would have generated three million kilowatts for Arizona and Southern California and would have been a boon to Utah's economy. But opposition had been building ever since the consortium announced its plans in 1962. The Sierra Club and the National Park Service argued that the plant would pour at least 300 tons of pollutants a day into the air in a region that included 11 national parks and recreation areas. The Interior Department had delayed approval of construction while investigating objections, and two weeks before the project was abandoned, 31 members of Congress had asked Interior Secretary Thomas Kleppe for another delay pending further study.

Also influencing the decision were the slowdown in the growth of demand for electrical power and rising costs—partially stemming from federal insistence on better protection of the environment. Concluded Michael McCloskey, executive director of the Sierra Club: "Kaiparowits was a project at the wrong time and in the wrong place."

GEOLOGY

Delving into the past, geologists reconstructed a view of the world during the last ice age, found evidence of global flooding that may have given rise to the Biblical story of the Deluge and pinpointed the probable source of King Solomon's fabulous gold supply. They also gained a futuristic new tool to keep a precise check on various earth movements.

BIBLICAL FLOODS

The folklore of almost every culture includes tales of a great flood that swept away early civilizations. Many of these tales are vague about the time of the Deluge, but Plato's account of the inundation of Atlantis—inspired by the stories of generations of Egyptian priests—placed the great flood at 9600 B.C. *(Nature/Science Annual 1973, pages 140-153).* In September 1975, University of Miami scientists reported in *Science* that there had indeed been widespread flooding about that time.

The conclusion of paleoclimatologist Cesare Emiliani and his colleagues was based on sediment cores from the floor of the Gulf of Mexico. Such cores contain fossil shells that, when they were formed, absorbed two sorts of oxygen: the normal type with 16 neutrons and the isotope O 18, which has two extra neutrons; the latter is more abundant in sea water than in fresh water. Analyzing the oxygen content of the shells, the researchers found a marked reduction of O 18 in shells from one particular sedimentary level.

They calculated that the salinity of the Gulf had suddenly declined by about 20 per cent when that layer of sediment had been laid down. By carbon-14 dating of the shells, they determined that the layer had been deposited around 9600 B.C. —the date of the destruction of Atlantis.

Previous research had indicated that worldwide temperatures began to rise about that time. Evidently, this warming of the earth's climate melted the base of the Arctic icecap. The lubricating effect caused the ice sheet to suddenly surge southward, spreading into what is now the northern United States, where it melted rapidly. As a result, the scientists theorized, fresh water surged down the Mississippi into the Gulf, decreasing its salinity. Meanwhile, fresh water from the melting glacier was also pouring into Hudson Bay and the North Atlantic, raising sea levels. The ensuing flooding of low-lying coastal areas—said the report —gave rise to the Deluge stories.

KING SOLOMON'S MINES

According to the Bible (I Kings: 4-10), King Solomon brought 1,086 gold talents to Jerusalem from a mine named Ophir. That account's accuracy has long been questioned by historians and, recently, by mining engineers, since it meant that the ancient mine must have produced at least 31 metric tons (a talent was about 28.5 kilograms) of gold—about half the known supply of the ancient world. It seemed highly unlikely that any mine in the region of Ophir (now Saudi Arabia) could have contained so rich a lode. But in May 1976, a team of U.S. Geological Survey scientists, working with Saudi Arabian counterparts, reported that the Biblical account may have been correct. Their study showed that Saudi Arabia's recently abandoned Mahd adh Dhahab gold and silver mine could easily be the fabled Ophir.

The United States-Arabian team analyzed samples of the million tons of waste material left by ancient miners and found that the rock contained an average of .6 ounce of gold per ton—a high assay. The mined ore must have been much richer. Further sampling of the deposits and a check of modern production figures compiled during the mine's last years (1939-1954) indicated that gold was plentiful near the surface during Biblical times. In fact, it was so abundant that the first 420 talents or so of King Solomon's treasure could have easily been separated from the ore by simple panning or winnowing. Recovery of the remaining 666 talents would have been more difficult; it probably involved many workers using crude copper and stone tools to mine the hard, gold-bearing, underground quartz veins. The ore brought out was then crushed with stone hammers and grindstones.

Mahd adh Dhahab is located on a natural north-south trade route that has been used for 4,000 years and was easily accessible from Aqaba, the port from which Solomon's ships sailed. Gold taken from the mine was probably carried by caravan to the closest point on the Red Sea, 149 miles away, and then by ship another 471 miles through the Red Sea and the Gulf of Aqaba. With favorable winds, a round trip would have taken no more than three months. Given the new evidence, said a U.S. Geological Survey spokesman, "We believe that the legendary King Solomon's Lost Mines are no longer lost."

ICE AGES REPORT

What was the world like 18,000 years ago? According to a report that appeared in *Science* in March 1976, thick ice sheets covered vast expanses of land in the Northern Hemisphere and extended over the seas in the Southern Hemisphere; sea levels were some 300 feet lower than they are today; worldwide precipitation was about 15 per cent less; and areas of desert, grassland and steppes were expanding, while forests were in retreat.

These conclusions were reached by an international consortium of scientists involved in a project called CLIMAP (Climate Long-Range Investigation Mapping and Prediction). Beginning in 1971, the researchers examined deep-core samples taken from the land, ocean bottom and the Greenland icecap. Among other things, they were looking for traces of pollen or the remains of sea organisms deposited at the peak of the last ice age, 18,000 years ago. From the fossils of small surface-dwelling sea animals, they determined the approximate temperature of surface waters. Pollen samples identified the type of vegetation—and hence the climate—on land.

Some of the other CLIMAP findings:

•Though average air temperatures were probably about 10° F. below what they are today, the average temperature of the oceans was only 4.1° F. cooler.

•Ice sheets in east-central Canada were 9,500 feet thick.

•Though the ice sheets advanced as far south as the Carolinas in North America, large areas of Alaska and Asia remained unglaciated because of a lack of precipitation.

CLIMAP researchers plan to reconstruct climate profiles of other eras, including an unusually warm period about 120,000 years ago—between the last two ice ages—to help explain why the earth undergoes major and rapid climate changes.

DO SOLID ROCKS EVAPORATE?

Most solid substances change to a gas or vapor only by going through a liquid stage. But some—like iodine crystals or frozen carbon dioxide (dry ice)—sublimate: that is, they pass from solid form directly into vapor. In March 1976, Edward Goldberg, a chemist at the Scripps Institution of Oceanography, theorized that such unlikely substances as silicates and other minerals in the earth's crust may also be slowly sublimating. He based his theory on the concentration of trace metals found in air and in rainwater samples collected from around the world. In general, discounting man-made air pollution, lead was the most abundant, followed by zinc, copper, manganese and nickel.

Goldberg was struck by the fact that this ranking corresponded to the relative readiness of common compounds of these metals to vaporize as temperatures rise; lead compounds vaporize first and then—at increasing temperatures—zinc, copper, manganese and nickel compounds. This correlation led him to conclude that even at normal surface temperatures the earth's rocks slowly sublimate—lead-bearing minerals faster than, say, manganese compounds.

LASER BALL IN THE SKY

Lofted into a 3,600-mile orbit by NASA in May 1976, the satellite resembled a giant golf ball. Its two-foot aluminum surface was dimpled with 426 cube-corner prism reflectors, which reflect light striking them at any angle back to the source. This ability enables LAGEOS (laser geodynamic satellite) to serve as a celestial bench mark for measurements of continental drift, movement along faults, the rotation rate of the earth and the wobble of its axis.

The measurements are made by aiming high-powered pulses of laser light at LAGEOS and noting the time it takes for the pulses to return to their source; the return time indicates the distance between the light source and the satellite with exactitude. Laser stations placed on the dozen or so tectonic plates that make up the earth's surface will track the rate and direction of their movement.

Success in measurement requires that LAGEOS maintain a very stable orbit. To ensure that stability, engineers gave LAGEOS a solid brass core, which contributes most of the 903-pound satellite's weight. Because LAGEOS is so small and yet has such mass, its orbit will be little affected by traces of atmosphere at its 3,600-mile altitude, by particles in the solar wind or by variations in the earth's gravity field. As a result, scientists expect to be able to detect earth movements of as little as .4 inch a year.

WORKER IN DUST-FREE SUIT INSPECTS LASER BALL.

MEDICINE

Medical researchers reported encouraging progress in their efforts to develop vaccines against two crippling diseases, held an unorthodox family reunion to counsel on a rare genetic malady and showed how hugging could save thousands of lives each year.

HOPE FOR A SYPHILIS VACCINE . . .

Some 25,000 new syphilis cases are reported in the United States yearly, and the real incidence is surely much higher. Penicillin cures the disease in the early stages, but many cases go undetected until an advanced stage, when syphilis can damage the brain, bones, heart and other organs—and may cause death.

For decades, medical science has been unsuccessfully seeking a way to immunize humans against this scourge, which is caused by the spiral bacterium *Treponema pallidum.* In February 1976 a team of Florida researchers announced encouraging progress toward a vaccine. Reporting in the *British Journal of Venereal Diseases,* a team led by microbiologist Ronald H. Jones claimed it had achieved two goals: it had grown *T. pallidum* in the test tube, and developed a vaccine that partially protected test animals against the bacterium.

Jones's team, from the Medical Research Institute of the Florida Institute of Technology, cultivated cell lines containing the syphilis organisms by using bacteria from animals that had been infected for 30 days or longer. Once they succeeded in growing the bacteria in the laboratory they discovered that some of the organisms were covered with a layer of slime and others were not. Only the slime-covered variety caused the disease, and it appeared that earlier experimenters had washed off the slime during their vaccine-making process, thus guaranteeing failure.

Preparing a vaccine containing killed, slime-covered bacteria, Jones and his colleagues vaccinated rabbits and then injected them with a massive dose of live syphilis organisms. The rabbits were infected, but far less severely than unvaccinated rabbits in a control group. The Florida scientists are now working on a more effective vaccine. They hope to test it on chimpanzees in two years and on humans a year or two afterward.

... AND AN MS VACCINE TOO

Multiple sclerosis is a mysterious disease of the nervous system that attacks hundreds of thousands of Americans, usually between the ages of 20 and 40, causing tremors, speech disturbances, paralysis and even death. Hope of a vaccine was raised in 1972, when a team of New York City researchers headed by Richard Carp announced the apparent discovery of an MS virus.

Carp reported that material taken from the brains of human multiple sclerosis victims had been used to infect mice, and that material from the brains of these mice had then been used to infect other mice. The size of the infecting agent—it could pass through a .00005-millimeter filter but not through one with openings half that size—led Carp to believe that the disease was caused by a virus approximately as big as those that cause polio or influenza. During the next few years, however, other researchers were unable to duplicate Carp's experiments, and the fight against MS seemed to be as far from success as ever.

In February 1976, there was a dramatic turnaround. A group of Philadelphia researchers headed by a husband and wife team, Drs. Werner and Gertrude Henle, reported in the British journal *The Lancet* that they had not only duplicated Carp's work, but also carried it several steps further. In experiments at the Joseph Stokes Jr. Research Institute, they discovered that large amounts of the virus were present in the brains of patients with active MS cases and smaller amounts in patients whose illnesses were in remission. The existence of the MS virus was further supported by the finding of antibodies—produced by the body to fight the invading viruses—in the blood of patients, their relatives and their nurses. Tests show that these antibodies neutralized the effect of the virus in mice and other test animals.

Concluded *The Lancet* report: The American findings place MS "squarely in the sector of infectious diseases, although the precise nature of the virus has yet to be determined."

THE JOSEPH ILLNESS

Portuguese immigrant Antone Joseph fathered six children before he died of a rare degenerative nerve disease in California in the mid-19th Century. The same strange illness has since claimed the lives of at least 48 of his 300 or so descendants. In September 1975, after being tracked down with the help of the National Genetics Foundation, nearly 100 of Joseph's descendants gathered for a bizarre family reunion in the auditorium of the Oakland Children's Hospital. There, pediatrician and geneticist William Nyhan of the University of California at San Diego and neurologist Roger Rosenberg of the University of Texas Southwestern Medical School in Dallas explained the hereditary disease, examined family members for symptoms and gave genetic counseling.

Nyhan spelled out the symptoms of the disease, which he called the Joseph Illness. Caused by a defective gene, it can show up as early as age 16 or as late as 70, but usually appears in the middle to late twenties. Victims first notice a loss of coordination, a staggering gait and gradual slurring of speech. Over the years, swallowing becomes difficult, and the muscles of the chest and abdomen become paralyzed. Death occurs about 20 years after the onset of the disease, usually from pneumonia stemming from paralysis of the breathing muscles. The illness can be passed on only by those afflicted; each of their offspring has a 50-50 chance of inheriting it.

Of the Joseph descendants gathered in Oakland, 10 were found to have the illness; 26 others, the children of afflicted parents, may develop it. For those already ill, Nyhan and Rosenberg offered no hope. They mentioned several drugs that may slow the progress of the disease, but said there is no cure. For those still free of symptoms, they could only suggest careful consideration of the risks of having children.

LIFESAVING HUG

It happens as often as 4,000 times a year in the United States. During mealtime, someone suddenly stops talking, clutches at his throat or chest, turns blue, collapses and in four or five minutes is dead. Though the symptoms are similar to those of a heart attack, the victim has really suffered what some doctors call a café coronary—his windpipe has been blocked by food.

For years, first-aid experts have recommended a variety of methods for saving the choking victim: bending the person over and slapping him hard between the shoulder blades; removing the food with fingers or with specially designed plastic tweezers; or even cutting a hole in the victim's windpipe with any available sharp instrument. In October 1975, however, both the American Medical Association and the American Red Cross endorsed a new and more effective method developed by Henry Heimlich, director of surgery at the Jewish Hospital in Cincinnati.

In Dr. Heimlich's procedure, the rescuer gets behind the choking victim, wraps his arms around him above the navel and below the rib cage, makes a fist with one hand and grasps the fist with the other hand. Then he presses the thumb side of that fist into the victim's abdomen with a quick upward thrust, repeating the motion if necessary. This elevates the diaphragm and compresses the lungs, increasing air pressure in the windpipe and forcing the obstruction out.

At the time that his hugging technique received A.M.A. and Red Cross approval, Heimlich reported, it had already been used on at least 374 potential choking and drowning victims. All survived.

PHYSICS

Seeking confirmation of the existence of gravity waves that measure millions of miles from trough to crest, physicists proposed a detection system that would have a terminal beyond Mars. Meanwhile, investigations of the ultrasmall realm of atomic particles provided a surprise: there are at least two—and possibly four—naturally occurring elements heavier than any known before.

LONG-LIVED SUPERHEAVY ELEMENTS

Using particle accelerators, physicists in the past three decades have produced upward of a dozen elements more massive than uranium, the heaviest of the 92 elements known to exist in nature. Aside from plutonium, none of these artificially created materials lasts more than a fraction of a second; they promptly decay into lighter, naturally occurring elements. However, in June 1976, scientists from the Oak Ridge National Laboratory, Columbia Union College, the University of California at Davis and Florida State University reported finding evidence of two extremely heavy elements that have great stability and may have existed on earth since it was formed.

The two new elements would be Numbers 116 and 126 on the table of elements, which lists substances according to the number of protons in the atomic nucleus. The suspected traces of these superheavy elements (and possibly of Numbers 124 and 127) were found in specimens of mica that have unusually large halos—microscopic rings caused by radiation. These halos had been produced by emissions more powerful than those from uranium, and the researchers believed the radiation had occurred during the decay of unstable elements with very high atomic numbers.

In the hope that this decay had left behind a superheavy but stable element, the scientists devised an ingenious detection technique. They bombarded the mica with protons to knock electrons loose from the atoms in the crystals; in less than a billionth of a second, new electrons took their place, emitting X-rays characteristic of the atoms.

In studying the X-ray patterns produced by the bombardment, the scientists found that some of them matched patterns that had been predicted by theory for the putative elements 116 and 126. There were also less distinct match ups with patterns predicted for elements 124 and 127. Though the crystals contained only minuscule traces of the superheavy atoms, the evidence was sufficient to convince some nuclear physicists that the elements existed.

GRAVITY WAVE DETECTOR

Many of the strange relativistic phenomena predicted by Albert Einstein in the early part of the century have since been confirmed by elaborate tests. But one —the existence of gravitational waves —has proved to be more elusive. According to the Einstein equations, gravitational waves should be generated by the accelerated motion of massive bodies, just as electromagnetic waves are produced by the acceleration of charged particles. Moreover, gravitational waves should produce slight variations in the motion of any object they pass. In February 1976, physicists Kip Thorne of the California Institute of Technology and Vladimir Braginsky of Moscow State University suggested a scheme to detect these subtle motions.

Writing in *The Astrophysical Journal,* the scientists proposed setting up a tracking antenna on Earth to steadily transmit radio signals to a spacecraft flying beyond the orbit of Mars; the craft would amplify the signals and send them back to Earth. This long-distance relay system would, in effect, serve as a detector of gravity waves with wavelengths of six million miles or more (such waves, thought to be produced by such stupendous celestial events as the explosions of stars, are theoretically the most powerful and most easily detected of gravitational emissions). According to Thorne and Braginsky's scheme, when the waves pass the spacecraft and the earth, they would produce jiggles in the motion of both bodies; these motions could be perceived as irregular variations in the elapsed time required for the relay of the radio signals.

Once the waves are observed, Thorne said, astronomers will be able to use them to study the innards of celestial bodies. "Because gravitational waves come from the interiors of objects," he said, "they can be very powerful tools in revealing cosmic activity that we have never seen before."

SPACE

Scientists probing the mysteries of the solar system were richly rewarded when an unmanned United States spacecraft settled on Mars and relayed to Earth the first pictures taken on the surface of the Red Planet. Another study of the planets revealed that remote Pluto has a covering of methane ice, and in Houston, NASA unveiled a simplified rescue device for space travelers.

SUCCESSFUL MARS LANDING

Seven years to the day after Apollo astronaut Neil Armstrong became the first man to walk on the moon, and after an 11-month, 420-million-mile journey through space, the unmanned Viking 1 landing craft settled gently onto the surface of Mars and began photographing the surrounding landscape of Chryse Planitia (Gold Plain). Within two hours after the historic July 20, 1976, landing, scientists at the Jet Propulsion Laboratory (J.P.L.) in Pasadena, California, were studying the first photographs shot on the surface of Mars.

The initial picture, taken with one of Viking's two cameras pointed down, showed a spacecraft footpad resting on soil covered with small rocks and pebbles. The photograph, relayed by telemetry from the lander to the orbiting mother ship and then transmitted 212 million miles across space to J.P.L., was remarkably clear, distinguishing even the rivets on the footpad. The second picture, an eye-level, 300° panoramic view, showed a flat, rock-strewn plain reminiscent of desert areas in Arizona and Mexico. Clearly visible were sand dunes, a depression that could be a small crater, bright patches of sand and, on the horizon about two miles away, a ridge that scientists thought might be the rim of a large impact crater. There was another early dividend from Viking's descent to the Martian surface. On the way down, the lander sniffed out small amounts of argon (one and a half per cent)—an indication that the atmosphere was once much more dense—and nitrogen (three per cent), an element essential to living terrestrial organisms. The presence of both gases increased the possibility that some form of life had evolved on Mars.

The robot lander was originally scheduled to touch down on July 4; it was kept in orbit when cameras aboard the mother ship revealed that the prime landing site in the Chryse region was filled with deep crevasses, rough channels apparently carved out by running water, steep slopes and giant boulders. Revised plans for a July 17 touchdown were also abandoned when Viking's cameras, and radar mapping by the giant radio telescope at Arecibo, Puerto Rico, showed that an alternate site was also extremely rough, and therefore too risky for the 1,300-pound, instrument-crammed craft to attempt a landing.

Once the Viking 1 lander was safely down on July 20 taking atmospheric and geophysical readings and ready to begin testing Martian soil for evidence of living organisms, scientists were prepared to assume greater risks with its twin, the Viking 2 lander, scheduled to go into orbit around Mars on August 7. They began considering landing sites that were geologically different—and probably more hazardous—than Chryse Planitia.

Whatever the fate of the second lander, the one-billion-dollar Viking mission was already a resounding success.

THE OUTERMOST PLANET

The least-known member of the solar system is the outermost planet Pluto, which orbits the sun at a distance that varies between 2.8 and 4.6 billion miles; the planet appears only as a pinpoint of light through even the largest telescopes. In April 1976, however, three University of Hawaii astronomers announced that the exceedingly faint light from Pluto is sufficient to indicate a surface consisting largely of frozen methane. Using the 158-inch telescope at Kitt Peak National Observatory, the astronomers observed the infrared reflections of Pluto through two highly selective filters—one designed to admit infrared light waves associated with reflections from water ice and the other to pass light waves reflected off methane ice.

The result, reported astronomer Dale Cruikshank, "was exactly as predicted for methane ice." Just to ensure that the system was working properly, the scientists tested it on several moons of Saturn known to have frozen water on their surfaces. The reflections indicated water ice, as expected, but no methane ice.

Finding methane ice on Pluto established that the surface temperature must be at least as cold as −373° F., the freezing point of methane in a near-vacuum environment like Pluto's. The discovery also threw doubt on estimates of Pluto's size that were based on the planet's observed brightness. With methane ice on its surface to reflect sunlight, Pluto may be little more than 2,000 miles in diameter, instead of the previously estimated 4,000 miles. If so, Pluto's smaller size would lend credence to the theory that it was once a moon of Neptune but was torn from its orbit by the gravity of some passing body and launched onto its highly elliptical path around the sun.

SPACE RESCUE BALL

In the 1980s, the United States plans to ferry scientists and other personnel between Earth and an orbiting laboratory by means of a space shuttle—a combination rocket and plane. Should the shuttle run into trouble, passengers could literally have a ball. The possibility was revealed in March 1976, when engineers at the Johnson Space Center in Houston demonstrated a proposed rescue ball in which a passenger could transfer from a disabled shuttle to a nearby rescue craft.

In the event the shuttle is stranded in orbit, each passenger, instead of donning a costly space suit like those worn by the crew members, will zip himself into a relatively inexpensive 34-inch-diameter, 14-pound enclosure made of layers of synthetic fabrics. The ball will then be inflated to its full diameter with pure oxygen and—while its cramped occupant gazes out of a small plastic window—will be towed by a space-suited astronaut or conveyed by a clothesline-like transfer system across empty space to the rescue ship.

AN INFLATABLE BALL MAY SAVE LIVES.

WILDLIFE

The decades-old search for the Loch Ness monster continued, while some all-too-real, crop-consuming African elephants were successfully rounded up and relocated. Rarities made news: birdwatchers sighted an uncommon visitor on the wrong side of the Atlantic, the vanishing bald eagle gained a sanctuary, and biologists discovered how a tropical vine finds trees to climb.

HOW VINES FIND TREES

Most plants grow phototropically, or toward light, but in November 1975, two Florida State University biologists described a vine that violates the normal code of plant behavior. While studying insects in a Costa Rican rain forest, Donald Strong Jr. and Thomas Ray Jr. noticed a tree surrounded by thousands of bright green seedlings of the tropical vine *Monstera gigantea,* which is a relative of the split-leaf philodendron. What seemed so strange to the biologists was that all of the *Monstera* seedlings were snaking toward the tree, irrespective of where the light fell.

After a series of tests that involved setting up vertical cloth panels of varying translucency near the seedlings, the scientists discovered that the little vines seemed attracted not by light but by darkness. Their conclusion: the seedlings, in search of a host to climb, find it by a sort of botanical radar that senses the closest dark object, usually the black bark of a nearby tree.

The *Monstera* seedlings can use this response, which the biologists named skototropism (growth toward darkness), to search out trees as far as 27.5 inches away. Once the vine has found the tree and begins to climb, however, it reverts to normal plant behavior. The *Monstera* puts out saucer-shaped leaves, reaches toward the sun and begins manufacturing its food through photosynthesis.

FIRST EAST-COAST SMEW

For birdwatchers across the country, it was the most exciting event since the 1974 sighting of a Ross's gull in Newburyport, Massachusetts. In January of 1976, the National Audubon Society confirmed that a smew—a waterfowl normally found in Siberia and Northern Finland—had been spotted at Green End Pond in Newport, Rhode Island. Never before had a smew even been glimpsed on the Atlantic Coast, and only a handful of sightings had been reported elsewhere in North America.

To preclude the possibility that the white-and-black male bird had escaped from captivity somewhere in the vicinity, Audubon officials called the only two persons in the eastern United States known to keep smews. One reported that his birds were all accounted for; the other said that he was no longer keeping birds. By that time, some of the birdwatchers who had flocked to Green End Pond had crept close enough to the unusual bird to see that it had no identification bands or other markings indicating that it had been in captivity. Furthermore, the smew was observed repeatedly diving for fish—feeding behavior that, according to the Audubon Society, could be learned only in the wild.

FIRST SMEW EVER SEEN ON ATLANTIC COAST.

What had brought the smew so far from home? One expert speculated that it might have migrated across the Atlantic from northern Europe because of severe winter weather on the continent. Another suggested that it might have been blown across the Atlantic by an unusual high pressure system that at the time stretched from Poland to Greenland. In any case, the smew appeared to like what it found; it began keeping company with a flock of American mergansers, settling in for the duration of the winter in Rhode Island.

HAVEN FOR THE BALD EAGLE

As the Bicentennial Year began, the National Wildlife Federation took action to prevent the extinction of a bird that has been the nation's symbol since 1782: the American bald eagle. The Wildlife Federation announced in January that it had purchased a 150-acre tract in Wisconsin that is one of the prime roosting spots of the bald eagle (the birds nest primarily in wilderness areas of the northern United States and Canada). The heavily wooded site, located along the Wisconsin River near Madison, will be called the Ferry Bluff Eagle Sanctuary. As is the case at a similar 1,100-acre sanctuary previously established in South Dakota, the Ferry Bluff sanctuary will be off limits to humans during the eagles' winter roosting season.

The Wildlife Federation's action comes none too soon. A southern race of the species has already been listed as endangered by the U.S. Fish and Wildlife Service; a mere 600 or so survive. And only about 1,800 of the larger, northern bald eagles remain in the lower 48 states, although they are still present in large numbers in Canada and Alaska. To help in implementing further aid for the survivors, the Wildlife Federation is organizing a computerized "eagle data bank" in Washington, D.C. The data bank will contain all the known information about the bald eagle and its habits and will pinpoint its nesting and roosting sites.

NESSIE

Nessie, the fabled monster of Scotland's Loch Ness, achieved a degree of scientific respectability in December 1975, when *Nature* magazine published several murky underwater photographs, including one that to some seemed to show an overall view of a long-necked, horned creature that bore a resemblance to the plesiosaurs that inhabited the seas 150 million years ago.

The pictures had been taken in Loch Ness during the summer of 1975 by an expedition led by Robert Rines, a Boston lawyer and physicist who had visited Loch Ness every summer since 1970 to carry on the search for Nessie. In an accompanying report, which was coauthored by Sir Peter Scott, who is a British naturalist, Rines proposed that the creature be given a scientific name

—*Nessiteras rhombopteryx*—so that the creature could be protected under British conservation laws.

Publication of the report immediately precipitated a controversy, particularly after a London newspaper noted that the scientific name is an anagram for "monster hoax by Sir Peter S." Some experts suspected that the article was just that. However, George Zug, curator of reptiles and amphibians at the Smithsonian Institution, was sufficiently impressed by the photos to speculate that there might even be several such creatures in Loch Ness. Still other scientists thought that Rines's photographs might represent the wreckage of an ancient Viking ship or might simply be the head of a Highland steer that had drowned in the lake.

The *Nature* article nonetheless gave the search for Nessie a respectability that it had lacked in the past. Following the publication of Rines's photographs in *Technology Review* and *Smithsonian* magazines, *The New York Times* announced that it would cosponsor, with Rines's Boston-based Academy of Applied Sciences, "the most thorough and technologically sophisticated" hunt ever conducted for Nessie, using photography, infrared sensors and sonar, during the summer of 1976.

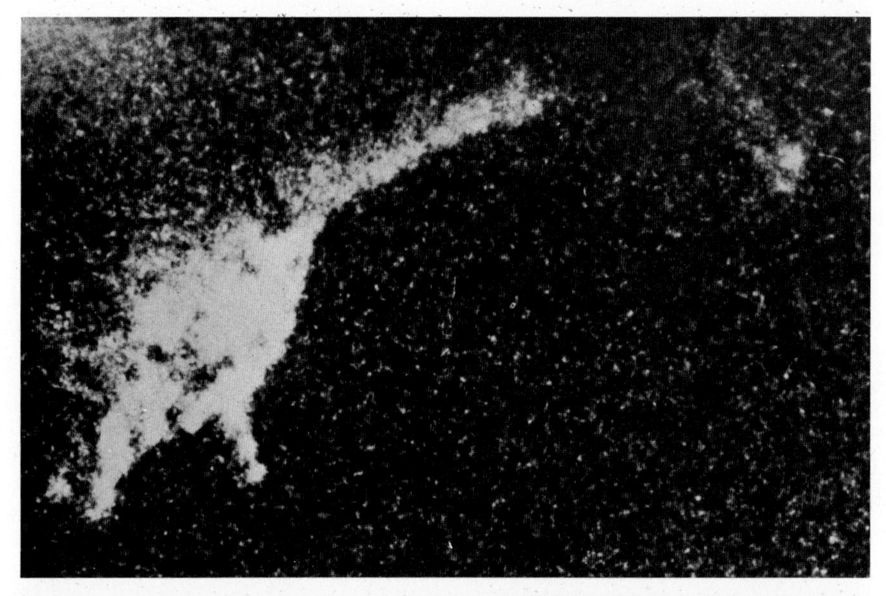

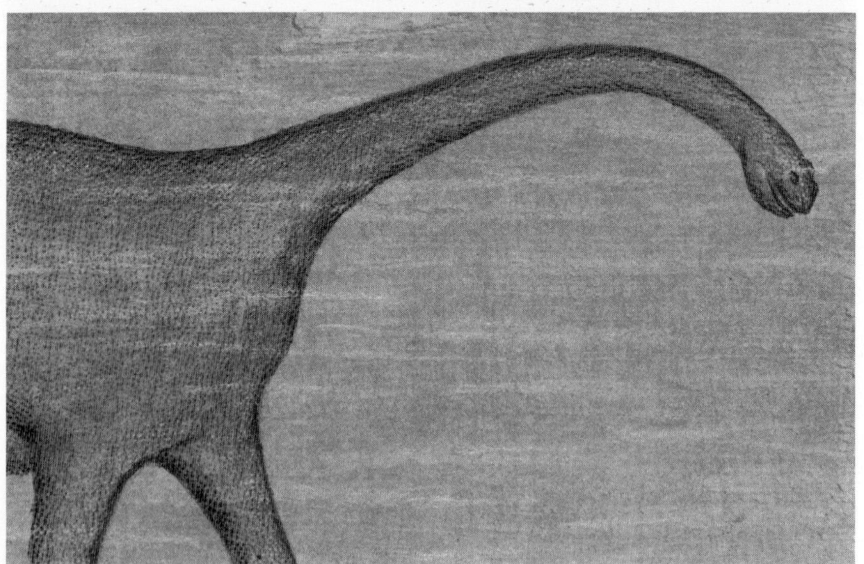

AN UNDERWATER PHOTO, CLARIFIED IN A SKETCH, REPUTEDLY SHOWS THE LOCH NESS MONSTER.

AIRBORNE ELEPHANTS

ELEPHANT IS AIRLIFTED TO RWANDA PARK.

General Juvénal Habyalimana, president of Rwanda in east-central Africa, felt he had no other choice. The 140-odd elephants living in his 10,000-square-mile country were competing with the four million human inhabitants for food. As near-starving tribesmen increasingly cultivated former forest acreage, less and less land was left for the elephants. Deprived of their natural forage, the pachyderms raided peasants' subsistence plots. Finally, in March 1975, as Rwanda's food crisis worsened, the president acted. Turning down as too time consuming and costly a plan to tame all of the animals and drive them nearly 100 miles to the Akagera National Park, he ordered that they be "culled."

Army helicopters drove elephants toward hunters armed with rifles and trappers equipped with dart guns. When the animals were about 15 yards away, the men opened fire, killing the adult elephants and shooting tranquilizing darts into the younger ones. In all, 106 were killed and 26 captured. The small elephants were then airlifted by helicopter or floated down a river in crates to a compound, where they were readied for a truck journey to the Akagera sanctuary.

By May 1976, all of the 26 surviving elephants (except one, which escaped) seemed to be thriving in the protected park, where they can forage and breed without endangering crops.

Nobel Prize Winners

In 1975 four Americans and four Europeans shared the Nobel Prizes in physiology or medicine, physics and chemistry awarded in October by the Caroline Institute and the Royal Swedish Academy of Sciences in Stockholm. The award in each category, split equally by the winners, was worth $143,000.

PHYSIOLOGY OR MEDICINE

Until 1970, virtually all scientists believed that genetic information within a cell was invariably passed from the master molecule, DNA, to a messenger molecule, RNA, which in turn instructed the cell to manufacture various proteins. For successfully challenging that dogma, and for providing what the Caroline Institute called a "conceptual foundation" that will foster investigations of the links between cancer and viruses, three biologists were awarded the prize in physiology or medicine.

One of the laureates, Howard Temin, 41, a University of Wisconsin researcher, had speculated a decade earlier that tumor viruses containing only RNA could work in reverse, utilizing an intermediary substance to transcribe their genetic information into a cell's DNA, which would then order the production of more RNA viruses. Around the same time, the second prizewinner, David Baltimore, 38, was pursuing similar research at M.I.T. In 1970, in two separate reports to *Nature,* both reported the discovery of "reverse transcriptase," the substance that Temin had hypothesized.

Both Temin and Baltimore had studied under the man who shared their prize, Italian-born Renato Dulbecco, 62, a naturalized United States citizen. While doing research at the Salk Institute and at the California Institute of Technology, he developed ingenious cancer research techniques, including one for introducing into an animal cell a small number of viral genes and determining which was responsible for cancerous change. Using and building upon Dulbecco's procedures enabled Temin and Baltimore to make their simultaneous discoveries. Recalling the long years of viral research conducted by the trio, Temin wryly noted that their key discovery resulted from "a process," not from "a Eureka thing where we sat in a bathtub."

PHYSICS

The prize in physics was shared by James Rainwater, 58, of Columbia University; Aage Bohr, 54, a Dane who succeeded his Nobel laureate father Niels as head of Copenhagen's Niels Bohr Institute; and Benjamin Mottelson, 50, a Chicago-born naturalized Danish citizen with the Nordic Institute of Technical Atomic Physics in Copenhagen. All were cited by the Swedish Academy for their work in nuclear physics, and particularly for "development of the theory of the structure of the atomic nucleus."

The stage was set for their efforts by the discovery in the late 1940s that the nuclei of some atoms acted as though they were asymmetrical, rather than perfectly spherical, as had been assumed. In 1950 Rainwater proposed that interactions between the swiftly moving particles on the periphery of the nucleus and other particles swirling around deep inside might account for the asymmetry.

Bohr then shared an office at Columbia with Rainwater; when he returned to Copenhagen, he worked with Mottelson to devise a more detailed explanation of the nuclear deformation. According to their "collective motion" theory, the distortion of the nucleus is caused in part by the centrifugal effect of the outer particles in the nucleus—just as the centrifugal force of the earth's spin causes the planet to bulge at the equator.

Because their work was published so long ago—between 1950 and 1953—Rainwater admitted that the award had come as "a complete surprise."

CHEMISTRY

Research that was "of fundamental importance to an understanding of biological processes" won the chemistry prize for Vladimir Prelog, 70, a naturalized Swiss citizen born in Yugoslavia, and John Cornforth, 58, a native Australian who did his work in Great Britain.

Prelog, a professor at the Swiss Federal Institute of Technology, elaborated a theory of the three-dimensional nature of molecules and pioneered in developing a system for identifying *d* and *l* isomers—right- and left-handed compounds with identical chemical formulas that are mirror images of each other. He also devised methods for determining which of these are biologically active.

Cornforth, a professor at the University of Sussex who also focused on the three-dimensional structure of molecules, specialized in the synthesis of naturally occurring substances. During World War II, he helped unravel the structure of penicillin. Later, he synthesized compounds ranging from cholesterol to the female sex hormone progesterone. He also demonstrated how the structure of enzymes enables them to rearrange the structure of molecules and thus influence various kinds of biological activity. Cornforth attributed part of his success to his deafness; as his wife and collaborator remarked, "He can't be interrupted easily."

TEMIN

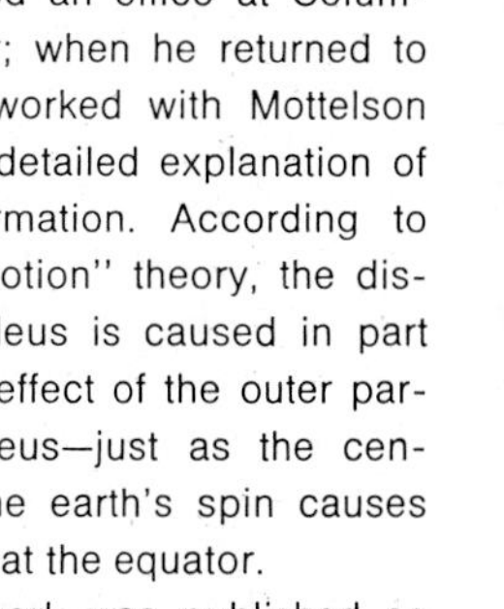
BOHR

BALTIMORE

MOTTELSON

DULBECCO

PRELOG

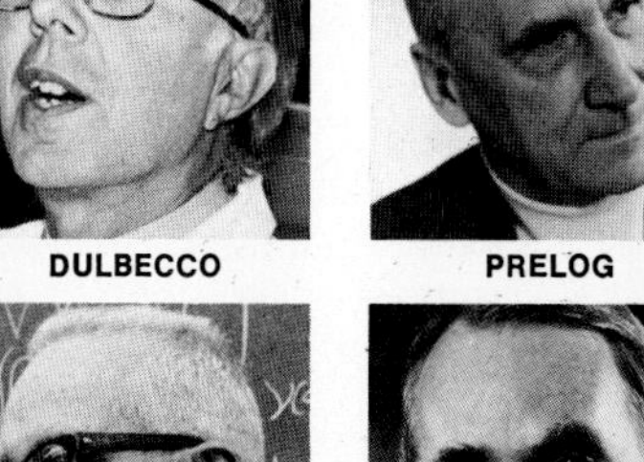

RAINWATER

CORNFORTH

Credits

Sources for the illustrations in this book are shown below. Credits from left to right are separated by semicolons, from top to bottom by dashes.

Cover—Heinz Meng. 6—Map by Nicholas Fasciano. 7—Theo W. Brown. 8—Keith Gillett. 9—Flip Schulke from Black Star (2)—Ben Cropp. 10,11 —Flip Schulke from Black Star; Glenn Millott—Ron and Valerie Taylor. 12—Keith Gillett. 13—Drawing by Patricia J. Wynne. 14—Ron and Valerie Taylor from Ardea Photographics; Douglas Faulkner—Allan Power from Bruce Coleman Ltd.; Walter Deas—Allan Power from Bruce Coleman Ltd.; Robert Dickson from Ben Cropp Productions. 15—Walter Deas—T. L. Tansy—Robert Dickson from Ben Cropp Productions. 16 —Keith Gillett—Douglas Faulkner—Keith Gillett. 17—Douglas Faulkner; Walter Deas—Allan Power from Bruce Coleman Inc.; Douglas Faulkner—Walter Deas; Douglas Faulkner. 18,19—Ron and Valerie Taylor from Ardea Photographics. 20,21—Jean-Pierre Laffont from Sygma. 23—Courtesy of Clarence R. Allen, California Institute of Technology. 24—Map by J. Kuhl. 26—David E. Scherman from TIME-LIFE Picture Agency. 29—Drawing by Walter Johnson, courtesy S. T. Algermissen and David M. Perkins, U.S. Geological Survey. 33—Ralph Crane from TIME-LIFE Picture Agency. 34—Drawing by Nicholas Fasciano. 35 —Henry Groskinsky. 36,37—Corning Glass Works. 38—Norton Company, Worcester, Massachusetts, except bottom left, Corning Glass Works. 39—Corning Glass Works. 40—Drawing by Nicholas Fasciano; Corning Glass Works. 41—Fritz Goro. 42—Ford Motor Company. 43 —Drawings by Nicholas Fasciano. 44,45—Norton Company, Worcester, Massachusetts; Mitchell Funk. 46—Gordon S. Smith from National Audubon Society Collection/Photo Researchers. 48—George Schaller from Bruce Coleman Inc. 50—Drawings by Patricia J. Wynne. 51—Stern Magazine-Black Star. 54,55—Bill Ray from TIME-LIFE Picture Agency. 57—N. Myers from Bruce Coleman Inc. 58—Drawing by Seymour Chwast. 61—T. S. Satyan from TIME-LIFE Picture Agency. 62,63—Ray Utt, Cities Service Company, Tulsa. 64—Arkansas Game and Fish Commission Photo by Bill Bailey; U.S.D.A. Soil Conservation Service—Fish Farming Experiment Station, Fish and Wildlife Service, Stuttgart, Arkansas (2). 66—Fred Myers. 67—Courtesy Rodale Press; John C. Stevenson from Animals, Animals—Sven-Olof Lindblad. 68,69—Sven-Olof Lindblad. 70,71—African Wildlife Leadership Foundation/ Tomasyan. 72—Noel D. Vietmeyer. 73—Edward S. Ayensu. 74,75 —World Health Organization. 77—World Health Organization. 80,81 —World Health Organization photograph by D. Henrioud—U.N. Photo; World Health Organization photograph by P. Almasy. 83—World Health Organization photograph by A. Kuchar. 87—Henry Groskinsky. 88,89 —Drawings by Nicholas Fasciano—photographs by Ralph Morse. 90,91 —Ralph Morse. 92—Stanley Cohen, Stanford University Medical Center. 94—Jack Griffith, Stanford University Medical Center. 95 —Drawing by Nicholas Fasciano. 98,99—Thomas D. Mangelsen. 102,103—Rod Drewien (2)—Thomas D. Mangelsen. 106—The Peregrine Fund, Cornell University; New York State College of Agriculture and Life Sciences at Cornell University. 111—Heinz Meng. 112,113—John Zimmerman from TIME-LIFE Picture Agency. 114—The Bettmann Archive. 116—Drawing by George V. Kelvin. 117—Robert Perron © 1975. 120,121—John Zimmerman from TIME-LIFE Picture Agency except bottom left, John Zimmerman. 123—Solar Energy Facility, S. Ilario, Genoa. 124—David Austen, copied from the Mitchell Library, from Perry's *Arcana*. 125—George Holton from National Audubon Society Collection/ Photo Researchers. 126,127—David Austen, from the Clarence River Historical Society—Graham Pizzey. 128—Harold J. Pollock; Graham Pizzey. 129—Bill N. Kleeman from Tom Stack and Associates—Graham Pizzey. 130—John Dominis from TIME-LIFE Picture Agency —Warren Garst from Tom Stack and Associates. 131—John Carnemolla. 132—Henry Groskinsky. 136,137—Drawings by Nicholas Fasciano. 139—Morton Tadder. 142 through 149—© Stephen Dalton from the book *Borne on the Wind* published by Readers Digest Press. 150,151 —San Diego Museum of Man, photograph by Spencer L. Rogers. 153 —Map by Rafael D. Palacios. 156,157—Fritz Goro. 159—Courtesy University of Pittsburgh. 163—NASA. 164,165—Document Lucien Rudaux, courtesy Librairie Larousse (2); Drawing adapted from original artwork by Paul Calle. 166,167—Tass from Sovfoto (2)—Novosti Press Agency. 168—NASA drawing adapted by Nicholas Fasciano. 169 —NASA, Ames Research Center. 170—Thomas Eisner, Irmgard Kriston and Daniel Aneshansley, Cornell University. 171—Earl Gustie from the Chicago Tribune. 172—From *Prehistoric Animals,* by Professor J. Augusta and Z. Burian, published by Paul Hamlyn, Ltd. 173—Larry Dale Gordon from TIME-LIFE Picture Agency. 174—David Rubinger from TIME-LIFE Picture Agency. 177—The Bettmann Archive. 181—Wide World. 184—NASA. 185—National Audubon Society Collection/Photo Researchers. 186—Dr. Robert Rines from Phototrends—Drawing by Ed Frank; Mohamed Amin from Camerapix. 187—Wide World (2)—Wide World; United Press International—United Press International; No Credit—United Press International; Camera Press Ltd.

Acknowledgments

The editors are particularly indebted to Leon Jaroff, who wrote portions of this book. The index for this book was prepared by Gail Liss. The editors also wish to thank the following persons and institutions for their assistance: R. D. Adams, Superintendent, Seismological Observatory, Department of Scientific and Industrial Research, Wellington, New Zealand; Martin L. Albert, Assistant Professor of Neurology, Department of Neurology, Medical School, Boston University, Boston, Massachusetts; S. T. Algermissen, Geophysicist, U.S. Geological Survey, Denver, Colorado; Clarence R. Allen, Professor of Geology and Geophysics, California Institute of Technology, Pasadena, California; Richard A. Alliegro, Director of Research, Industrial Ceramics Division, Norton Company, Worcester, Massachusetts; Don L. Anderson, Director, Seismological Laboratory, California Institute of Technology, Pasadena, California; James W. Atz, Curator, Department of Ichthyology, The American Museum of Natural History, New York City; Jim Ayers, Fishery Marketing Specialist, National Marine Fisheries Service, Little Rock, Arkansas; William Bailey Jr., Special Projects Coordinator, Arkansas Game and Fish Commission, Lonoke, Arkansas; Dr. Arthur F. Battista, Professor of Neurosurgery, New York University Medical Center, New York City; Frederick M. Bayer, Curator, Department of Invertebrate Zoology (Echinoderms), National Museum of Natural History, Smithsonian Institution, Washington, D.C.; John Biewener, Staff Vice President, RCA Corporation, New York City; Kent D. Broadbent, Vice President, MCA Disco-Vision, Inc., Torrance, California; Thomas J. Cade, Professor of Ornithology and Director, Peregrine Fund, Laboratory of Ornithology, Cornell University, Ithaca, New York; Lawrence Colin, Pioneer Venus Project Scientist, NASA-Ames Research Center, Moffett Field, California; Hilary Crawford, Assistant to the Press Officer, Australian Information Service, New York City; James Dieterich, Geophysicist, U.S. Geological Survey,

Menlo Park, California; Sandra Donavan, Technical Director, Horizons Research, Inc., Beachwood, Ohio; Susan Drennan, Associate Editor, *American Birds,* National Audubon Society, New York City; Rod Drewien, Idaho Cooperative Wildlife Research Unit, University of Idaho, Moscow, Idaho; Robert Endean, Reader, Department of Zoology, University of Queensland, Brisbane, Queensland, Australia; Ray C. Erickson, Assistant Director for Endangered Wildlife Research Program, Patuxent Wildlife Research Center, U.S. Fish and Wildlife Service, Laurel, Maryland; David Fleay, Zoologist, West Burleigh Fauna Reserve, Queensland, Australia; Edgar Frankel, Department of Geology and Geophysics, University of Sydney, Sydney, New South Wales, Australia; Dr. Avram Goldstein, Professor of Pharmacology, Stanford University, and Director of the Addiction Research Foundation, Palo Alto, California; Robert M. Hamilton, Chief, Office of Earthquake Studies, U.S. Geological Survey, Reston, Virginia; P. Edgar Hare, Organic Geochemist, Geophysical Laboratory, Carnegie Institution of Washington, Washington, D.C.; Clyde A. Hill, Curator of Mammals, San Diego Zoological Garden, San Diego, California; John Hughes, Unit for Research on Addictive Drugs, Marischal College, University of Aberdeen, Aberdeen, Scotland; Malcolm Johnston, Geophysicist, U.S. Geological Survey, Menlo Park, California; Robert Katz, U.S. Army Materials and Mechanics Research Center, Watertown, Massachusetts; Donovan Kelly, Technical Information Specialist, U.S. Geological Survey, Reston, Virginia; Richard A. Kenchington, Research Fellow, Department of Biological Sciences, James Cook University of North Queensland, Townsville, Queensland, Australia; Cameron B. Kepler, Research Behaviorist, Endangered Wildlife Research Program, Patuxent Wildlife Research Center, U.S. Fish and Wildlife Service, Laurel, Maryland; Richard G. Klein, Associate Professor of Anthropology, University of Chicago, Chicago, Illinois; Dr. Hans W. Kosterlitz, Director of the Unit for Research on Addictive Drugs, Marischal College, University of Aberdeen, Aberdeen, Scotland; George J. Kukla, Senior Research Associate, Lamont-Doherty Geological Observatory, Palisades, New York; Michael Lane, Director, Bureau of Smallpox Eradication, Center for Disease Control, Atlanta, Georgia; Leonard Laub, Manager, Electro-Optics Section, Research Department, Zenith Radio Corporation, Chicago, Illinois; David Lipton, Vice President, Public Relations Department, MCA Disco-Vision, Inc., Universal City, California; John S. Lucas, Senior Lecturer in Zoology, James Cook University of North Queensland, Townsville, Queensland, Australia; Richard MacNeish, Robert S. Peabody Foundation for Archeology, Andover, Massachusetts; Thomas D. Mangelsen, Boulder, Colorado; J. Mayo Martin, Extension Biologist, U.S. Fish and Wildlife Service, Fish Farm Experimental Station, Stuttgart, Arkansas; Arthur F. McLean, Turbine Development, Ford Motor Company, Dearborn, Michigan; Heinz Meng, Professor of Biology, State University College, New Paltz, New York; Dennis Mog, Corning Glass Works, Corning, New York; Dr. José M. Musacchio, Professor of Pharmacology, New York University Medical Center, New York City; David M. Perkins, Geophysicist, U.S. Geological Survey, Denver, Colorado; Dr. Edward R. Perl, Professor and Chairman of Physiology, University of North Carolina, Chapel Hill, North Carolina; Waverly Person, Geophysicist, U.S. Geological Survey, Denver, Colorado; Agu Pert, Adult Psychiatry Branch, National Institute of Mental Health, Bethesda, Maryland; Candace B. Pert, Adult Psychiatry Branch, National Institute of Mental Health, Bethesda, Maryland; Marc Podems, Project Director, Research and Development Group, Rodale Press, Inc., Organic Park, Emmaus, Pennsylvania; Philip S. Portoghese, Professor of Medicinal Chemistry, University of Minnesota, Minneapolis, Minnesota; Frank Press, Head, Department of Earth and Planetary Sciences, Massachusetts Institute of Technology, Cambridge, Massachusetts; Richard W. Rigby, Manager, Bosque del Apache National Wildlife Refuge, San Antonio, New Mexico; Joseph Rosewater, Curator, Department of Invertebrate Zoology (Mollusks), National Museum of Natural History, Smithsonian Institution, Washington, D.C.; Carl Sagan, Laboratory of Planetary Studies, Cornell University, Ithaca, New York; Christopher Scholz, Associate Professor of Geology, Lamont-Doherty Geological Observatory, Palisades, New York; Eric J. Simon, Professor of Experimental Medicine, New York University Medical Center, New York, New York; Thomas Smylie, Public Affairs Officer, U.S. Fish and Wildlife Service, Albuquerque, New Mexico; Dr. Solomon H. Snyder, Professor of Psychiatry and Pharmacology, Johns Hopkins University School of Medicine, Baltimore, Maryland; Violette Solt, Public Affairs Officer, U.S. Fish and Wildlife Service, Denver, Colorado; William J. Spence, Geophysicist, U.S. Geological Survey, Denver, Colorado; Noel Vietmeyer, Professional Associate, Board on Science and Technology for International Development, Office of the Foreign Secretary, National Academy of Sciences, Washington, D.C.; Franklin Wang, Professor of Engineering, State University of New York at Stony Brook, Stony Brook, New York; Charles L. Ward, Aransas National Wildlife Refuge, Austwell, Texas; James D. Weaver, Technical Associate, Peregrine Fund, Laboratory of Ornithology, Cornell University, Ithaca, New York; Kenneth Whitham, Director, Earth Physics Bureau, Department of Energy, Mines and Resources, Ottawa, Canada; Edward O. Wilson, Professor of Zoology and Curator in Entomology, Museum of Comparative Zoology, Harvard University, Cambridge, Massachusetts.

Index

Numerals in italics indicate an illustration of the subject mentioned.

PRINTED IN U.S.A.